Introduction to

MOLECULAR SPECTROSCOPY

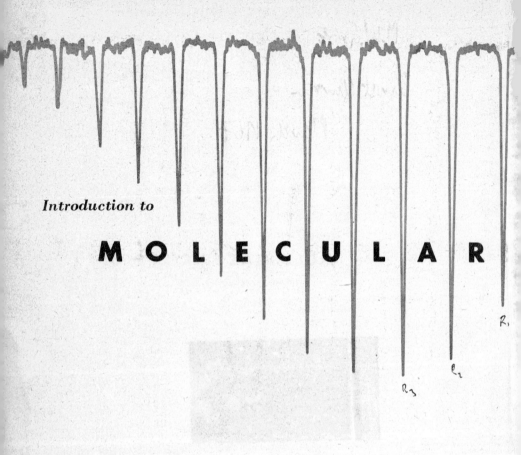

Introduction to

MOLECULAR

INTERNATIONAL STUDENT EDITION

McGRAW-HILL *Book Company, Inc.*

NEW YORK   SAN FRANCISCO   TORONTO   LONDON

KŌGAKUSHA *Company, Ltd.*

TOKYO

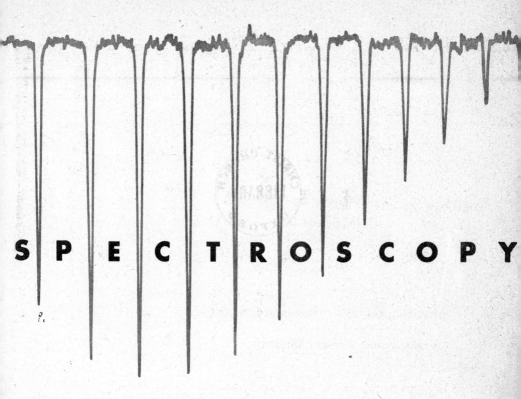

SPECTROSCOPY

GORDON M. BARROW

Professor of Chemistry
Case Institute of Technology

INTRODUCTION TO MOLECULAR SPECTROSCOPY

INTERNATIONAL STUDENT EDITION

Library of Congress Catalog Card Number 62-12478

Tosho Printing Co., Ltd., Tokyo, Japan

PREFACE

Molecular spectroscopy cannot be regarded as the private domain of the physicist or physical chemist who describes himself as a spectroscopist. Both organic and inorganic chemists make use of infrared and ultraviolet spectrometers as if they were standard tools of the trade. Analytical chemists base many of their analytical techniques on the methods of spectroscopy. Furthermore, almost all chemists make frequent use of molecular-structure data, and much of this has been obtained from spectroscopic measurements.

One can, it is true, make very considerable use of spectroscopy as a tool for the characterization, identification, and analysis of materials with little or no understanding of the way in which the observed spectrum is related to the properties of the absorbing, or emitting, molecules. Likewise, data on molecular properties can be used even if the way in which they were obtained is not understood. The tendency of many chemists, who are not molecular spectroscopists, to proceed with this lack of appreciation for the elementary theory of molecular spectroscopy persists, in, part, because of the lack of suitable introductory material. This book is, therefore, intended to bridge the gap between the very cursory treatment of spectroscopy generally given in undergraduate textbooks and the detailed treatments written for the specialist and research worker that are given in books in the various areas of molecular spectroscopy. The reader will here be provided with the basic theory which makes understandable the relationship of the amount and wavelength of radiation absorbed or emitted by a sample and the properties of the molecules of the sample. This introduction should not only allow the organic, inorganic, or analytical chemist to make surer use of spectroscopy as a tool, but should also provide that comfortable feeling of knowing "what is happening" when spectroscopic techniques, or results obtained by these techniques, are used.

No special background is necessary for the study of this book. Although the Schrödinger wave equation is introduced and simple problems to illustrate its relation to quantities that are important in spectroscopy are solved, no prior knowledge of quantum mechanics is assumed. In a similar way, some of the theory known as "group theory" is given and some analyses are based on the methods of group theory. Again no previous knowledge of this subject is necessary. The use of quantum mechanics and group theory is carefully confined to areas of specific value in this introduction to spectroscopy. The level of treatment is maintained by avoiding the many additional avenues that these subjects open up.

This introduction to molecular spectroscopy will show how molecular spectra can be interpreted in terms of molecular behavior and how, from such interpretations, molecular properties can be obtained. The level of understanding of the theory of molecular spectroscopy that this book seeks to achieve is that from which the student can enter into the specialized reference books and the research literature of molecular spectroscopy. In fact the goal of much of the material presented could be considered to be that of providing readier access for the student to the two important molecular spectroscopy books, frequently referred to throughout the book, by G. Herzberg. It is hoped that the student will be able to understand and appreciate advanced and current spectroscopic material if, after studying this book, he pays some additional attention to the details and nomenclature surrounding a particular spectroscopic subject. With this background the inorganic chemist should, for example, be able to appreciate the very important guides to the nature of bonding in coordination compounds that are now being based, to a large extent, on spectroscopic results. The organic chemist, to use a specific example, should be able to make increased use of the information on the nature and energies of excited states that are being discovered and analyzed by the spectroscopist.

The problems of selection of material and depth of treatment are, of course, considerable in a book which attempts to serve as an introduction to a field as extensive as spectroscopy. Judgement as to the relative importance of the topics to be treated and the depths to which these treatments should be taken are, it is recognized, greatly influenced by one's particular interests and background. I have attempted, however, to maintain a uniform introduction to the areas of rotational, vibrational, and electronic spectroscopy that are generally of interest to chemists.

Several sections are concerned in some detail with subjects that are perhaps of special rather than general interest. These sections, marked with an asterisk, can be omitted without destroying the continuity of the book.

I would like to express my appreciation to my colleagues, Dr. Wm. Abrahamson and Dr. W. E. Thompson, and to the graduate students at Case Institute, Mrs. Carol Haberman, Miss Kim Vo, and Mr. I. Chu, for the assistance they have given me by carefully working through many sections of the manuscript. I am also indebted to my wife, Harriet, for the improvements that she made in the style of the presentation and to Mrs. Julia Dasch for typing the manuscript.

Gordon M. Barrow

CONTENTS

INTRODUCTION

Molecular spectroscopy is the study of the absorption or emission of electromagnetic radiation by molecules. The experimental data that such studies provide are the frequencies, or wavelengths, of the radiation and the amount of radiation emitted or absorbed by the sample.

One can often understand the nature of the molecular changes that are responsible for the emission or absorption of the radiation. In such cases, the experimental spectroscopic data can be used to determine quantitative values for various molecular properties. In this way, as will be seen, remarkably detailed and exact measurements of the size, shape, flexibility, and electronic arrangement of a molecule can be obtained. It will become apparent that spectroscopy offers one of the most powerful tools for a great variety of molecular-structure studies.

Only brief mention will be made of the experimental techniques used to obtain the spectra that are discussed. A number of books, listed at the end of this section, deal in part or wholly with these techniques. In practice, furthermore, many commercial spectrometers operating in the various spectral regions are available. With such equipment, spectra can be obtained and used without a detailed understanding of the behavior of the components of the instrument.

There will, furthermore, be no attempt to deal in detail with the tremendous body of very useful empirical data that has been accumulated, primarily from studies of infrared and ultraviolet spectra. References to some treatments and collections of these data are given below.

Classifications of Spectroscopy

When the theory of molecular spectra is treated, it is convenient to classify spectra according to the type of molecular energy that is being altered in the emission or absorption process. In this way the principal headings for the material that is to be presented can be arrived at. These are:

Rotational spectra—due to changes in the rotational energy of the molecule

Vibrational spectra—due to changes in the vibrational energy of the molecule

Electronic spectra—due to changes in the energy of the molecule due to different electron arrangements

It is allowable, generally to a good approximation, to treat the energy of a free molecule as made up of separate rotational, vibrational, and electronic components as has been implied by this classification. We will see, however, that spectra may result from transitions in which more than one type of molecular energy changes. Thus an absorption of energy due primarily to a change in the vibrational energy may show the effects of accompanying rotational energy changes.

One can also divide spectroscopy according to the instrumentation used. It happens that the categories obtained in this way are similar to those based on molecular energies. The instrumentation classification might be given as:

Microwave spectrometer: klystron source, wave guide, and crystal detector—molecular rotation spectra

Infrared spectrometer: hot ceramic source, rock-salt prism or grating, thermocouple detector—molecular vibration spectra

Visible and ultraviolet spectrometer: tungsten lamp or hydrogen discharge tube source, glass or quartz prism or grating, photomultiplier detector—electronic spectra

It should also be mentioned that vibrational spectra can be obtained by means of Raman spectroscopy and that this technique uses a visible or ultraviolet spectrometer.

In addition to the types of molecular spectroscopy listed above, there are two closely related types that play a comparable role in chemistry. These are nuclear magnetic resonance (nmr) and electron spin resonance (esr) spectroscopy. The energy levels that are studied in these spectroscopic categories result, in contrast to those normally studied in rotational, vibrational, and electronic spectroscopy, from the action of a magnetic field on the molecules of the sample. In nuclear magnetic resonance spectroscopy the effect of the magnetic field is to orient certain nuclei in certain directions with respect to the direction of the field. These different orientations correspond to different energies, and radiation of a suitable frequency can then be used to study the energy-level separations. Similarly, in electronic spin resonance spectroscopy the spin of an electron of the sample molecule is oriented one way or the other with respect to the field, and again the resulting energy-level separation of these two orientations is studied by radiation of suitable frequency.

A number of recent books have appeared which provide excellent introductions, suitable for the chemist, to nuclear magnetic resonance and electronic spin resonance spectroscopy. Of particular interest are "Nuclear Magnetic Resonance," McGraw-Hill Book Company, Inc., New York, 1959, and "An Introduction to Spin-Spin Splitting in High-Resolution Nuclear Magnetic Resonance Spectra," W. A. Benjamin, Inc., New York, 1961, both by J. D. Roberts, and "Applications of Nuclear Magnetic Resonance Spectroscopy in Organic Chemistry," Pergamon Press, Inc., New York, 1959, by M. L. Jackman. In view of these treatments, which are at the same level as the treatments of rotational, vibrational, and electronic spectroscopy given here, no discussion of nuclear magnetic resonance and electronic spin resonance will be included.

Wavelength, Frequency, and Energy of Radiation

Before the emission or absorption of radiation by molecular systems can be treated, some of the terms used to describe electromagnetic radiation must be summarized.

The wave nature description of electromagnetic radiation associates oscillating electric and magnetic fields with the radiation. Ordinary radiation traveling in the z direction, for example, can be treated in terms of electric and magnetic fields perpendicular to each other and to the direction of propagation. Polarized radiation, which is more convenient for discussion here, can be obtained. Figure 1 indicates the

FIG. 1   Plane-polarized electromagnetic radiation.

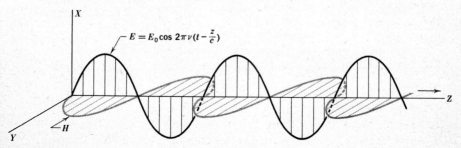

$$E = E_0 \cos 2\pi \nu \left(t - \frac{z}{c} \right)$$

electric and magnetic fields that are associated with polarized electromagnetic radiation which has only the xz plane component of the electric
field. In spectroscopy almost all attention is centered on the electric
field, but, for completeness, Fig. 1 shows that this plane polarized radiation has the magnetic field component in the plane perpendicular to that
of the electric field.

The oscillation of the electric field, and also of the associated magnetic field, travels out in the z direction, the direction of propagation,
with a velocity c. The value of the electric field along the z axis at a
given time and at a given point on the z axis as a function of time can be
expressed by the formula

$$E = E_0 \cos 2\pi\nu \left(t - \frac{z}{c} \right) \tag{1}$$

This formula, it should be recognized, gives the behavior shown in Fig. 1
for a given value of t, $t = 0$ for example, while at a given value of z the
oscillation of E with respect to time is given.

With this wave picture of radiation, electromagnetic radiation consists of waves of varying electric and magnetic field strength traveling
with the velocity of light and having a given wavelength and frequency.
As can be readily verified by considering a position with some fixed value
of z and asking how many cycles pass this position in the time c seconds,
the relation between the wavelength and the frequency of oscillation of
the wave is

$$\nu = \frac{c}{\lambda} \tag{2}$$

Although, as will be seen later, the frequencies of the radiation that
are absorbed or emitted in a spectral study are more directly related to
the molecular energy changes that cause the absorption or emission, it is
often customary to deal as well with the wavelength of the radiation.

The corpuscular description of electromagnetic radiation views this
radiation as a stream of energy packets, called photons in the visible
region, traveling with the velocity of light.

Basic to an understanding of spectra is the relation of Planck that
brings together the wave and corpuscular theories of radiation. His
equation

$$\Delta\epsilon = h\nu \tag{3}$$

where h, a constant known as Planck's constant, with the value 6.624 $\times$ 10^{-27} erg-sec, ties together the corpuscular quantity $\Delta\epsilon$, the energy of a radiation energy packet, or quantum, with the wave nature concept of the frequency of the radiation.

In the various types of spectroscopy one makes use of $\Delta\epsilon$, ν, or λ to characterize the particular radiation emitted or absorbed. One additional unit which is proportional to ν has convenient numerical values and is often used. This unit, quite commonly called a frequency unit, differs from ν by the factor c. It is designated as $\bar{\nu}$ and is defined as

$$\bar{\nu} = \frac{1}{\lambda} \tag{4}$$

The units of $\bar{\nu}$ are invariably those of cm^{-1}, called reciprocal centimeters or *wave numbers*. It should be kept in mind that $\bar{\nu}$ is essentially a measure of frequency, being different from ν by the constant factor of the velocity of light.

The ranges of electromagnetic radiation, expressed in the units usually used for each region, are shown in Table 1. While it may seem unfortunate that a consistent set of units, such as the cgs wavelength unit of centimeters, is not used throughout, it is a historical fact that each area of spectroscopy developed pretty much on its own, independent of developments in other areas, and each acquired its own convenient set of units.

It is frequently necessary to convert from one description of radiation, such as given by a value of λ, for example, to another, such as given by ν, or $\bar{\nu}$, or by the value of $\Delta\epsilon = h\nu$. Conversion factors for all the interconversions that are likely to be encountered are shown in Table 2. It should be pointed out, with regard to the entries in Table 2, that a term such as cal/mole is intended to mean calories per Avogadro's number of particles, where the "particles" may be molecules, atoms, or quanta.

TABLE 1 The Spectral Regions of Electromagnetic Radiation

	Microwave	Infrared	Visible	Ultraviolet
λ (cm)	30–0.1	0.003–0.00025	7×10^{-5}–3×10^{-5}	3×10^{-5}–1×10^{-5}
λ (A)			7,000–3,000	3,000–1,000
ν	1000–300,000 megacycles/sec			
$\bar{\nu}$		300–4,000 cm^{-1}		

TABLE 2   Energy Conversion Factors

	erg/molecule	ev	cm^{-1}	cal/mole
erg/molecule......	1	6.242×10^{11}	5.036×10^{15}	1.439×10^{16}
ev..............	1.602×10^{-12}	1	8,067	23,060
cm^{-1}.............	1.986×10^{-16}	1.2396×10^{-4}	1	2.858
cal/mole........	6.949×10^{-17}	4.338×10^{-5}	0.3499	1

Exercise 1.   Complete Table 1 by filling in all the blank spaces.

Exercise 2.   Verify the conversion factors along a row of Table 2.

Exercise 3.   Calculate typical energies of an Avogadro's number (6.023×10^{23}) of quanta in the four regions of electromagnetic radiation shown in Table 1.   Compare these values with the classical thermal kinetic energy of $\frac{1}{2}RT = 600$ cal/mole per degree of freedom at room temperature and with chemical bond energies of 50 to 100 kcal/mole.

PRINCIPAL REFERENCES

Experimental Methods

1. Harrison, G. R., R. C. Lord, and J. R. Loofbourow: "Practical Spectroscopy," Prentice-Hall, Inc., Englewood Cliffs, N.J., 1948.
2. Gordy, W., W. V. Smith, and R. F. Trambarulo: "Microwave Spectroscopy," John Wiley & Sons, Inc., New York, 1953.
3. Sawyer, R. A.: "Experimental Spectroscopy," Prentice-Hall, Inc., Englewood Cliffs, N.J., 1944.

Applications

1. Bellamy, L. J.: "The Infrared Spectra of Complex Molecules," John Wiley & Sons, Inc., New York, 1954.
2. Lawson, K. E.: "Infrared Absorption of Inorganic Substances," Reinhold Publishing Corporation, New York, 1961.
3. Gillam, A. E., and E. S. Stern: "An Introduction to Electronic Absorption Spectroscopy in Organic Chemistry," Edward Arnold & Co., London, 1954.

1
INTRODUCTION TO
THE THEORETICAL TREATMENT OF
MOLECULAR SYSTEMS

The development of theories of atomic and molecular systems has, since about 1900, been closely tied to the study of their spectra.   The principal aspect of these theories that must be introduced here is their statements about the energy that an atom or molecule can have.   An appreciation of the restrictions that are placed on the energies of atomic and molecular systems is basic to an understanding of the spectra of these systems.

While many spectra can be understood to some extent without any further appreciation of the theories of molecular systems, a better understanding is usually obtained if some of the general features of these theories are known.   In this chapter, the general nature of theoretical treatments of atomic and molecular systems will be introduced to the extent needed for the treatments of molecular systems given in later chapters.

1-1. The Recognition of Quantum Restrictions

The earliest recognition of discrete energy jumps or quantum restrictions stems from Planck's studies of the radiation emitted by hot bodies. He was driven to assume, as was later stated, that the oscillating atoms of a hot body cannot have any energy of oscillation but can have only the energies that are integral multiples of $h\nu$, where ν is a frequency of oscillation and h is a proportionality constant, Planck's constant.   Furthermore, radiation from such an oscillating system consists of the energies emitted when an oscillator jumps from one of the allowed energy levels to a lower one.   The unit, or quantum, of energy given out in such a jump from one energy state to the next lowest one is, therefore,

$$\Delta\epsilon = h\nu$$

The idea of discrete energies and the prominent role played by the constant h were basic features of Planck's black-body radiation derivation.   They seemed, however, to be awkward and troublesome features since, in classical treatments, they could not be justified.   Planck's black-body theory was, however, a preview of the developments in molecular theory and spectroscopy that were to take place in the next half century.   His reluctantly proposed ideas of quantum restrictions were accepted and expanded into more elaborate theories of molecular behavior, and his interpretation of the continuous spectrum provided by a hot body was to be followed by analyses of spectra of great detail and complexity.

In the next few years after 1900 the ideas of Planck were applied and extended, as in Einstein's theories of the photoelectric effect and the heat capacity of solids.   The next major step of spectroscopic interest was the application of these ideas of quantum restrictions to atomic systems, in particular to the hydrogen atom, by Niels Bohr in 1913.

1-2. The Bohr Theory of the Hydrogen Atom

Although detailed theories of atomic structure are not pertinent to the discussion here, the Bohr theory provides a clear and concrete illustration of one of the most important quantum rules and is, therefore, worthy of study.   By 1913 it was recognized, as a result of the then recent work of Thomson and of Rutherford, that an atom, in particular the hydrogen atom, consisted of a small heavy nucleus carrying the positive charge and that the electron moved, or resided, in some manner outside the nucleus.

Bohr's interpretation of the behavior of the electron was based on the rather arbitrary assumption that it moved in a circular orbit about the nucleus in such a way that *its angular momentum was an integral multiple of $h/2\pi$*.   This statement and the ordinary rules of dynamics and electrostatics lead to allowed orbits for the electron, each allowed orbit having a certain energy.

The derivation, in brief, is as follows: the angular momentum postulate requires that

$$mvr = n\frac{h}{2\pi} \qquad n = 1, 2, 3, \ldots \tag{1}$$

where m is the mass of the electron, v its velocity, and r the radius of its orbit. The requirement that the electron should have the coulombic force of attraction to the nucleus balanced by the centrifugal force gives

$$\frac{e^2}{r^2} = \frac{mv^2}{r} \tag{2}$$

or

$$r = \frac{e^2}{mv^2} \tag{3}$$

where e is the charge of the electron. Elimination of v^2, by means of the quantum restriction of Eq. (1), gives the radii of the orbits in which, according to Bohr, the electron is allowed to travel as

$$r = n^2 \frac{h^2}{4\pi^2 me^2} \tag{4}$$

Substitution of numerical values for the constants gives the radii of the Bohr orbits as

$$r = 0.529n^2 \text{ angstrom} \qquad n = 1, 2, 3, \ldots \tag{5}$$

The convenient unit of angstroms, defined so that $1 \text{ A} = 10^{-8}$ cm, has been introduced.

Of more interest in spectroscopy are the energies of the allowed orbits. If the potential energy at infinite separation of the electron and proton is taken as zero, the potential energy at separation r is given by Coulomb's law as

$$PE = -\frac{e^2}{r} \tag{6}$$

Addition of the kinetic energy gives, for the total energy of the electron, the result

$$\epsilon = KE + PE$$
$$= \frac{1}{2}mv^2 - \frac{e^2}{r} \tag{7}$$

Use can now be made of the relation of Eq. (3) and the quantum restriction of Eq. (1) to obtain

$$\epsilon_n = -\frac{2\pi^2 me^4}{h^2}\left(\frac{1}{n^2}\right) \qquad n = 1, 2, 3, \ldots \tag{8}$$

where the fact that each value of n implies a value of ϵ has been recognized by writing ϵ_n. This result gives, according to the Bohr theory, the possible energies that the electron of the hydrogen atom can assume.

Elaborations of this result have been made to allow for elliptical orbits, to take into account that the electron and nucleus should be treated as rotating about the center of gravity, which is not quite at the nucleus, and to include the relativistic dependence of electron mass on velocity. These details need not, however, be treated here.

It is interesting to see that the condition that the angular momentum be quantized in units of $h/2\pi$ leads to a set of allowed energies. Furthermore, if the electron of the hydrogen atom is now assumed to jump from one orbit to another, say from that with $n = n_1$ down to that with $n = n_2$, the Bohr theory predicts that an amount of energy $\Delta\epsilon = \epsilon_{n_1} - \epsilon_{n_2}$ must be emitted. With the Planck relation $\Delta\epsilon = h\nu$, the Bohr theory leads to the prediction of emission of radiation with frequencies

$$\nu = \frac{\Delta\epsilon}{h} = \frac{2\pi^2 me^4}{h^3}\left(\frac{1}{n_2^2} - \frac{1}{n_1^2}\right) \qquad \text{with } n_1 > n_2 \tag{9}$$

In terms of the more often used units of cm^{-1}, one has the prediction

$$\bar{\nu} = \frac{\nu}{c} = \frac{2\pi^2 me^4}{ch^3}\left(\frac{1}{n_2^2} - \frac{1}{n_1^2}\right) \qquad cm^{-1} \tag{10}$$

which, on substitution of numerical values, gives

$$\bar{\nu} = 109{,}677\left(\frac{1}{n_2^2} - \frac{1}{n_1^2}\right) \qquad cm^{-1} \tag{11}$$

This corresponds almost exactly to the empirical expression known as the Rydberg expression, which summarizes the observed hydrogen-atom spectrum.

Exercise 1-1. Derive, according to the Bohr theory, the orbit radii and energies for an electron of the He^+ ion.

The principle of quantized angular momentum used by Bohr is, as will be seen, a very generally applicable one in atomic and molecular systems. A more complete statement of the principle applied to the simple Bohr hydrogen atom would recognize that not only must the total angular momentum be quantized but that, if a direction is imposed on the atom, as by an applied electric or magnetic field, the component of angular momentum in that direction must also be quantized in units of $h/2\pi$. Thus for the $n = 2$ orbit, for example, the total angular momentum of the electron is $2(h/2\pi)$, and there is the possibility of showing by the application of a directed field that this orbit can be inclined in five different directions corresponding to angular momentum components of $2(h/2\pi)$, $1(h/2\pi)$, 0, $-1(h/2\pi)$, and $-2(h/2\pi)$. The splitting of the energy of the original $n = 2$ state by the application of a field reveals that the original state is to be thought of as having five states, all with the same energy. One says that the $n = 2$ orbit, or state of the electron, has a multiplicity of 5 or is fivefold *degenerate*.

The details of atomic theory and spectra will not be developed further here. Instead, some further general theoretical developments which led finally to the more powerful and less *ad hoc* formulation of quantum restrictions than that of Bohr will be outlined.

1-3. The Wave Nature of Particles

In 1925, Louis de Broglie, reasoning from the generally symmetric nature of the physical world, proposed that electrons, protons, and so forth, as well as radiation quanta, should have wave properties associated with them. He further suggested that the wavelength associated with a particle with mass m and velocity v, i.e., with momentum mv, would be given by

$$\lambda = \frac{h}{mv} \tag{12}$$

This interesting relation can be used in a number of situations. For example, if it is postulated that the wave associated with an electron in a Bohr orbit should form a standing wave around the nucleus, the condition that $2\pi r = n\lambda$ where n is an integer and $2\pi r$ is the circumference of the electron orbit is imposed. This stipulation together with de Broglie's wavelength relation leads, interestingly, to the same requirement, i.e., $mvr = n(h/2\pi)$, as imposed by Bohr.

Even more indicative of the validity of the de Broglie relation were the experiments of Davisson and Germer in which an electron beam was shown to give diffraction effects corresponding to a wave with wavelength given by the de Broglie relation.

It became clear that the Bohr condition, while successful in explaining the hydrogen-atom spectrum, did not recognize in a sufficiently basic way this wave nature of the electron. The importance of the wave nature led ultimately to a formulation of a general approach to the mechanics of atomic-sized systems.

It seems best here to present and illustrate this approach by means of an equation given in 1926 by Erwin Schrödinger. It is of great value to appreciate the way in which atomic-scale problems are handled and described by the wave mechanics of Schrödinger.

1-4. The Time-independent Schrödinger Equation

Although the equation originally presented by Schrödinger allowed for the calculation of time-dependent behavior, it is convenient first to demonstrate the simpler time-independent features of the complete equation.

In a study of spectroscopy there is little need to perform wave-mechanical, or quantum-mechanical, calculations of the properties of molecular systems. It will, however, be very helpful to have performed a simple illustrative calculation. One can then better appreciate the nature of more general quantum-mechanical methods and solutions.

The Schrödinger equation is not really derivable and should be looked upon as the counterpart, applicable to atomic- and molecular-scale problems, of such classical formulations as Newton's $f = ma$ expression. The Schrödinger equation, like $f = ma$, is used and accepted, not because of a derivation showing its validity, but rather because it leads, wherever properly applied, to results in agreement with observation.

Use of the Schrödinger equation implies that we are interested in learning about the *energy* of a particle, which is subject to some potential energy, and the *position* adopted by the particle. (The Bohr theory of hydrogenlike atoms obtained just such information, and the information was in agreement with experiment. Bohr's method could not, however, be extended to more complicated systems. The Schrödinger equation accomplishes this extension.) The Schrödinger equation might, for example, be used to solve again the hydrogen-atom problem and predict the position and the energy of the electron exposed to the coulombic potential of the nucleus.

The Schrödinger equation, as will be seen, yields directly values for the allowed energies of the particle under study. The position of the particle is, however, given only in terms of a probability function. According to M. Born, the value at a given point of the square of the trigonometric or algebraic function that solves the Schrödinger equation gives the probability of the particle being found at that point. If we choose, for simplicity, to consider a simple problem in which the particle can move only along one dimension, say the x coordinate, the solution function, or *eigenfunction*, represented by ψ, will be a function of x. For emphasis one sometimes writes $\psi(x)$. The probability of the particle being at a given value of x along the x axis is then equal to the value of ψ^2 at the given value of x. (If ψ is a complex function, as is sometimes the case, the probability is given by $\psi^*\psi$, where ψ^* is the complex conjugate of ψ.)

The Schrödinger equation for a particle of mass m constrained to one dimension and subject to some potential function $U(x)$ is

$$-\frac{h^2}{8\pi^2 m}\frac{d^2\psi}{dx^2} + U(x)\psi = \epsilon\psi \qquad (13)$$

(The first term can, in fact, be associated with the kinetic energy of the particle, the second with the potential energy, and the sum, therefore, with the total energy. It is perhaps better at first merely to use the equation to calculate desired quantities much as one does with $f = ma$.)

Solution of a particular problem requires values of m and an expression for the potential function to be substituted. The function ψ that solves the resulting differential equation must then be found. Such a function will generally exist only for certain values of ϵ, and these values are the allowed energies of the system that are being sought. The square of the solution function gives, as mentioned, the probability of the particle being at various positions. The hydrogen-atom problem would require the value of m for the electron to be used and the expression $-e^2/r$ to be put in as the potential function. (The hydrogen-atom problem is, however, three dimensional.) Solution of the problem would give the allowed energies, which turn out to be identical with those obtained by Bohr. The ψ^2 function would give the probability of the electron being at various positions, and the probability that is found is related to, but not identical with, the Bohr orbits.

Before the equation is illustrated by a simple, but important, example, it is necessary to state some of the limitations that are imposed on the function ψ. Briefly, the function ψ, to be an acceptable solution, must be "well behaved." It must not, for example, go to infinity or be double valued. In the first case one would deduce from the infinite value of ψ^2 an infinite probability of the particle being at a given position; while in the second case one would have two different probabilities at the same position. Neither of these would be physically reasonable. Further restrictions are that the function must be continuous and that discontinuities in the slope can occur only at points where the potential energy goes to infinity. One understands these restrictions from the fact that the equation involves the second derivative of ψ and that this would go to infinity at a discontinuity in the slope.

The equation and its application are more understandable when applied to a specific problem.

1-5. The Particle-in-a-Box Problem

A very simple problem, which in fact has some counterparts of interest in real molecular problems, is that of determining the allowed energies and the position probability function of a particle that can move in only one dimension and is confined to a region of length a. This problem implies a potential-energy function that has some value, which can conveniently be taken as zero, between $x = 0$ and $x = a$, and is infinitely high outside this region.

An electron in a piece of wire, for example, is subject to a potential which for some purposes can be so represented. Of more spectroscopic interest, as will be shown in Chap. 11, is the fact that the double-bonding, or π, electrons of a conjugated system of double bonds in a molecule behave approximately as though the potential which they experience is such a simple square-well function.

In the region $0 < x < a$ the potential-energy function is $U(x) = 0$, and the Schrödinger equation in this region reduces to

$$-\frac{h^2}{8\pi^2 m}\frac{d^2\psi}{dx^2} = \epsilon\psi \tag{14}$$

It is now necessary to find well-behaved solutions for this equation. The function ψ must be zero outside the potential well since there the potential is infinitely high, and there is no probability of the particle being in such a region. To be well behaved, and prevent a discontinuity in ψ, the function ψ in the region between 0 and a must be such that it equals zero at $x = 0$ and at $x = a$. Functions which solve the differential equation and also satisfy these boundary conditions can be seen by inspection to be

$$\psi = A \sin\frac{n\pi x}{a} \qquad \text{where } n = 1, 2, 3, \ldots \tag{15}$$

and A is some constant factor. The expression $n\pi x/a$ has, as can be checked, been arranged so that the function goes to zero at $x = 0$ and at $x = a$ for any integral value of n. That the function satisfies the Schrödinger equation can be tested by substitution in Eq. (14) to give

$$\text{Left side} = -\frac{h^2}{8\pi^2 m}\left(-\frac{n^2\pi^2}{a^2}\right) A \sin\frac{n\pi x}{a}$$

$$= \frac{n^2 h^2}{8ma^2}\left(A \sin\frac{n\pi x}{a}\right) \tag{16}$$

$$\text{Right side} = \epsilon\left(A \sin\frac{n\pi x}{a}\right) \tag{17}$$

The left and right sides of Eq. (14) are equal, and the expression

$$\psi = A \sin \frac{n\pi x}{a}$$

gives solutions of Eq. (14) if

$$\epsilon = \frac{n^2 h^2}{8ma^2} \qquad n = 1, 2, 3, \ldots \tag{18}$$

No really different solutions can be found, and no energies other than these will result. [The value $n = 0$ in Eq. (15) provides a solution to Eq. (14) but gives a wave function that is everywhere zero. This leads to a zero probability of a particle being anywhere in the box and is therefore unacceptable.] The allowed energies ϵ, which are represented in Fig. 1-1, are seen to be quantized as a result of the quite natural introduction of the integers in the solutions of the Schrödinger equation. A similar situation occurs generally in atomic and molecular problems. The quantum phenomena, which were so arbitrarily introduced in the Bohr theory, are seen to result much more naturally in Schrödinger's approach.

FIG. 1-1 Energies, wave functions, and probability functions for the particle-in-a-box problem.

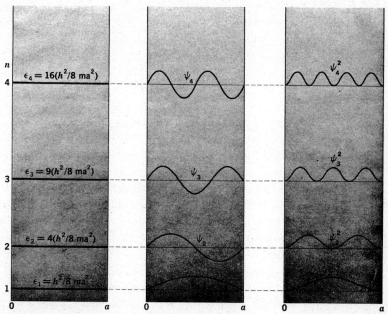

The solution functions, or *eigenfunctions*,

$$\psi = A \sin \frac{n\pi x}{a}$$

and the probability functions

$$\psi^2 = A^2 \sin^2 \frac{n\pi x}{a} \tag{19}$$

are shown opposite the corresponding energy level in Fig. 1-1.

This simple problem illustrates many of the characteristics of more difficult quantum-mechanical calculations on atomic and molecular systems. One finds that solutions exist for the Schrödinger equation only for certain values of ϵ and that the solution functions and the corresponding energies are characterized by an integer, called a quantum number. A number of situations will arise in later chapters where solution of the Schrödinger equation will present some mathematical complexities that cannot be dealt with here. In these cases, if the general features of Schrödinger equation solutions are appreciated, it will be sufficient to have the solution functions and allowed energies stated without derivation.

As an illustration of this Schrödinger equation problem the one-dimensional square-well, or "particle-in-a-box," solution can be applied to the question of the energies of the double-bonding or π electrons of a conjugated system. These electrons are apparently delocalized and are relatively free to move throughout the length of the molecule. One can therefore approximate such a system by representing the molecule as a one-dimensional region of uniform potential bounded by regions of infinitely high potential. The allowed energies of the π electrons, ignoring electron-electron repulsions, are then those given by the previous derivation; i.e., $\epsilon = n^2 h^2/8ma^2$. To apply this square-well approximation to the π electrons of a conjugated system, it remains to recall the Pauli exclusion principle which requires that no two electrons of a molecule have all their quantum numbers the same. Since the spin of an electron can be oriented to give a spin quantum number of $+\frac{1}{2}$ or $-\frac{1}{2}$, two electrons can be accommodated in a state represented by a single value of n. The occupancy of the energy levels by the six π electrons of hexatriene is represented in Fig. 1-2. The success of this simplification of the factors affecting π electrons in conjugated systems is judged by the comparison of the energy calculated for the promotion of one of the highest energy electron pair to the next higher energy state with the energy of the radiation quanta absorbed in an electronic spectral study. The agreement, as Exercise 1-2 illustrates, is remarkably good.

Exercise 1-2. Calculate the wavelength of the radiation that will be absorbed in the lowest energy π-electron transition of hexatriene according to the square-well model. The length of the molecule can be taken as about 7.3 A. Compare with the observed value of 2,580 A.

1-6. Normalization of Wave Functions

It is frequently convenient, when a wave function ψ is obtained for a particle, to arrange it so this function shows that there is a value of unity for the total probability of the particle being found somewhere in space. In terms of a one-dimensional problem this implies that

$$\int_{-\infty}^{+\infty} \psi^2 \, dx = 1 \tag{20}$$

For the particle-in-a-box problem, since ψ is zero everywhere outside the region 0 to a, the limits can be reduced to give

$$\int_{0}^{a} \psi^2 \, dx = 1 \tag{21}$$

A wave function that gives a total probability of unity is said to be *normalized*.

FIG. 1-2 The square-well model for the π electrons of hexatriene. The dashed arrow shows the transition that occurs when radiation is absorbed.

For the particle-in-a-box wave functions, normalization consists of evaluating A such that

$$\int_0^a A^2 \sin^2 \frac{n\pi x}{a}\, dx = 1 \tag{22}$$

The integration can be performed (or read from tables which give, if m is an integer, $\int_0^\pi \sin^2 my\, dy = \pi/2$) to give

$$\int_0^a \sin^2 \frac{n\pi x}{a}\, dx = \frac{a}{2} \tag{23}$$

For normalization, therefore,

$$A^2 \left(\frac{a}{2}\right) = 1$$

or

$$A = \sqrt{\frac{2}{a}} \tag{24}$$

The normalized wave functions for a particle in a box are, therefore,

$$\psi = \sqrt{\frac{2}{a}} \sin \frac{n\pi x}{a} \tag{25}$$

In a similar way, wave functions for other molecular problems can, and usually are, normalized. In the general three-dimensional case, if $d\tau$ represents the differential element of volume, the normalization condition on a wave function ψ is that

$$\int_{-\infty}^{+\infty} \psi^2\, d\tau = 1 \tag{26}$$

or, if the wave functions are complex,

$$\int_{-\infty}^{+\infty} \psi^* \psi\, d\tau = 1 \tag{27}$$

1-7. Orthogonality

A general property of wave functions, i.e., functions that solve the Schrödinger equation for a particular problem, is that of *orthogonality*, a property of considerable importance in spectroscopic problems. Two wave functions ψ_l and ψ_m, where l and m imply different quantum numbers, are such that

$$\int_{-\infty}^{+\infty} \psi_l \psi_m\, d\tau = 0$$

or, more generally,

$$\int_{-\infty}^{+\infty} \psi_l^* \psi_m \, d\tau = 0 \tag{28}$$

if l and m describe states with different energies.

This property is stated without proof. It can, however, be readily illustrated by the particle-in-a-box eigenfunctions. It is necessary to show that

$$\int_0^a \sin \frac{l\pi x}{a} \sin \frac{m\pi x}{a} \, dx = 0 \tag{29}$$

for $l \neq m$. Substitution of the variable $y = \pi x/a$ converts the left side of Eq. (29) to

$$\int_0^\pi \sin ly \sin my \, dy$$

where, it should be kept in mind, l and m are integers. The integral in this form can be shown to be zero by, for example, replacing the sine terms by

$$\sin ly = \frac{1}{2i} \left(e^{ily} - e^{-ily} \right)$$

and

$$\sin my = \frac{1}{2i} \left(e^{imy} - e^{-imy} \right) \tag{30}$$

and performing the integration on the exponential form of the integral. In this way one obtains zero for the integral and verifies the orthogonality statement of Eq. (29).

This is an example of the general orthogonality result that is applicable to the wave functions for states with different energies. Some additional features must be considered when there are several states, i.e., wave functions, corresponding to a single energy of the system.

A summary of this and the previous section can be given by the statement that if ψ_l and ψ_m are normalized, real, wave functions corresponding to nondegenerate states of a system

$$\int_{-\infty}^{+\infty} \psi_l \psi_m \, d\tau \begin{cases} = 0 & \text{for } l \neq m \\ = 1 & \text{for } l = m \end{cases} \tag{31}$$

These properties, it will be seen, lead to considerable simplification in a number of spectroscopic problems.

1-8. Symmetry Properties of Wave Functions

A general property of wave functions that is important in many spectroscopic problems is their form when, as is often the case, the potential-energy function is a symmetric one. The potential of the particle-in-a-box problem, for example, is symmetric about the point $x = a/2$ in Fig. 1-1. It is apparent from the plots of the wave functions shown in Fig. 1-1 that those with even values of n are functions that are antisymmetric about the mid-point of the well while those with odd values of n are symmetric. Such symmetry properties are characteristic of wave functions that arise from a problem with a symmetric potential function.

Generally, it is more satisfactory to use the center of symmetry, such as the mid-point of the square well, as the origin of the coordinate system. If this is done in the square-well case, the solution functions are sines and cosines as shown in Fig. 1-3. It is then possible to investigate the symmetry properties of the wave functions by investigating what happens when y is replaced by $-y$ in a particular wave function. When this is done for the functions shown in Fig. 1-3, one sees mathematically that

FIG. 1-3 The symmetry properties of the particle-in-a-box wave functions. (The wave functions shown are not normalized.)

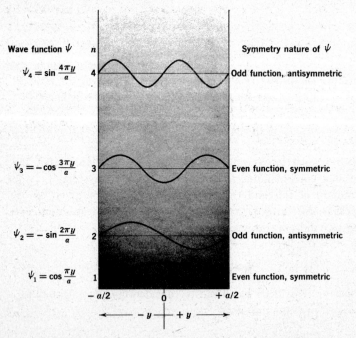

Wave function ψ	n		Symmetry nature of ψ
$\psi_4 = \sin \dfrac{4\pi y}{a}$	4		Odd function, antisymmetric
$\psi_3 = -\cos \dfrac{3\pi y}{a}$	3		Even function, symmetric
$\psi_2 = -\sin \dfrac{2\pi y}{a}$	2		Odd function, antisymmetric
$\psi_1 = \cos \dfrac{\pi y}{a}$	1		Even function, symmetric

$-a/2 \qquad 0 \qquad +a/2$

$\longleftarrow -y \ {\Large +}\ +y \longrightarrow$

For n odd

$$\psi(y) = \psi(-y)$$

For n even   (32)

$$\psi(y) = -\psi(-y)$$

Again one sees that for odd values of n the function is an even, or symmetric, function; while for even values of n the function is an odd, or antisymmetric, function.

*1-9. The Quantum-mechanical Average

Although the values of the allowed energies of a system are the quantum-mechanical results of prime importance for spectroscopy, we will have occasion to want to know the average value of some other properties. We will, for example, want to know the average position of a particle for which we have obtained an eigenfunction ψ from solution of the appropriate Schrödinger equation.

The method of finding a quantum-mechanical average, furthermore, allows the concept of operators, which will also be encountered later, to be introduced. In quantum mechanics every variable, such as position, momentum, and kinetic energy, has associated with it what is called an operator. If one of these variables is denoted by g and the operator for this function by G, then operation on the wave function of the system by G will give, in some cases, the value for the variable g times ψ, i.e.,

$$G\psi = g\psi$$ (33)

Only a few functions and their operators will be encountered, and these are listed in Table 1-1. The operator for kinetic energy can be used to illustrate the basic operator relation $G\psi = g\psi$. The kinetic-energy operator, denoted by T is, for one-dimensional motion along the x axis,

$$T_x = -\frac{h^2}{8\pi^2 m}\frac{\partial^2}{\partial x^2}$$ (34)

The calculation of the average value of the kinetic energy of a particle in a box can be used to illustrate this operator. Since $\psi = A \sin n\pi x/a$, operation on this function by T_x gives

$$T_x\psi = -\frac{h^2}{8\pi^2 m}\left(-\sqrt{\frac{2}{a}}\right)\left(\frac{n\pi}{a}\right)^2 \sin\frac{n\pi x}{a}$$

$$= \frac{n^2 h^2}{8ma^2}\sqrt{\frac{2}{a}}\sin\frac{n\pi x}{a} = \frac{n^2 h^2}{8ma^2}\psi$$ (35)

Here operation on ψ by T_x gives a quantity $n^2h^2/8ma^2$ times ψ. Since T_x is the kinetic-energy operator, the values of $n^2h^2/8ma^2$ are the allowed kinetic energies of the particle. This result, since the potential energy was taken as zero, agrees with that obtained previously.

One further feature of the nature of these operators must be pointed out. Sometimes an operator acts on ψ and does not lead to a number, such as $n^2h^2/8ma^2$ in the example, times the wave function. Thus the momentum operator acting on the particle-in-a-box wave function is

$$P_x\left(\sqrt{\frac{2}{a}}\sin\frac{n\pi x}{a}\right) = \frac{h}{2\pi i}\sqrt{\frac{2}{a}}\left(\frac{n\pi}{a}\right)\cos\frac{n\pi x}{a} \tag{36}$$

TABLE 1-1 Some Quantum-mechanical Operators
(In terms of cartesian coordinates x, y, z and polar coordinates r, θ, ϕ)

Variable	Operator
Position:	
x	x
y	y
z	z
Linear momentum:	
P_x	$\dfrac{h}{2\pi i}\dfrac{\partial}{\partial x}$
P_y	$\dfrac{h}{2\pi i}\dfrac{\partial}{\partial y}$
P_z	$\dfrac{h}{2\pi i}\dfrac{\partial}{\partial z}$
Angular momentum:	
M_x	$\dfrac{h}{2\pi i}\left(y\dfrac{\partial}{\partial z} - z\dfrac{\partial}{\partial y}\right)$ or
	$\dfrac{h}{2\pi i}\left(-\sin\phi\dfrac{\partial}{\partial\theta} - \cot\theta\cos\phi\dfrac{\partial}{\partial\phi}\right)$
M_y	$\dfrac{h}{2\pi i}\left(z\dfrac{\partial}{\partial x} - x\dfrac{\partial}{\partial z}\right)$ or
	$\dfrac{h}{2\pi i}\left(\cos\phi\dfrac{\partial}{\partial\theta} - \cot\theta\sin\phi\dfrac{\partial}{\partial\phi}\right)$
M_z	$\dfrac{h}{2\pi i}\left(x\dfrac{\partial}{\partial y} - y\dfrac{\partial}{\partial x}\right)$ or
	$\dfrac{h}{2\pi i}\left(\dfrac{\partial}{\partial\phi}\right)$
$M^2 = M_x^2 + M_y^2 + M_z^2$	$-\dfrac{h^2}{4\pi^2}\left[\dfrac{1}{\sin\theta}\dfrac{\partial}{\partial\theta}\left(\sin\theta\dfrac{\partial}{\partial\theta}\right) + \dfrac{1}{\sin^2\theta}\dfrac{\partial^2}{\partial\phi^2}\right]$
Kinetic energy:	
$\frac{1}{2}m(v_x^2 + v_y^2 + v_z^2)$	$-\dfrac{h^2}{8\pi^2 m}\left(\dfrac{\partial^2}{\partial x^2} + \dfrac{\partial^2}{\partial y^2} + \dfrac{\partial^2}{\partial z^2}\right)$
Potential energy:	
$V(x,y,z)$	$V(x,y,z)$

In such cases one is to understand that the variable being investigated is not a constant for one of the allowed states. Rather it has various values at various positions. For such functions, the *average* value of the variable is obtained according to the general rule

$$g = \frac{\int_{-\infty}^{+\infty} \psi^* G \psi \, d\tau}{\int_{-\infty}^{+\infty} \psi^* \psi \, d\tau} \tag{37}$$

For normalized functions the denominator is of course equal to unity. For normalized, real functions, the average value of a variable is, therefore,

$$g = \int_{-\infty}^{+\infty} \psi G \psi \, d\tau \tag{38}$$

One obtains the average momentum with this relation as

$$
\begin{aligned}
P_{av} &= \int_0^a \left(\sqrt{\frac{2}{a}} \sin \frac{n\pi x}{a} \right) \frac{h}{2\pi i} \sqrt{\frac{2}{a}} \left(\frac{n\pi}{a} \right) \cos \frac{n\pi x}{a} \, dx \\
&= \frac{nh}{ia^2} \int_0^a \sin \frac{n\pi x}{a} \cos \frac{n\pi x}{a} \, dx \\
&= \frac{nh}{ia^2} \left(\frac{a}{2n\pi} \right) \left[\sin^2 \frac{n\pi x}{a} \right]_0^a \\
&= 0
\end{aligned}
\tag{39}
$$

The result of an average momentum of zero reflects the fact that the classical picture of the motion of the particle would ascribe both positive and negative values to the momentum since the particle would move in either direction.

Exercise 1-3. Obtain the average position of a particle in a box in the $n = 1$ state using the operator method of Eq. (38).

Similar applications of Eq. (37), or (38), will be made in a number of spectroscopic problems.

1-10. The Boltzmann Distribution

Spectra can be interpreted in terms of the energies of the allowed states if one can decide which of the allowed states will in fact be occupied by the molecules of the sample. In the particle-in-a-box example the question that would have to be asked is: If some large number (frequently it is convenient to consider an Avogadro's number 6×10^{23}) of particles are placed in such a potential well, how many will behave according to the $n = 1$ wave function, i.e., occupy the $n = 1$ level; how many the $n = 2$ level; and so forth? (In Sec. 1-5 the tacit assumption that the lowest available levels would be occupied was made.)

The answer to such questions is given by the Boltzmann distribution which states that the number of particles N_i occupying a state with energy ϵ_i will be related to the number N_j occupying some state with energy ϵ_j, which is lower than ϵ_i, by the relation

$$\frac{N_i}{N_j} = e^{-(\epsilon_i - \epsilon_j)/kT} \tag{40}$$

where k is Boltzmann's constant, 1.380×10^{-16} erg/deg molecule. If it is more convenient to measure the energies of the states in calories per mole, the appropriate expression is

$$\frac{N_i}{N_j} = e^{-(E_i - E_j)/RT} \tag{41}$$

where R, equal to Nk, is 1.987 cal/mole deg.

Most often one is interested in the number of molecules in a state with an energy ϵ_i compared to the number in the lowest energy state ϵ_0. The appropriate form of the Boltzmann distribution is then

$$N_i = N_0 e^{-(\epsilon_i - \epsilon_0)/kT} \tag{42}$$

Sometimes, as was mentioned in Sec. 1-2, there are several states with the same energy. The population of the energy level is then correspondingly greater. Thus if g_i is the multiplicity of the ith energy level, i.e., the number of states with energy ϵ_i, and as is usually the case, the lowest energy level is a single state, the number of molecules with energy ϵ_i compared to the number with energy ϵ_0 is

$$N_i = g_i N_0 e^{-(\epsilon_i - \epsilon_0)/kT} \tag{43}$$

[Note that the number in each state at energy ϵ_i is still $N_0 e^{-(\epsilon_i - \epsilon_0)/kT}$. There are, however, g_i states at energy ϵ_i.]

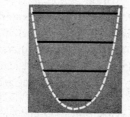

2

THE VIBRATIONAL ENERGIES OF A DIATOMIC MOLECULE

The general introduction to the theory of atomic and molecular systems of the preceding chapter can now be applied to the particular case of simple vibrating systems.   First the classical behavior of a single particle and a pair of particles will be treated according to classical mechanics. Then the corresponding problem with molecular-sized units and quantum mechanics will be studied.   The energy levels deduced in these calculations will then be compared with the separation between these energy levels indicated by spectroscopic transitions.

We will see that changes in the vibrational energy of the simple systems dealt with here lead, in spectroscopic studies, to absorption of radiation in the infrared spectral region.   The chemist may well be already familiar with the complicated absorption pattern, like that of Fig. 2-1b, which large molecules show in this region.   The rather "mechanical" treatment of simple vibrating systems in this chapter constitutes an introduction to these more complex, but chemically more interesting, systems.

In later chapters a number of points that are here mentioned in passing will be dealt with in greater detail.   Thus, Chap. 4 will deal with the transition process that takes a molecule from one energy level to another, and Chap. 6 will recognize that gas-phase molecules engage in simultaneous rotation and vibration and that it must be shown to what extent these motions can be treated separately.   It seems desirable,

25

however, to present some introductory material before these questions
are raised.

2-1. The Vibrations of a Single Particle (Classical)

It will be apparent from the next few sections that an understanding
of the behavior of macroscopic, i.e., ordinary-sized, particles which can
be described by classical mechanics is very helpful when the quantum-
mechanical behavior of molecules is encountered.   The simplest classical
vibrational problem is that illustrated in Fig. 2-2.   The effect of gravity
is here ignored.

The question that is asked is: What type of vibrational motion does
the particle of mass m undergo?

The answer clearly depends, among other things, on the nature of
the spring.   It is found that many springs are such that if the particle is
removed a distance from its equilibrium position, it experiences a restoring force that is proportional to its displacement from the equilibrium

FIG. 2-1   The absorption of radiation in the infrared spectral region by (a) a diatomic
molecule and (b) a polyatomic molecule.   In general, the greater the number of atoms
in a molecule, the more ways the molecule can vibrate and the more complex is the
infrared absorption spectrum.

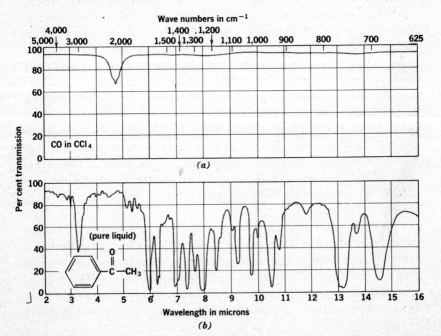

position.   A spring which behaves in this manner is said to obey Hooke's law.   For such behavior one can write

$$f \propto x \tag{1}$$

or

$$f = -kx \tag{2}$$

where x, the measure of the displacement from the equilibrium position, is the *displacement coordinate*, f is the force which the spring imposes on the particle, and k is a proportionality constant called the *force constant*. It should be appreciated that k, which will also appear in molecular problems, measures the stiffness of the spring; i.e., it gives the restoring force for unit displacement from the equilibrium position.   The minus sign, written explicitly in Eq. (2) so that k will be positive, enters because

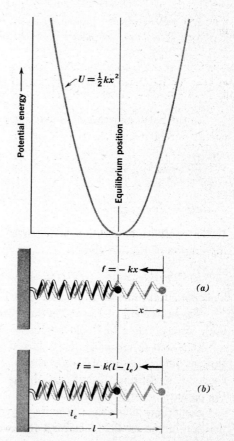

FIG. 2-2 The restoring force and potential-energy function for a ball-and-spring system obeying Hooke's law. The displacement from the equilibrium position is measured in (a) from the equilibrium position and in (b) from the point of attachment of the spring.

as x increases in one direction the force increases but is directed in the opposite direction.

Before proceeding to the problem of the nature of the vibrations, it is important to point out that Hooke's law implies that the potential energy of the particle increases parabolically as the particle moves in either direction from the equilibrium position. The work that must be done to displace the particle a distance dx is $f_{applied}\, dx$, and this work is stored as potential energy U. Thus

$$dU = f_{applied}\, dx \tag{3}$$

It is more convenient to deal with the force f that the spring exerts on the particle and, since it is this force that the applied force acts against, one has $f = -f_{applied}$ and

$$dU = (-f)\, dx$$
or
$$\frac{dU}{dx} = -f \tag{4}$$

This is an important and general relation between force and potential energy.

In the particular case of Hooke's law, where $f = -kx$, the potential-energy derivative is

$$\frac{dU}{dx} = kx$$
or
$$dU = kx\, dx \tag{5}$$

If the equilibrium position is taken as that of zero potential energy, integration of Eq. (5) gives

$$U = \tfrac{1}{2}kx^2 \tag{6}$$

This potential function is illustrated in Fig. 2-2.

The statement of Eq. (6) is therefore equivalent to that of Eq. (2), both corresponding to Hooke's law.

It is well to recognize here, since it will be encountered again later, that, as differentiation of Eq. (6) shows, k is equal to d^2U/dx^2. The force constant, measuring the stiffness of a spring, is equal to the curvature of the potential-energy function.

Sometimes a problem is more conveniently set up in terms of the position of the particle measured from some other reference point than the equilibrium position.   If, as Fig. 2-2b indicates, the length of the spring is l and the equilibrium length is l_e, the previous results are expressed as

$$f = -k(l - l_e) \qquad \text{and} \qquad U = \tfrac{1}{2}k(l - l_e)^2 \tag{7}$$

The equation describing the motion of the particle can now be set up. One way of doing this is to substitute into Newton's $f = ma$ equation to obtain

$$-kx = m\frac{d^2x}{dt^2} \qquad \text{or} \qquad -kx = m\ddot{x} \tag{8}$$

It is often more convenient to start with statements about the kinetic and potential energies of the particle.   One then writes

$$\begin{aligned} \text{Kinetic energy} &= T = \tfrac{1}{2}m\dot{x}^2 \\ \text{Potential energy} &= U = \tfrac{1}{2}kx^2 \end{aligned} \tag{9}$$

An equation equivalent to the $f = ma$ equation that can then be used to solve for the nature of the motion of the particle is that of Lagrange

$$\frac{d}{dt}\left(\frac{dT}{d\dot{x}}\right) + \frac{dU}{dx} = 0 \tag{10}$$

One can note that, since

$$\frac{dT}{d\dot{x}} = m\dot{x} \qquad \text{and} \qquad \frac{d}{dt}\left(\frac{dT}{d\dot{x}}\right) = m\ddot{x}$$

the same expression

$$m\ddot{x} + kx = 0 \qquad \text{or} \qquad -kx = m\ddot{x} \tag{11}$$

as set up by Newton's $f = ma$ relation, is obtained.

The differential equation, Eq. (11), has a solution of the form

$$x = A\,\cos\,(2\pi\nu t + \varphi) \tag{12}$$

The correctness of this solution can be verified by substituting Eq. (12) and its second derivative with respect to time

$$\ddot{x} = -4\pi^2\nu^2 A\,\cos\,(2\pi\nu t + \varphi) \tag{13}$$

back into the differential equation.   When this is done one obtains an equality if

$$-4\pi^2\nu^2 m = -k$$

or

$$\nu = \frac{1}{2\pi}\sqrt{\frac{k}{m}} \tag{14}$$

This equation is the important *classical* result. It shows that a particle with mass m held by a spring with force constant k will vibrate according to Eq. (12) with the frequency ν given by Eq. (14). Only this frequency is allowed. The energy with which the particle vibrates can be shown to depend on the maximum displacement, i.e., the amplitude A of the vibration.

The quantum-mechanical result will differ from this (not all vibrational energies will be allowed), but it will be seen that the quantum-mechanical solution retains a considerable similarity to Eq. (14).

2-2. The Vibrations of Two Particles Connected by a Spring (Classical)

It is worth while treating one additional problem in a completely classical manner before we proceed to molecular systems. Consider the macroscopic system of a spring and two particles, which provides the counterpart of the diatomic-molecule problem. The particles will, for simplicity, be allowed to move only along the line of the system. Again it is asked: What is the nature of the motion that these particles undergo?

FIG. 2-3 The shape of the potential energy–bond length curve for a diatomic molecule. The displacement coordinate q is defined as $q = r - r_e$.

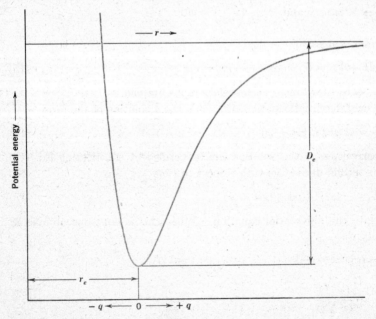

If x_1 and x_2 represent displacements of the particles of mass m_1 and m_2 from initial positions in which the particles were separated by their equilibrium distance, and if Hooke's law is assumed for the spring, the kinetic and potential energies can be written as

$$T = \tfrac{1}{2}(m_1\dot{x}_1^2 + m_2\dot{x}_2^2)$$

and (15)

$$U = \tfrac{1}{2}k(x_2 - x_1)^2$$

Although one could solve the problem by writing $f = ma$ for each particle, the use of Lagrange's equation, which will be important in later work, will be illustrated here. For each particle i, one writes the Lagrange equation as

$$\frac{d}{dt}\left(\frac{\partial T}{\partial \dot{x}_i}\right) + \frac{\partial U}{\partial x_i} = 0 \qquad (16)$$

Since the simultaneous motion of two particles is being considered, two equations in two unknowns will be obtained. Two methods of solution, which are presented here because they introduce methods that will be encountered in molecular vibrational problems, can be used.

a. Direct Solution. With either Lagrange's equations or $f = ma$ applied to each particle, one obtains

$$m_1\ddot{x}_1 - k(x_2 - x_1) = 0$$

and (17)

$$m_2\ddot{x}_2 + k(x_2 - x_1) = 0$$

Let us again see if solutions of the type found for the single-particle problem exist. We try, therefore,

$$x_1 = A_1 \cos (2\pi \nu t + \varphi)$$

and (18)

$$x_2 = A_2 \cos (2\pi \nu t + \varphi)$$

where the amplitudes A_1 and A_2 may be different but where, if a vibrational solution is to be found, the frequency will be that of the system and must be the same for particles 1 and 2. Substitution of

$$\ddot{x}_1 = -4\pi^2\nu^2 A_1 \cos (2\pi \nu t + \varphi)$$

and (19)

$$\ddot{x}_2 = -4\pi^2\nu^2 A_2 \cos (2\pi \nu t + \varphi)$$

and Eqs. (18) into Eqs. (17) gives, on rearranging,

$$(-4\pi^2\nu^2 m_1 + k)A_1 - kA_2 = 0$$

and (20)

$$-kA_1 + (-4\pi^2\nu^2 m_2 + k)A_2 = 0$$

One can now eliminate A_1 or A_2 from these two equations to get a relation for ν. This is most conveniently done by recalling that for such linear homogeneous equations *nontrivial solutions for the A's will exist only if the determinant of the coefficients of the A's is zero.* That is,

$$\begin{vmatrix} (-4\pi^2\nu^2 m_1 + k) & -k \\ -k & (-4\pi^2\nu^2 m_2 + k) \end{vmatrix} = 0 \qquad (21)$$

This determinant, on expansion, yields the equation

$$(4\pi^2\nu^2)^2 m_1 m_2 - 4\pi^2\nu^2 k(m_1 + m_2) + k^2 - k^2 = 0 \qquad (22)$$

which has the roots

$$\nu = 0 \qquad (23)$$

and

$$\nu = \frac{1}{2\pi}\sqrt{\frac{k}{\mu}} \qquad \text{where} \qquad \mu = \frac{m_1 m_2}{m_1 + m_2} \qquad (24)$$

The quantity μ which is introduced here will be frequently encountered and is given the name the *reduced mass*. There are, therefore, two natural frequencies for the system, one of the frequencies being zero.

The motions that correspond to these frequencies can be recognized if the relation of the two amplitudes A_1 and A_2 is found.

Substitution of $\nu = 0$ in either of the equations of Eqs. (20) gives, after rearranging,

$$A_1 = A_2 \qquad (25)$$

and, therefore, $x_1 = x_2$. Thus the motion corresponding to $\nu = 0$ consists of displacement of the particles by the same amount and in the same direction. The $\nu = 0$ root corresponds, therefore, to a translational motion of the entire system.

Substitution of $\nu = 1/2\pi\sqrt{k/\mu}$ in either of Eqs. (20) gives, after substitution of $\mu = m_1 m_2/m_1 + m_2$ and rearranging,

$$\frac{A_1}{A_2} = -\frac{m_2}{m_1}$$

and $\qquad\qquad\qquad\qquad\qquad\qquad\qquad\qquad\qquad\qquad\qquad\qquad (26)$

$$\frac{x_1}{x_2} = -\frac{m_2}{m_1}$$

If the two masses are equal, one gets $A_1 = -A_2$ and $x_1 = -x_2$. The motion corresponding to $\nu = 1/2\pi\sqrt{k/\mu}$ can be generated, in view of Eqs. (18), by displacing the particles from their equilibrium position by equal and opposite amounts. The motion that will occur will clearly be one of vibration and will have the frequency $\nu = 1/2\pi \sqrt{k/\mu}$.

It should be recognized from Eq. (26) that if the masses of the two particles are not equal, the lighter one will move with a greater amplitude than the heavier one. Thus if m_1 is less than m_2, Eq. (26) shows that the amplitude of particle 1 will be correspondingly greater than that of particle 2.

Exercise 2-1. Obtain the relation between A_1 and A_2 for the two roots of Eq. (21) by comparing the appropriate minors of the determinant.

b. *Solution in Terms of an Internal and a Center-of-mass Coordinate.* The existence of a translational mode and a vibrational one can be recognized at the outset, and the problem can be set up in terms of coordinates which are especially suited to describe these motions. Thus, rather than displacements x_1 and x_2, one could choose to use the coordinates

$$q = x_2 - x_1$$

and

$$X = \frac{m_1 x_1 + m_2 x_2}{m_1 + m_2} \qquad (27)$$

Now q is a measure of the displacement of the distance between the particles from the original equilibrium value, and X is a measure of the displacement of the center of mass of the system. In terms of these coordinates one can immediately write down the potential energy as

$$U = \tfrac{1}{2}k(x_2 - x_1)^2 = \tfrac{1}{2}kq^2 \qquad (28)$$

The kinetic energy is always easily written in terms of simple cartesian coordinates. Thus

$$T = \tfrac{1}{2}(m_1 \dot{x}_1^2 + m_2 \dot{x}_2^2)$$

This expression must be converted to one involving q and X.

From Eqs. (27) one obtains by rearrangement, or by forming the inverse transformation,

$$x_1 = X - \frac{m_2}{m_1 + m_2} q$$

and

$$x_2 = X + \frac{m_1}{m_1 + m_2} q \qquad (29)$$

These allow the kinetic energy to be written as

$$T = \frac{1}{2}(m_1 + m_2)\dot{X}^2 + \frac{1}{2}\left(\frac{m_1 m_2}{m_1 + m_2}\right)\dot{q}^2 \qquad (30)$$

The Lagrange equation, applied to the coordinate q, then gives

$$\frac{m_1 m_2}{m_1 + m_2} \ddot{q} + kq = 0$$

or   (31)

$$\mu\ddot{q} + kq = 0$$

This can be recognized as identical to Eq. (11) for the vibration of a single particle.   Only a change in notation from m to μ and x to q has occurred. The solution to Eq. (31) is, therefore, the same as that for Eq. (11), and we can write down the solution as

$$q = A \cos (2\pi\nu t + \varphi)$$ (32)

and

$$\nu = \frac{1}{2\pi} \sqrt{\frac{k}{\mu}}$$ (33)

The Lagrange equation for X retains only the kinetic-energy term and leads to

$$(m_1 + m_2)\ddot{X} = 0$$

or   (34)

$$\ddot{X} = 0$$

A solution which is formally like that obtained previously is

$$X = A \cos (2\pi\nu t + \varphi)$$

with $\nu = 0$.   Alternatively one can write the solution velocity as $\dot{X} = $ const t representing a uniform velocity of the center of mass of the system.

The advantage of this procedure of recognizing the existence of translational and vibrational modes initially is that one ends up with one equation which determines the vibrational motion and another which determines the translational motion.   Previously, two simultaneous equations were obtained, and these had to be solved to extract the desired information on the vibrational motion.   For problems of much complexity it is of great value to eliminate the translational and rotational motions before the vibrational problem is developed.

Exercise 2-2.   By finding the inverse of the transformation matrix for the x's in terms of q and X, obtain the expressions of Eq. (29).

2-3. The Potential-energy Function for a Chemical Bond

A preliminary to the study of the vibrations of a molecule, as with a macroscopic mass and spring system, is a consideration of the nature of the variation of the potential energy with the position of the atoms. More particularly, for a diatomic molecule, one asks about the change in potential energy of the molecule as a function of the distortion of the bond of the molecule from its equilibrium distance.

Except for the case of H_2, it has not been possible to calculate the energy of the molecule as a function of internuclear distance from the interactions between the bonding electrons and the atomic nuclei. The general shape of the potential-energy versus bond-length curve can, however, be sketched. One knows, for example, that if a bond is stretched far enough it will break, i.e., a molecule can be dissociated, and that bonds strongly resist compression, as is revealed, for example, by the relative incompressibility of solids. Such qualitative ideas, and more exact ones that will be developed, lead to a potential curve of the form shown in Fig. 2-3.

Although no exact mathematical expression for the potential energy curves of all molecules is known, a simple and often convenient one that yields curves of the shape of that in Fig. 2-3 has been given by P. M. Morse. He has suggested the relation

$$U(q) = D_e(1 - e^{-\beta q})^2 \tag{35}$$

where, as before, q measures the distortion of the bond from its equilibrium length; D_e is the dissociation energy measured from the equilibrium position, i.e., from the minimum of the curve; and β is a constant for any given molecule and can be said to determine the narrowness, or curvature, of the potential well. The Morse curve with the values of D_e and β that are appropriate to HCl is shown in Fig. 2-4.

Exercise 2-3. The value of β in the Morse equation can be conveniently calculated from the relation

$$\beta = \bar{\omega}_e \sqrt{\frac{2\pi^2 c\mu}{D_e h}}$$

Determine β for H_2 for which $\bar{\omega}_e = 4{,}395$ cm^{-1} and $D_e = 38{,}310$ cm^{-1}. Plot the harmonic oscillator, using $k = 5.2 \times 10^5$ dyne/cm, and Morse curves for H_2 as has been done for HCl in Fig. 2-3. (The quantity $\bar{\omega}_e$ is related to the vibrational level spacing as will be shown in Sec. 2-6.)

A straightforward procedure for deducing the allowed vibrational energies would be to substitute the Morse function into the Schrödinger equation and, in much the same way as was done for the square-well problem, to look for functions that solve the resulting differential equation. The pattern of allowed energies, known in terms of D_e and β, could then be compared with the observed spectrum. Some mathematical difficulties arise in this procedure, and a simpler and more fruitful procedure is followed.

It will be seen shortly that the vibrations of a molecule result in only small distortions of the bond from its equilibrium length. In a study of the vibrational motion of a molecule we are, therefore, particularly interested only in an expression for the potential energy near the minimum in the potential-energy curve. This suggests that a suitable expression for the potential energy can be obtained by a series expansion about the minimum. If q is the displacement of the bond from its equilibrium length, a Maclaurin series expansion about $q = 0$ gives

$$U(q) = U_{q=0} + \left(\frac{dU}{dq}\right)_{q=0} q + \frac{1}{2}\left(\frac{d^2U}{dq^2}\right)_{q=0} q^2 + \cdots \tag{36}$$

The usual choice of $U = 0$ at $r = r_e$, or $q = 0$, sets $U_{q=0}$ equal to zero. Furthermore, at $q = 0$ the potential energy is a minimum, and therefore $(dU/dq)_{q=0}$ must be zero. If only the next higher term in the expansion is

FIG. 2-4 The harmonic oscillator (dashed line) and Morse (solid line) potential-energy functions for HCl.

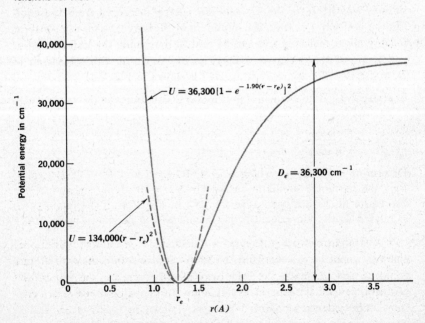

$$U = 36,300[1 - e^{-1.90(r - r_e)}]^2$$

$$D_e = 36,300 \text{ cm}^{-1}$$

$$U = 134,000(r - r_e)^2$$

Potential energy in cm^{-1}

$r(A)$

retained, we have the approximation, valid near the equilibrium position,

$$U(q) = \frac{1}{2}\left(\frac{d^2U}{dq^2}\right)_{q=0} q^2 \tag{37}$$

This result should be recognized, by comparison with Eq. (6), as identical to that which would have been obtained if it had been assumed that a chemical bond behaves as a spring following Hooke's law.   (For a true Hooke's law spring, d^2U/dq^2 is equal to k at all values of q; i.e., U is a parabola.   For a chemical bond the curve can be said to approximate a parabola only near the minimum.   The force constant is then the value of d^2U/dq^2 near the minimum.)   Figure 2-4 shows the parabola that fits the Morse curve for HCl near the minimum.

When the parabolic potential function is used to approximate the potential of a chemical bond, the system is said to be treated as a *harmonic oscillator*.

2-4. The Quantum-mechanical Solutions of the Harmonic Oscillator

The solution of the two-particle problem by method b in Sec. 2-2 showed that the vibrational equation that arises for the vibration of the two-particle system is identical in form to that for a single vibrating particle.   It is only necessary to replace m by μ and x, the displacement of the single particle from its equilibrium position, by $q = x_2 - x_1$, the distortion of the distance between the two particles from the equilibrium bond length.   The same situation is true in the quantum-mechanical problem.   The Schrödinger equation for a single atom of mass m subject to a potential of $U = \frac{1}{2}kx^2$ is

$$-\frac{h^2}{8\pi^2 m}\frac{d^2\psi}{dx^2} + \left(\frac{1}{2}kx^2\right)\psi = \epsilon\psi \tag{38}$$

while that for the vibrations of a diatomic molecule with reduced mass μ is, correspondingly,

$$-\frac{h^2}{8\pi^2 \mu}\frac{d^2\psi}{dq^2} + \left(\frac{1}{2}kq^2\right)\psi = \epsilon\psi \tag{39}$$

The deduction of solution functions will not be followed through here but can be found in any textbook on quantum mechanics.   The procedure should be recognized to be essentially that followed in the simpler square-well problem.   (The solution functions for the two problems are in fact similar, and those which will be given as solutions to the harmonic-oscillator problem should be compared with those previously obtained for the square-well problem.)

It is found, as would be expected from the similar square-well problem, that solution functions exist for certain values of ϵ and that these functions, and the values of ϵ, are characterized by a quantum number. Thus, there are again certain allowed states, and each of these states has a specified energy. The integer that describes these states is usually represented by v. It can take on the values 0, 1, 2, ...

The energies of the allowed states are given by the expression

$$\epsilon_v = \left(v + \frac{1}{2}\right) \frac{h}{2\pi} \sqrt{\frac{k}{\mu}} \qquad \text{where } v = 0, 1, 2, \ldots \tag{40}$$

These allowed energies are shown, along with the potential-energy function, in Fig. 2-5. The appearance in Eq. (40) of the same quantities as in the classical calculation of a vibrating system should be noted. This

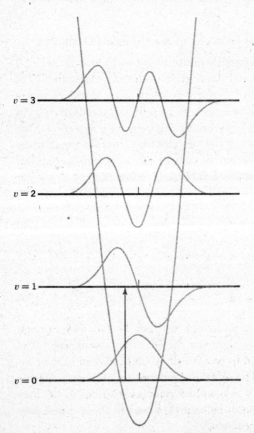

FIG. 2-5 The harmonic-oscillator wave functions and the fundamental vibrational transition.

relation to the classical problem is sometimes made use of by writing

$$\epsilon_v = (v + \tfrac{1}{2})h\omega \tag{41}$$

where $\omega = 1/2\pi \sqrt{k/\mu}$ is written for the frequency with which, according to Eq. (14), the system would vibrate if it behaved classically. (In what follows, ω will be used for a molecular vibrational property and ν will be reserved for the frequency of radiation.)

The form of the solution functions, or eigenfunctions, is also shown in Fig. 2-5. Although little will be done with the solution wave functions themselves, it can be mentioned that each involves a set of series terms known as a Hermite polynomial. If one introduces α as

$$\alpha = \frac{2\pi \sqrt{\mu k}}{h} \tag{42}$$

the solution functions can be written as

$$\psi_v = N_v e^{-\frac{1}{2}\alpha q^2} H_v(\sqrt{\alpha}q) \qquad \text{where } v = 0, 1, 2, \ldots \tag{43}$$

and H_v is the Hermite polynomial of degree v. The normalizing factor N_v is

$$N_v = \left(\frac{\sqrt{\alpha}}{2^v v! \sqrt{\pi}}\right)^{\frac{1}{2}} \tag{44}$$

For most purposes it will be enough to recognize the form of the solution functions shown in Fig. 2-5. For those unfamiliar with the Hermite polynomials it may be informative, however, to write down a few of the first solution functions.

$$\begin{aligned}
\psi_0 &= \left(\frac{\alpha}{\pi}\right)^{\frac{1}{4}} e^{-\frac{1}{2}\alpha q^2} \\
\psi_1 &= \sqrt{2\alpha} \left(\frac{\alpha}{\pi}\right)^{\frac{1}{4}} q e^{-\frac{1}{2}\alpha q^2} \\
\psi_2 &= \frac{1}{\sqrt{2}} \left(\frac{\alpha}{\pi}\right)^{\frac{1}{4}} (2\alpha q^2 - 1) e^{-\frac{1}{2}\alpha q^2} \\
\psi_3 &= \sqrt{\frac{\alpha}{3}} \left(\frac{\alpha}{\pi}\right)^{\frac{1}{4}} (2\alpha^{\frac{3}{2}} q^3 - 3\alpha^{\frac{1}{2}} q) e^{-\frac{1}{2}\alpha q^2} \\
\psi_4 &= \frac{1}{\sqrt[2]{6}} \left(\frac{\alpha}{\pi}\right)^{\frac{1}{4}} (4\alpha^2 q^4 - 12\alpha q^2 + 3) e^{-\frac{1}{2}\alpha q^2}
\end{aligned} \tag{45}$$

The spectral absorptions or emissions attributable to changes in the vibrational energy of a molecule will now be discussed in terms of the energy levels of Fig. 2-5.

2-5. Vibrational Absorption Spectra of Diatomic Molecules

The previous section has shown that the allowed energy levels of a vibrating molecule form a pattern of equally spaced levels with a separation that is related to the molecular properties by the relation

$$\Delta\epsilon = \epsilon_{v+1} - \epsilon_v = \frac{h}{2\pi}\sqrt{\frac{k}{\mu}} \tag{46}$$

The spectral transitions that are to be expected to arise from such an energy-level pattern can be predicted if one also knows what transitions can occur with the absorption or emission of radiation and what energy levels are appreciably populated at the temperature of the experiment.

Although the interaction of molecules with radiation will be dealt with in Chap. 4, some of the results that will be obtained can be mentioned here. First of all, it will be shown that a vibrating molecule cannot interact with electromagnetic radiation unless a vibrating, or oscillating, dipole moment accompanies the molecular vibration. Qualitatively, one can picture an oscillating dipole as coupling with the electric field of the radiation so that energy can be exchanged between the molecule and the radiation. This stipulation that the vibration be accompanied by a dipole-moment change implies that all homonuclear diatomic molecules, which necessarily have zero dipole moment for all bond lengths, will fail to interact with radiation and will exhibit no vibrational spectral transitions. On the other hand, a heteronuclear diatomic molecule will generally have a dipole moment and, generally, the dipole moment will be dependent on the internuclear distance. The vibration of a heteronuclear diatomic molecule will, therefore, be generally accompanied by an oscillating dipole moment. Such molecules can interact with radiation and can absorb energy of the radiation and can thereby change their vibrational state to one of higher energy. They can, also, emit radiation energy and thereby change their vibrational state to one of lower energy.

One further transition restriction, which will be discussed in Chap. 4, must be mentioned. Even for those molecules that have an oscillating dipole moment there is the further restriction, which is rigorously applicable only to harmonic oscillator type systems, that the vibrational quantum number can change only by one unit. Transitions are allowed, therefore, only if

$$\Delta v = \pm 1 \tag{47}$$

This restriction is an example of a *selection rule*. For absorption experiments, which are those most commonly performed, the applicable part of the selection rule is, of course, $\Delta v = +1$.

Now that the allowed transitions have been stated, it is only necessary to decide in which state, or states, the molecules are likely to be found at the beginning of an experiment. It will be shown that the energy spacing between vibrational energy levels is typically of the order of 2×10^{-13} erg/molecule or 3000 cal/mole. With Boltzmann's distribution one can calculate the number of molecules in the $v = 1$ state compared with the number in the $v = 0$ state at 25°C as

$$\frac{N_{v=1}}{N_{v=0}} = e^{-2\times10^{-13}/298(1.38\times10^{-16})}$$

$$= 0.008 \tag{48}$$

Thus, less than 1 per cent of the molecules are in the $v = 1$ state, and negligibly small numbers will be in still higher energy states. It follows that, in experiments not much above room temperature, the transitions that begin with the $v = 0$ state will be of major importance.

The selection rule and population statements allow the vertical arrow of Fig. 2-5 to be drawn to indicate the expected spectral vibrational transition for an absorption experiment with a heteronuclear diatomic molecule.

It is found experimentally that such molecules do lead to the absorption of radiation quanta in the infrared spectral region and that this absorption can be attributed to the vibrational transition. Thus, HCl absorbs radiation with $\bar{\nu} = 2,890$ cm^{-1} or

$$\nu = 3 \times 10^{10}(2,890) = 8.67 \times 10^{13} \text{ cycles/sec}$$

The energy of the quanta of this radiation is

$$\Delta\epsilon = h\nu = 6.62 \times 10^{-27}(8.67 \times 10^{13})$$
$$= 5.74 \times 10^{-13} \text{ erg} \tag{49}$$

It is this energy that must correspond to the energy difference between the $v = 0$ and $v = 1$ levels, i.e., to

$$\Delta\epsilon = \frac{h}{2\pi}\sqrt{\frac{k}{\mu}} \tag{50}$$

By equating these two results for $\Delta\epsilon$ and using

$$\mu_{HCl} = \frac{m_H m_{Cl}}{m_H + m_{Cl}} = 1.627 \times 10^{-24} \text{ g}$$

one obtains

$$k = 4.84 \times 10^5 \text{ dynes/cm} \tag{51}$$

In this way it is seen that the spectral absorption is understood in terms of a molecular-energy-level pattern and that new quantitative information about the molecule is gained.

The frequencies of radiation absorbed by some diatomic molecules and the deduced force constants are shown in Table 2-1. One should recall that the force constant measures the stiffness of the bond and should see that the force constants of Table 2-1 are to some extent understandable in terms of qualitative ideas about these chemical bonds.

It should be mentioned finally that it is not customary to convert from radiation frequency to quantum energies in comparing spectral absorptions with energy-level patterns. It is more convenient to use the conversion factor h between energy and frequency, i.e., $\Delta\epsilon = h\nu$, and to convert the energies of allowed energy levels to frequency units.

TABLE 2-1 Frequencies of Fundamental Vibrational Transitions $v = 0$ to $v = 1$ and the Bond Force Constants Calculated from These Data
(Values for homonuclear molecules are from Raman spectral studies)

Molecule	$\bar{\nu}(\text{cm}^{-1})$	k (dynes/cm)
H_2	4,159.2	5.2×10^5
D_2	2,990.3	5.3
HF	3,958.4	8.8
HCl	2,885.6	4.8
HBr	2,559.3	3.8
HI	2,230.0	2.9
CO	2,143.3	18.7
NO	1,876.0	15.5
F_2	892	4.5
Cl_2	556.9	3.2
Br_2	321	2.4
I_2	213.4	1.7
O_2	1,556.3	11.4
N_2	2,330.7	22.6
Li_2	246.3	1.3
Na_2	157.8	1.7
NaCl	378	1.2
KCl	278	0.8

Thus the energy levels of the harmonic oscillator can be written as

$$\epsilon_v = \left(v + \frac{1}{2}\right)\frac{h}{2\pi}\sqrt{\frac{k}{\mu}} \qquad \text{ergs} \tag{52}$$

$$\epsilon_v = \left(v + \frac{1}{2}\right)\frac{1}{2\pi}\sqrt{\frac{k}{\mu}} \qquad \text{cycles/sec} \tag{53}$$

$$\bar{\epsilon}_v = \left(v + \frac{1}{2}\right)\frac{1}{2\pi c}\sqrt{\frac{k}{\mu}} \qquad \text{cm}^{-1} \tag{54}$$

The symbol $\bar{\epsilon}$ will be used for energies expressed in units of cm^{-1} to be consistent with frequencies or quantum energies of radiation that are written as $\bar{\nu}$ if expressed in cm^{-1}. With the last of these expressions one can compare the energy separation between two levels directly with the wave number $\bar{\nu}$ of the radiation absorbed or emitted in a transition between these levels; i.e., $\Delta\bar{\epsilon}$ will be the same as $\bar{\nu}$ for the radiation.

Exercise 2-4. Calculate the numbers of molecules in the $v = 1$ state compared to the number in the $v = 0$ state at 25°C for Br_2, which has the rather small vibrational energy-level spacing of 323 cm^{-1}, and for H_2, which has a vibrational spacing of about 4,159 cm^{-1}, the largest for any molecule.

2-6. The Anharmonicity of Molecular Vibrations

That the harmonic oscillator expression $U = \frac{1}{2}kq^2$ is only an approximate representation of the correct potential-energy function shows up in the presence of weak spectral absorption corresponding to $\Delta v = +2$, $+3, \ldots$, in violation of the $\Delta v = +1$ selection rule, and in the fact that the frequencies of these overtone absorptions is not exactly 2, 3, $\ldots$ times that of the fundamental, $\Delta v = +1$, absorption.

The retention of one additional term in the Maclaurin series expansion of Eq. (37) provides a better approximation to the potential energy. One has, then,

$$U = \frac{1}{2!}\left(\frac{d^2U}{dq^2}\right)_{q=0}q^2 + \frac{1}{3!}\left(\frac{d^3U}{dq^3}\right)_{q=0}q^3 \tag{55}$$

This expression for the potential can be used in the Schrödinger equation to deduce the energy levels of the allowed states of the anharmonic oscillator. The solution is obtained by an approximation, or perturbation, method and leads to an energy-level expression that can be written as

$$\bar{\epsilon}_v = \bar{\omega}_e(v + \tfrac{1}{2}) - \overline{\omega_e x_e}\,(v + \tfrac{1}{2})^2 \tag{56}$$

Here $\bar{\omega}_e$ has been written for convenience in place of $1/2\pi c \sqrt{k_e/\mu}$ where $k_e = (d^2U/dq^2)_{q=0}$. This quantity $\bar{\omega}_e$ is, therefore, the spacing of the energy levels, expressed in cm^{-1}, that would occur if the potential curve were a parabola with the curvature that the actual curve has at the minimum, or equilibrium, position. The coefficient $\overline{\omega_e x_e}$ of the squared quantum-number term is known as the *anharmonicity constant*. It is always much less than the principal term $\bar{\omega}_e$. With the minus sign written explicitly in Eq. (56) it is found that $\overline{\omega_e x_e}$ is always a positive quantity. The energy-level expression of Eq. (56) shows, therefore, that the separation between successive vibrational levels is not constant but rather decreases slightly with increasing values of v, as shown in Fig. 2-6.

It should be recognized that the broadening out of the potential curve, shown in Figs. 2-3 and 2-4, as a bond stretches, confines the

FIG. 2-6   The vibrational energy levels calculated for HCl.   Pattern (a) is based on the harmonic-oscillator approximation and the frequency of the fundamental transition. Pattern (b) is based on the anharmonic values of Table 2-2.

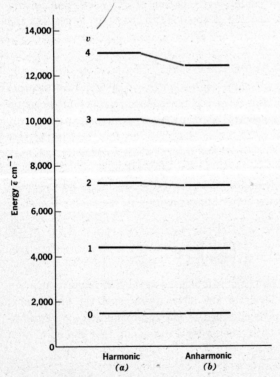

vibrating particles less closely than would a parabolic curve. Such loosening of the restrictions on the motion of particles always leads to more closely spaced allowed energy levels. The anharmonicity term introduces, therefore, an effect which decreases the spacing of the higher energy levels, as shown in Fig. 2-6.

If one observes some of the overtone bands, i.e., transitions from $v = 0$ to $v = 2$, $v = 3$, and so forth, one can check the success of the energy-level expression of Eq. (56) and determine the constants $\bar{\omega}_e$ and $\overline{\omega_e x_e}$. Table 2-2 shows the data obtained for the fundamental and first four overtones of HCl. These data can be compared with those derived from Eq. (56) for the energies of the transitions from $v = 0$ to $v = v$; i.e.,

$$\bar{\epsilon}(v) - \bar{\epsilon}(0) = \bar{\omega}_e(v) - \overline{\omega_e x_e}v(v + 1) \tag{57}$$

One finds, for $\bar{\omega}_e = 2{,}988.90$ cm^{-1} and $\overline{\omega_e x_e} = 51.60$ cm^{-1}, that Eq. (57) provides a very satisfactory fit to the observed frequencies of HCl.

One notices that $\bar{\omega}_e$ is considerably larger than the quantity $\bar{\epsilon}(1) - \bar{\epsilon}(0)$ which would have been identified with the coefficient of the $(v + \frac{1}{2})$ term in the expression based on a harmonic potential. It follows that the force constants calculated from these two quantities will be different. The distinction is that $\bar{\omega}_e$ is a measure of the curvature of the potential curve at the very bottom of the curve, where a hypothetical $v = -\frac{1}{2}$ level would be. The harmonic-oscillator approximation takes the difference in energy of the $v = 0$ and $v = 1$ levels as a measure of the curvature of the potential curve and therefore gets a lower value. Thus for HCl

$$\bar{\omega}_e = 2{,}988.90 \text{ cm}^{-1} \qquad k_e = 5.1574 \times 10^5 \text{ dynes/cm}$$

TABLE 2-2 Frequencies of the Vibrational Transitions of HCl. Comparison of the Observed Frequencies with Those Calculated from the Harmonic Oscillator Approximation and with Those from the Anharmonic Expression $\bar{\epsilon}_v - \epsilon_0 = 2{,}988.90(v) - 51.60v(v + 1)$

Δv	Description	$\bar{\nu}_{obs}$ cm^{-1}	$\bar{\nu}_{calc}$ cm^{-1}	
			Harmonic oscillator	Anharmonic oscillator
$0 \rightarrow 1$	Fundamental	2,885.9	(2,885.9)	2,885.70
$0 \rightarrow 2$	First overtone	5,668.0	5,771.8	5,668.20
$0 \rightarrow 3$	Second overtone	8,347.0	8,657.7	8,347.50
$0 \rightarrow 4$	Third overtone	10,923.1	11,543.6	10,923.6
$0 \rightarrow 5$	Fourth overtone	13,396.5	14,429.5	13,396.5

while

$$\bar{\epsilon}(1) - \bar{\epsilon}(0) = 2,885.90 \text{ cm}^{-1} \qquad k = 4.806 \times 10^5 \text{ dynes/cm}$$

The use of $\bar{\omega}_e$ instead of the observed fundamental energy is, in a number of ways, more satisfactory, but its use requires information on the overtone frequencies. For polyatomic molecules, this information is not always available.

Exercise 2-5. The fundamental and overtone frequencies of the CH stretching vibration of $CHCl_3$ are reported by Herzberg to be at 3,019, 5,900, 8,700, 11,315, 13,860, and 16,300 cm^{-1}. Fit these frequencies with a suitable equation that allows for anharmonicity. What value of $\bar{\omega}_e$ can be deduced?

PRINCIPAL REFERENCE

1. Herzberg, G.: "Spectra of Diatomic Molecules," chap. 3, D. Van Nostrand Company, Inc., Princeton, N.J., 1950.

3

THE ROTATIONAL
ENERGIES OF LINEAR MOLECULES

In the previous chapter it has been shown that changes in the vibrational energy of simple molecules can lead to absorption, or emission, of radiation in the infrared spectral region and that information on the frequency of the radiation absorbed, or emitted, can be used to determine the stiffness of the bond holding the atoms together. It is now natural to ask whether the rotational energy of a molecule is also quantized, whether changes in the rotational energy can lead to the absorption, or emission, of radiation, and, if so, what molecular property can be deduced from a study of the frequencies of radiation emitted or absorbed.

The nature of the rotational energies of molecules can be introduced by a consideration of the particularly simple systems of linear molecules. Although diatomic molecules provide most of the examples of linear molecules, the theory that is developed is equally applicable to linear polyatomic molecules. It is again convenient to consider first the classical behavior of a linear mass system and then to see the difference in behavior that is imposed when the system is of molecular dimensions and the quantum restrictions become important.

No attempt will be made in this introductory treatment to allow for the fact that the molecules undergo simultaneous rotation and vibration. The rotational effects will be considered by themselves. A treatment that assumes that the molecular dimensions are independent of molecular vibrations and undisturbed by molecular rotation is known as the *rigid-rotor* approximation. A final section will consider the slight modifications that occur as a result of the centrifugal distortion the rotation produces. Such a treatment is said to deal with the *nonrigid rotor*.

3-1. The Rotation of a Linear System (Classical)

The rotation of any system is most conveniently treated in terms of the angular velocity ω and the moment of inertia I.

It will be recalled that ω is defined as the number of radians of angle swept out in unit time by the rotating system. For a particle moving with a linear velocity v a distance r from the center of gravity, the revolutions per unit time, usually a second, are given by $v/2\pi r$ and the angular velocity by

$$\omega = 2\pi\left(\frac{v}{2\pi r}\right) = \frac{v}{r} \tag{1}$$

It follows also that the number of revolutions per unit time, i.e., the distance traveled per unit time divided by the circumference of the particle path, is $v/2\pi r$ or $\omega/2\pi$.

The moment of inertia of a system is defined as

$$I = \sum_i m_i r_i^2 \tag{2}$$

where r_i is the distance of the ith particle from the center of gravity of the system. For any particular system, the value of I can be worked out by first locating the center of gravity and then applying Eq. (2).

For a diatomic molecule, for instance, the masses and distances of Fig. 3-1 lead to the center of gravity being located so that

$$m_1 r_1 = m_2 r_2$$

FIG. 3-1   Location of the center of gravity of a diatomic molecule.

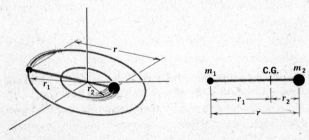

or, since $r_1 + r_2 = r$, to the relations

$$r_1 = \frac{m_2}{m_1 + m_2} r$$

and (3)

$$r_2 = \frac{m_1}{m_1 + m_2} r$$

Application of the defining equation, Eq. (2), for the moment of inertia now gives

$$
\begin{aligned}
I &= \frac{m_1^2 m_2}{(m_1 + m_2)^2} r^2 + \frac{m_1 m_2^2}{(m_1 + m_2)^2} r^2 \\
&= \frac{m_1 m_2}{m_1 + m_2} r^2 \\
&= \mu r^2
\end{aligned}
$$ (4)

where μ, the reduced mass, is defined as in the previous chapter as

$$\mu = \frac{m_1 m_2}{m_1 + m_2}$$ (5)

The kinetic energy of a system of moving macroscopic particles is given by $\sum_i \frac{1}{2} m_i v_i^2$. If the system performs a rotational motion, the particle velocities are more conveniently treated in terms of the angular velocity ω of the system. One then can write the kinetic energy T as

$$
\begin{aligned}
T &= \frac{1}{2} \sum_i m_i v_i^2 \\
&= \frac{1}{2} \sum_i m_i \omega^2 r_i^2 = \frac{1}{2} \omega^2 \sum_i m_i r_i^2 \\
&= \frac{1}{2} I \omega^2
\end{aligned}
$$ (6)

Equation (6) shows that a system of particles that obeys classical mechanics has a kinetic energy that is dependent on the moment of inertia of the system and on the angular velocity. No restriction, furthermore, is placed on the angular velocity with which the system can rotate. It can now be expected that when the same problem is treated for a molecular system some restrictions on the allowed rotational energy will appear.

Exercise 3-1. Calculate the moment of inertia of (a) HCl^{35}, HCl^{37}, and DCl^{35}, all of which have an equilibrium bond length of 1.275 A, and (b) N$_2$O, which is linear and has N—N and N—O bond lengths of 1.126 and 1.191 A, respectively.

3-2. The Rotation of a Linear System (Quantum Mechanical)

Although a complete quantum-mechanical description, i.e., the wave functions and energies of the allowed states, can be obtained by solving the Schrödinger equation for a rotating linear system, it is, at first, more informative to see what result is obtained by applying Bohr's condition that the angular momentum be quantized in units of $h/2\pi$.

The angular momentum of a rotating system is defined as

$$\sum_i (m_i v_i) r_i$$

which, in view of the definition of I as $\Sigma m_i r_i^2$ and ω as v_i/r_i, is

$$\sum_i m_i r_i^2 \left(\frac{v_i}{r_i}\right) = I\omega \tag{7}$$

Thus, the quantized angular momentum condition requires that

$$I\omega = J\frac{h}{2\pi} \quad \text{with } J = 0, 1, 2, \ldots \tag{8}$$

where the quantum number, following customary notation, has been designated by J. This stipulation leads to the allowed rotational energies of

$$\epsilon_J = \tfrac{1}{2}I\omega^2 = \frac{\tfrac{1}{2}(I\omega)^2}{I}$$

$$= \frac{h^2}{8\pi^2 I}J^2 \tag{9}$$

The correct result, obtained, for example, by solution of the Schrödinger equation, is only slightly different, being

$$\epsilon_J = \frac{h^2}{8\pi^2 I}J(J+1) \tag{10}$$

The correct quantum-mechanical treatment turns out to allow, if J is an integral quantum number, angular momenta given by

$$\sqrt{J(J+1)}\,\frac{h}{2\pi}$$

rather than by the simpler form $J(h/2\pi)$ introduced by Bohr and used in early quantum-mechanical treatments. If this term, $\sqrt{J(J+1)}\,\dfrac{h}{2\pi}$, is introduced for $I\omega$ in the classical energy expression, the correct quantum-mechanical result is obtained.

Solution of the molecular-rotation problem, and hence derivation of Eq. (10), by application of the Schrödinger equation will not be carried out here. Any textbook on quantum mechanics can be consulted for such a derivation. The problem consists of setting up the Schrödinger equation for three dimensions, using the convenient polar coordinates of Fig. 3-2. For a free gaseous molecule, rotation is unhindered, and the potential-energy function can be set equal to zero. Solutions are found for the resulting differential equation only if the energies have the values indicated in Eq. (10). The wave functions themselves need not now concern us. It can be mentioned, however, that they are identical to the angular part of the solutions for the behavior of the electron of the hydrogen atom. Thus for $J = 0$, the rotational wave function $\psi_{J=0}$ has the same form as the angular part of an s orbital wave function. For $J = 1$, the wave function is the same as that for the p_x, p_y, and p_z orbitals, and so forth.

For spectroscopic work, the expression for the energies of the rotational states allowed by the quantum restrictions is of prime importance. These allowed energies, as given by Eq. (10), are shown schematically in Fig. 3-3. Again it is more convenient to express these energies in wave-number units; in these units we have the expression

$$\bar{\epsilon}_J = \frac{h}{8\pi^2 I c} J(J + 1) \qquad cm^{-1} \tag{11}$$

The group of terms $h/8\pi^2 I c$ is sufficiently frequently encountered in

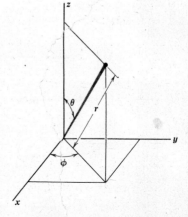

FIG. 3-2 Polar coordinates.

molecular spectroscopy to merit a symbol, and one uses the symbol $\bar{B}$ defined as

$$\bar{B} = \frac{h}{8\pi^2 Ic} \qquad cm^{-1} \tag{12}$$

Again the barred symbol is used to emphasize the units of cm^{-1}. The allowed rotational energies of a linear molecule can now be written as

$$\bar{\epsilon}_J = \bar{B}J(J + 1) \qquad cm^{-1} \tag{13}$$

FIG. 3-3 The energy-level pattern for a rotating linear molecule. The degeneracy, or multiplicity, of each rotational level is indicated by the number of levels that would appear if an electric field were applied to the rotating molecule.

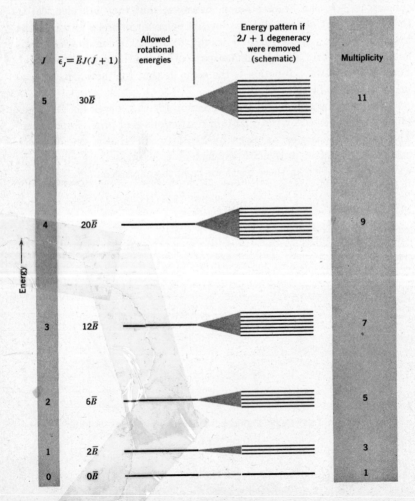

3-3. Rotational Energy-level Populations

The next step in laying the foundation for an understanding of rotational spectra involves a discussion of the populations of the rotational states whose energies are given by Eq. (10), (11), or (13).

Now as with the hydrogen atom treated in Sec. 1-2, there are, in general, a number of rotational states corresponding to a given rotational energy. This can most easily be seen from the condition that the component of the angular momentum in a direction imposed on a rotating molecule be quantized in units of $h/2\pi$. It follows, as Fig. 3-3 indicates, that there are $2J + 1$ states with energy $\bar{B}J(J + 1)$. The number $2J + 1$ arises from the states with angular momentum components of $J, J - 1$, $J - 2, 0, -1, -2, -J + 1, -J$ times $h/2\pi$ that would appear if an external field were applied.

In view of this $2J + 1$ degeneracy of the Jth energy level, the Boltzmann distribution expression for the populations of the rotational energy levels is

$$N_J = (2J + 1)N_0 e^{-J(J+1)h^2/8\pi^2 IkT} \tag{14}$$

It will be seen later that the allowed rotational energies typically have small energy spacings compared to the room-temperature value of kT. For example, N_2O has an N—N bond length of 1.126 A and an N—O bond length of 1.191 A. The moment of inertia can be calculated, as suggested in Exercise 3-1, to be 66.8×10^{-40} g cm^2, and at 25°C the energy-level population expression is

$$N_J = (2J + 1)N_0 e^{-J(J+1)(0.00202)} \tag{15}$$

The population of the levels of N_2O is shown as a function of J in Fig. 3-4.

FIG. 3-4 The relative populations of rotational energy levels of N_2O at 25°C.

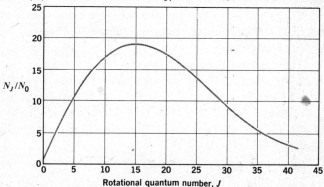

The result of this example, that quite a few of the allowed rotational energy levels are appreciably populated, is generally valid. It follows that, in an absorption experiment, we must expect transitions starting from energy levels corresponding not only to $J = 0$ but also to higher J values to be important.

Exercise 3-2. Make a population versus J value diagram like Fig. 3-4 for HCl at 25 and 1500°C.

3-4. Rotational Spectra of Rigid Linear Molecules

It is again necessary to anticipate the results that will be obtained in the following chapter when the transitions that electromagnetic radiation can induce will be studied.

The first requirement for the absorption of radiation by a rotational energy transition is that the *molecule must have a permanent dipole*. The rotating dipole can be thought of as interacting with the electric field of the radiation and allowing energy to be exchanged between the molecule and the radiation. The requirement is seen to be equivalent to that stated in the previous chapter where the vibration of a molecule had to be accompanied by an oscillating dipole for such interaction to occur.

There is a further restriction on rotational transitions even for those molecules which have dipole moments. The selection rule for rotational transitions of linear molecules that occur with the absorption or emission of electromagnetic radiation is

$$\Delta J = \pm 1 \tag{16}$$

For studies of the absorption of radiation, the experiment that is invariably done when rotational spectra are obtained, the appropriate part of the selection rule is $\Delta J = +1$.

With this selection rule, and the population results obtained in the previous section, the expected transitions can be indicated by the vertical arrows of Fig. 3-5.

The general expression for the energies that are absorbed in the transitions indicated by arrows in Fig. 3-5 can be obtained from the allowed energies given in Eq. (13). If the quantum number for the lower level involved in a transition is J and that for the upper level is $J + 1$, the energy difference in cm^{-1}, and therefore the value of $\bar{\nu}$ for the absorbed radiation, is

$$\bar{\nu} = \bar{B}(J + 1)(J + 2) - \bar{B}J(J + 1)$$
$$= 2\bar{B}(J + 1) \tag{17}$$

We thus expect, since the levels $J = 0, 1, 2, \ldots$ will generally be populated, absorptions of radiation at frequencies of $2\bar{B}, 4\bar{B}, 6\bar{B}, \ldots$ and should therefore observe a set of lines spaced by a constant amount. This amount can then be identified with $2\bar{B}$.

One observes in the microwave spectral region such series of absorption lines when linear molecules with dipole moments are studied. Table 3-1 shows the frequencies of absorption, attributable to rotational transitions, observed for the linear molecule OCS.

FIG. 3-5 Rotational energy levels and transitions for a rigid-rotor linear molecule. The symbol $\bar{B}$ is used to represent the quantity $h/8\pi^2 Ic$.

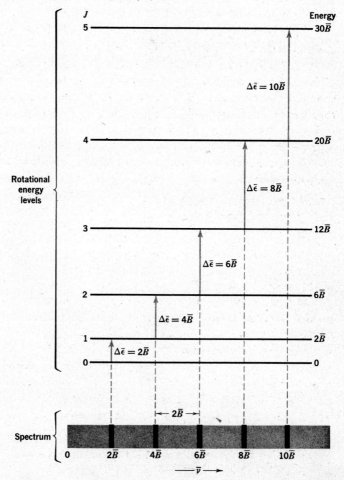

From these data one can obtain an average value of the absorption line spacing of 12,162.7 megacycles/sec and

$$\bar{B} = \frac{12{,}162.7 \times 10^6}{2(2.99790 \times 10^{10})} = 0.20285 \text{ cm}^{-1} \tag{18}$$

Therefore, since $\bar{B} = h/8\pi^2 Ic$, the moment of inertia of the OCS molecule can be calculated to be

$$I_{\text{OCS}} = 138.0 \times 10^{-40} \text{ g cm}^2 \tag{19}$$

It should be apparent that from this single experimental result it is not possible to deduce both the CO and CS distances of the molecule. In such cases, what is done whenever possible is to obtain the rotational spectrum of different isotopic species. Thus, more detailed analyses of the rotational spectra of $O^{16}C^{12}S^{32}$ and $O^{16}C^{12}S^{34}$ reported by Strandberg, Wentink, and Kyhl [*Phys. Rev.*, **75**: 270 (1949)] give

$$\bar{B}_{O^{16}C^{12}S^{32}} = 0.202864 \text{ cm}^{-1} \quad \text{and} \quad I_{O^{16}C^{12}S^{32}} = 138.0 \times 10^{-40} \text{ g/sq cm} \tag{20}$$

$$\bar{B}_{O^{16}C^{12}S^{34}} = 0.197910 \text{ cm}^{-1} \quad \text{and} \quad I_{O^{16}C^{12}S^{34}} = 141.4 \times 10^{-40} \text{ g/sq cm}$$

From these moment-of-inertia data, and the assumption that the bond lengths are independent of the isotopic species, one deduces that in the OCS molecule

$$\begin{aligned} r(\text{CO}) &= 1.161 \pm 0.001 \text{ A} \\ r(\text{CS}) &= 1.559 \pm 0.001 \text{ A} \end{aligned} \tag{21}$$

It is easier, as one will discover, to verify that these distances are consistent with the moment-of-inertia data than to derive the bond lengths from the moments of inertia.

Measurements of the spacing of rotational spectral frequencies have

TABLE 3-1   Absorptions of $O^{16}C^{12}S^{32}$ in the Microwave Region Due to Rotational Transitions*

Transition $J \to J+1$	Frequency ν (megacycles/sec)
$0 \to 1$	
$1 \to 2$	24,325.92
$2 \to 3$	36,488.82
$3 \to 4$	48,651.64
$4 \to 5$	60,814.08

* From Strandberg, Wentink, and Kyhl, *Phys. Rev.*, **75**: 270 (1949).

led to very accurate values for the moments of inertia and, in many cases, for the lengths of the bonds of molecules. Some of these results are shown in Table 3-2.

Close examination of data such as those of Table 3-1 reveals that the spacing between adjacent spectral lines is not, in fact, exactly constant. The constant spacing expected from the treatment given here is that obtained from the rigid-rotor approximation. Now we can see (although this is a minor matter that can be passed over) what alterations to the theory arise from the recognition that molecules are not rigid, but are flexible, and can be expected to stretch under the influence of the centrifugal forces that arise when they rotate.

Exercise 3-3. The rotational constant term $B = c\bar{B}$ is given by Gordy, Smith, and Trambarulo [2] for $HC^{12}N^{14}$ as 44,315.97 megacycles and for $DC^{12}N^{14}$ as 36,207.40 megacycles. Deduce moments of inertia for these molecules. Assuming that the bond lengths are independent of isotopic substitution, calculate the H—C and C—N bond lengths.

*3-5. The Nonrigid Rotor

The stretching effect of the centrifugal forces on the bond lengths, and therefore on the moment of inertia of a rotating system, can first be calculated on the basis of classical behavior. Consider, for simplicity,

TABLE 3-2 Some Bond Lengths Obtained from Microwave Spectroscopy of Linear Molecules*

Molecule	Bond	Bond distance (A)
CO	C≡O	1.1282
NaCl	Na—Cl	2.3606
HCN	C—H	1.064
	C≡N	1.156
ClCN	C—Cl	1.629
	C≡N	1.163
HC≡CCl	C—H	1.052
	C≡C	1.211
	C—Cl	1.632
HC≡C—C≡N	C—H	1.057
	C≡C	1.203
	C—C	1.382
	C≡N	1.157

* From W. Gordy, W. V. Smith, and R. F. Trambarulo, "Microwave Spectroscopy," John Wiley & Sons, Inc., New York, 1953.

a single particle of mass m rotating about a fixed point with an angular velocity of ω. Assume that, when there is no rotation, the particle is a distance r_0 from the fixed point and that this length increases to a value of r when the particle rotates.

The centrifugal force of $mr\omega^2$ is balanced by a restoring force of $k(r - r_0)$ that accompanies bond stretching. The extent of bond stretching that occurs for an angular velocity of ω is, therefore, given by the expression

$$k(r - r_0) = mr\omega^2 \tag{22}$$

On rearrangement, this gives the distorted bond length as

$$r = \frac{kr_0}{k - m\omega^2} \tag{23}$$

Since the energy of the rotating system is made up of kinetic- and potential-energy contributions, the total energy can be written as

$$\epsilon = \tfrac{1}{2}I\omega^2 + \tfrac{1}{2}k(r - r_0)^2 \tag{24}$$

which, with Eq. (22), becomes

$$\begin{aligned}
\epsilon &= \frac{1}{2}I\omega^2 + \frac{1}{2}\frac{km^2r^2\omega^4}{k^2} \\
&= \frac{1}{2}I\omega^2 + \frac{1}{2}\frac{(I\omega^2)^2}{kr^2}
\end{aligned} \tag{25}$$

The quantum restriction that the angular momentum $I\omega$ be quantized according to $\sqrt{J(J+1)}\,(h/2\pi)$ will convert this classical result to a quantum-mechanical result. The correct allowed energies are, therefore, deduced to be

$$\begin{aligned}
\epsilon_J &= \frac{h^2}{8\pi^2 I} J(J+1) + \frac{h^4}{32\pi^4 I^2 r^2 k} J^2(J+1)^2 \\
&= \frac{h^2}{8\pi^2 mr^2} J(J+1) + \frac{h^4}{32\pi^4 m^2 r^6 k} J^2(J+1)^2
\end{aligned} \tag{26}$$

It is finally necessary to relate the distorted distance r in the first term, which is of major importance in Eq. (26), to r_0 by means of Eq. (23). In this way, and approximating r by r_0 in the second, minor term of Eq. (26), one obtains

$$\begin{aligned}
\epsilon_J &= \frac{h^2}{8\pi^2 mr_0^2} J(J+1) - \frac{h^4}{16\pi^4 m^2 r_0^6 k} J^2(J+1)^2 \\
&\qquad\qquad\qquad\qquad + \frac{h^4}{32\pi^4 m^2 r_0^6 k} J^2(J+1)^2 \\
&= \frac{h^2}{8\pi^2 mr_0^2} J(J+1) - \frac{h^4}{32\pi^4 m^2 r_0^6 k} J^2(J+1)^2
\end{aligned} \tag{27}$$

In terms of wave-number units, this result becomes

$$\bar{\epsilon}_J = \frac{h}{8\pi^2 Ic} J(J+1) - \frac{h^3 m}{32\pi^4 I^3 kc} J^2(J+1)^2$$

$$= \bar{B} J(J+1) - \frac{4\bar{B}^3}{\bar{\omega}^2} J^2(J+1)^2 \tag{28}$$

where $\bar{\omega}$ is the vibrational-energy term $1/2\pi c \sqrt{k/m}$ and, as before, $\bar{B} = h/8\pi^2 Ic$.

It is customary to write this expression for the rotational energy levels as

$$\bar{\epsilon}_J = \bar{B} J(J+1) - \bar{D} J^2(J+1)^2 \tag{29}$$

where $\bar{D}$, known as the centrifugal distortion constant, is a quantity that can be evaluated from spectral results and, according to the above derivation, can be related to other spectroscopic molecular parameters by the relation

$$\bar{D} = 4\bar{B}^3/\bar{\omega}^2 \tag{30}$$

The value of $\bar{D}$ is always very much less than that of $\bar{B}$, and the difference between the rigid and nonrigid rotor treatments can, as Fig. 3-6

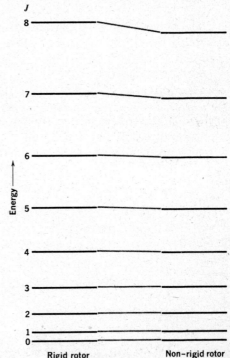

FIG. 3-6 The effect of centrifugal distortion shown by the comparison of the allowed rotational energy levels of a rigid (solid lines) and nonrigid (dashed lines) rotor.

TABLE 3-3   Absorptions Due to Rotational Transitions of HCl*

Transition $J \to J + 1$	$\bar{\nu}_{obs}$ (cm^{-1})	$\bar{\nu}_{calc} = 2\bar{B}(J + 1)$ (with $\bar{B} = 10.34$ cm^{-1})	$\bar{\nu}_{calc} = 2\bar{B}(J + 1) - 4\bar{D}(J + 1)^3$ ($\bar{B} = 10.395$, $\bar{D} = 0.0004$ cm^{-1})
$3 \to 4$	83.03	82.72	83.06
$4 \to 5$	104.1	103.40	103.75
$5 \to 6$	124.30	124.08	124.39
$6 \to 7$	145.03	144.76	144.98
$7 \to 8$	165.51	165.44	165.50
$8 \to 9$	185.86	186.12	185.94
$9 \to 10$	206.38	206.80	206.30
$10 \to 11$	226.50	227.48	226.55

* From G. Herzberg, "Spectra of Diatomic Molecules," D. Van Nostrand Company, Inc., Princeton, N.J., 1950.

suggests, be expected to show up only when high J value levels are involved.

The expression for the energies of the rotational transitions $\Delta J = +1$ for a nonrigid rotor are, according to Eq. (29),

$$\Delta\bar{\epsilon}(J \to J + 1) = 2\bar{B}(J + 1) - 4\bar{D}(J + 1)^3 \tag{31}$$

The data of Table 3-3 illustrate the improved fit to experimental absorption frequencies that can be obtained by allowing for centrifugal distortion.

PRINCIPAL REFERENCES

1. Herzberg, G.: "Spectra of Diatomic Molecules," chap. 3, D. Van Nostrand Company, Inc., Princeton, N.J., 1950.
2. Gordy, W., W. V. Smith, and R. F. Trambarulo: "Microwave Spectroscopy," John Wiley & Sons, Inc., New York, 1953.

4 THE ABSORPTION AND EMISSION OF RADIATION

In the two previous chapters it has been necessary to state, without adequate explanation or proof, that transitions between allowed energy levels can occur with the absorption or emission of electromagnetic radiation. Furthermore, selection rules governing the transitions that can thus occur have been quoted. Now that some introduction to allowed energy levels and to simple spectra has been given, it is appropriate to investigate the theoretical basis on which spectral transitions can be understood. A considerable amount of manipulation with quantum-mechanical expressions will be necessary. The net result of the derivation is, however, an expression that can often be used in a qualitative, or diagrammatic, way to understand what transitions will occur in a particular system and, moreover, the intensity of the absorption or emission band that will be observed. (The reader will notice that in the previous chapters the emphasis has been on the frequencies of absorption bands and little attention has been paid to their intensities.)

4-1. The Time-dependent Schrödinger Equation

The form previously given for the Schrödinger equation, and illustrated by the particle-in-a-box calculation, is known as the time-independent, or amplitude, equation. A more complete expression for Schrödinger's equation allows the calculation of atomic-scale phenomena as a function of time as well as of space. For one dimension the equation written for x and t is

$$-\frac{h^2}{8\pi^2 m}\frac{\partial^2 \Psi(x,t)}{\partial x^2} + U(x)\Psi(x,t) = -\frac{h}{2\pi i}\frac{\partial \Psi(x,t)}{\partial t} \tag{1}$$

The explicit indication that Ψ is a function of x and t, i.e., $\Psi(x,t)$, will not be continued. It will be understood that Ψ is a function of x and t and that ψ is a function only of x.

Previously it was shown that $\psi^*\psi$ described the system, i.e., gave information on the position of the particle, in the one-dimensional square-well potential. In a similar way, $\Psi^*\Psi$ describes the system in space and time.

To reduce equations such as the time-dependent Schrödinger equation to more manageable forms, it is customary to try to separate them into two equations each involving only one of the variables. With this approach one tries the general substitution

$$\Psi = \psi(x)\,\phi(t) \tag{2}$$

where $\psi(x)$ and $\phi(t)$ are functions of x and t, respectively. Substitution of this relation in Eq. (1), with the supposition that U is a function only of x, gives

$$-\frac{h^2}{8\pi^2 m}\frac{d^2\psi(x)}{dx^2}\,\phi(t) + U(x)\,\psi(x)\,\phi(t) = -\frac{h}{2\pi i}\psi(x)\frac{d\phi(t)}{dt}$$

or

$$\frac{1}{\psi(x)}\left[-\frac{h^2}{8\pi^2 m}\frac{d^2\psi(x)}{dx^2}\right] + U(x) = -\frac{h}{2\pi i}\frac{1}{\phi(t)}\frac{d\phi(t)}{dt} \tag{3}$$

The left side of this equation is a function only of x, and the right side is a function only of t. The equation can be valid for all values of x and t, only if each side is equal to a constant. The constant is called ϵ since it can be identified with the energy of the system. The two equations that are obtained by setting Eq. (3) equal to the constant ϵ are

$$\frac{d\phi(t)}{dt} = -\frac{2\pi i}{h}\,\epsilon\phi(t) \tag{4}$$

and

$$-\frac{h^2}{8\pi^2 m}\frac{d^2\psi}{dx^2} + U(x)\psi = \epsilon\psi \tag{5}$$

The second of these equations can be recognized as the time-independent Schrödinger equation introduced in Chap. 1. The time-dependent part of the complete Schrödinger equation can be readily solved, and the solution is

$$\phi(t) = e^{-(2\pi i/h)\epsilon_n t} \tag{6}$$

where ϵ_n is written because the values of ϵ that are required by Eq. (5) involve a quantum number which can be denoted by n. The solution to the complete equation for a general one-dimensional problem can, therefore, be written as

$$\Psi_n(x,t) = \psi_n(x)e^{-(2\pi i/h)\epsilon_n t} \tag{7}$$

If one thinks of the particle-in-a-box problem as an example, the solutions that would have been obtained from the time-dependent Schrödinger equation would have been

$$\Psi_n(x,t) = \sqrt{\frac{2}{a}}\left(\sin\frac{n\pi x}{a}\right)e^{-(2\pi i/h)\epsilon_n t}$$

where

$$\epsilon_n = \frac{n^2 h^2}{8ma^2} \tag{8}$$

The implications of the solution in x and t can be seen if the quantum-mechanical description of the system, as given by $\Psi^*\Psi$, is obtained. This is given in general by

$$\begin{aligned}\Psi^*\Psi &= \psi^*\psi e^{(2\pi i/h)\epsilon_n t}e^{-(2\pi i/h)\epsilon_n t}\\ &= \psi^*\psi e^{(2\pi i/h)(\epsilon_n-\epsilon_n)t}\\ &= \psi^*\psi\end{aligned} \tag{9}$$

Aside ③

The time-dependent part of the solution to the space and time equation is seen, therefore, to drop out, and the system is again described simply in terms of the time-independent wave functions. Systems, like the particle-in-a-box system studied in Chap. 1, which lead to solutions that are time independent, are said to have allowed *stationary states*. These are the allowed states that are obtained as solutions to the time-independent Schrödinger equation.

For a spectroscopic process to occur, a procedure must exist which causes a state to change from one stationary state to another. How a time dependence is introduced into a quantum-mechanical problem will now be investigated.

4-2. Induced Quantum Transitions

Much of spectroscopy is concerned with the absorption of radiant energy as a system goes from one stationary state to another under the influence of incident electromagnetic radiation. It is necessary to investigate, therefore, how radiation can disturb, or as one says *perturb*, a system so that a transition is induced.

In general any atomic or molecular system will have many allowed energy levels corresponding to the stationary states of the system. It is sufficient, and the notation is simplified, if a system is treated that is assumed to have only a lower energy state, with a wave function ψ_l, and an upper energy state, with a wave function ψ_m, where l and m are two different values of the quantum number for the system.

The complete time and space Schrödinger equation for one dimension is, as before,

$$-\frac{h^2}{8\pi^2 m}\frac{\partial^2 \Psi}{\partial x^2} + U(x)\Psi = -\frac{h}{2\pi i}\frac{\partial \Psi}{\partial t} \tag{10}$$

It is convenient to introduce the symbol H, called the Hamiltonian, to represent the terms

$$-\frac{h^2}{8\pi^2 m}\frac{\partial^2}{\partial x^2} + U(x)$$

(Although it is sufficient to treat H as a symbol, one should recognize that it is the quantum-mechanical operator for the total energy of the system.)   With this notation, Eq. (10) becomes

$$H\Psi = -\frac{h}{2\pi i}\frac{\partial \Psi}{\partial t} \tag{11}$$

The supposition that only the two stationary states described by ψ_l and ψ_m exist for the system implies that the only two solutions to Eq. (11) are

$$\Psi_l = \psi_l e^{-(2\pi i/h)\epsilon_l t}$$

and $\tag{12}$

$$\Psi_m = \psi_m e^{-(2\pi i/h)\epsilon_m t}$$

Since such solutions to the Schrödinger equation, as pointed out in Sec. 1-7, form an orthogonal set of functions, a general solution to the equation can be written as a series of these functions.   In this case, where only two solutions exist, the general solution is simply

$$\Psi = a_l \Psi_l + a_m \Psi_m \tag{13}$$

where a_l and a_m are weighting coefficients which are not functions of x but, as we will see, can be functions of time.   The two allowed stationary states of the system are described by the general expression with $a_l = 1$, $a_m = 0$ or $a_l = 0$, $a_m = 1$.

The potential energy of the system before it is disturbed, or perturbed, by electromagnetic radiation is now represented, more specifically, by U_0, and the corresponding Hamiltonian by H_0; i.e.,

$$H_0 = \frac{h^2}{8\pi^2 m}\frac{d^2}{dx^2} + U_0(x) \tag{14}$$

The Schrödinger equation for this initial, unperturbed case is then written as

$$H_0\Psi = -\frac{h}{2\pi i}\frac{\partial\Psi}{\partial t} \tag{15}$$

It is this equation that has the two solutions Ψ_l and Ψ_m.

Now let us assume that it is known that initially the system is in the lower energy state l with the wave function Ψ_l and energy ϵ_l. The initial state, at time $t = 0$, is therefore described by Eq. (13), with $a_l = 1$ and $a_m = 0$. As was seen from the previous discussion, the solution Ψ_l will lead to a description of the system as being time independent with the wave function ψ_l and energy ϵ_l. This state of affairs will continue as long as the system is undisturbed, i.e., as long as $U = U_0$.

Now let us suppose that electromagnetic radiation falls on the system. As will be shown later in more detail, the electric field of the radiation may act on the system and change the potential energy. The change in U is denoted by U' and that in H is denoted by H'. The new Hamiltonian is then $H_0 + H'$. The differential equation corresponding to the initial state of the system is therefore changed, and Ψ_l will not satisfy the new equation.

The more general expression

$$\Psi = a_l(t)\Psi_l + a_m(t)\Psi_m \tag{16}$$

where a_l and a_m are time-dependent parameters, can be used to provide a solution to the new Schrödinger equation that is applicable to the perturbed system.

This wave function, with undetermined a_l and a_m, can be substituted into this new Schrödinger equation to give

$$(H_0 + H')(a_l\Psi_l + a_m\Psi_m) = -\frac{h}{2\pi i}\frac{\partial}{\partial t}(a_l\Psi_l + a_m\Psi_m)$$

Expansion of this equation gives

$$a_l H_0\Psi_l + a_m H_0\Psi_m + a_l H'\Psi_l + a_m H'\Psi_m = -\frac{h}{2\pi i}\Psi_l\frac{da_l}{dt}$$
$$-\frac{h}{2\pi i}\Psi_m\frac{da_m}{dt} - \frac{h}{2\pi i}a_l\frac{\partial\Psi_l}{\partial t} - \frac{h}{2\pi i}a_m\frac{\partial\Psi_m}{\partial t} \tag{17}$$

The first two and last two terms cancel because Ψ_l and Ψ_m are solutions of the unperturbed wave equation. The remaining expression is simplified if it is multiplied through by Ψ_m^* and integrated over all space, i.e., from $x = -\infty$ to $x = +\infty$. The orthogonality of ψ_m and ψ_l eliminates one of the integrals, and the time-dependent part drops out of the $\Psi_m^*\Psi_m$ integral as in Sec. 4-1. On rearranging the remaining terms, and substituting Eqs. (12), one has

$$\frac{da_m}{dt} = -\frac{2\pi i}{h} a_l e^{-(2\pi i/h)(\epsilon_l - \epsilon_m)t} \int_{-\infty}^{+\infty} \psi_m^* H' \psi_l \, dx$$
$$-\frac{2\pi i}{h} a_m \int_{-\infty}^{+\infty} \psi_m^* H' \psi_m \, dx \quad (18)$$

It is known that initially $a_l = 1$ and $a_m = 0$ so that the final term does not initially contribute. It can be shown also that the final term does not contribute appreciably at longer times, and one has

$$\frac{da_m}{dt} = -\frac{2\pi i}{h} e^{-(2\pi i/h)(\epsilon_l - \epsilon_m)t} \int_{-\infty}^{+\infty} \psi_m^* H' \psi_l \, dx \quad (19)$$

This important equation gives the rate at which a system can be changed from one stationary state to another under the influence of a perturbing effect. The rate with which a_m increases corresponds to the rate at which the description of the system changes from ψ_l to ψ_m.

To proceed it is necessary to be more specific about the perturbation H'. Some features of the interaction between the electric field of the electromagnetic radiation and the molecular system that absorbs the system are now treated.

4-3. The Interaction of Electromagnetic Radiation with a Molecular System

When electromagnetic radiation falls on a molecule, the oscillating electric field of the radiation can in some cases disturb the potential energy of the molecule and allow it to escape from its initial stationary state, here assumed to be characterized by the quantum number l. It will be recalled from the discussion presented in the introduction that the electric field of the radiation oscillates at the point occupied by the molecule with a frequency ν. For example, the x component of the radiation can be described at the position occupied by the molecule by an equation which is usually written as

$$E_x = 2E_x^\circ \cos 2\pi\nu t \quad (20)$$

It is here more convenient to use the exponential form for the time dependency and write

$$E_x = E_x^\circ (e^{2\pi i \nu t} + e^{-2\pi i \nu t}) \qquad (21)$$

The derivation of the influence of the electric field on the molecule can, for simplicity, be followed through in terms of the x component of the interaction. At the end of the derivation, the effects of the interactions in the y and z directions can be added on.

The electric field E_x can act on a dipole-moment component μ_x to produce a change in energy of $E_x \mu_x$. This term adds to the potential energy of the system and is responsible for the change in H that occurs when radiation falls on the system. One can write, therefore,

$$H' = E_x \mu_x \qquad (22)$$

If the frequency dependence of E_x is shown explicitly, this becomes

$$H' = E_x^\circ (e^{2\pi i \nu t} + e^{-2\pi i \nu t}) \mu_x \qquad (23)$$

Substitution of this perturbation in Eq. (19) gives

$$\frac{da_m}{dt} = -\frac{2\pi i}{h} E_x^\circ \int_{-\infty}^{+\infty} \psi_m^* \mu_x \psi_l \, dx (e^{(2\pi i/h)(\epsilon_m - \epsilon_l + h\nu)t} + e^{(2\pi i/h)(\epsilon_m - \epsilon_l - h\nu)t}) \qquad (24)$$

The integral over x that appears here is customarily represented by $|\mu_{xlm}|$; i.e.,

$$|\mu_{xlm}| = \int_{-\infty}^{+\infty} \psi_m^* \mu_x \psi_l \, dx \qquad (25)$$

With this notation, and integration of the time-dependent functions of Eq. (24) over the time interval 0 to t, one obtains

$$a_m(t) = |\mu_{xlm}| E_x^\circ \left[\frac{1 - e^{(2\pi i/h)(\epsilon_m - \epsilon_l + h\nu)t}}{\epsilon_m - \epsilon_l + h\nu} + \frac{1 - e^{(2\pi i/h)(\epsilon_m - \epsilon_l - h\nu)t}}{\epsilon_m - \epsilon_l - h\nu} \right] \qquad (26)$$

The process of interest here is that in which the system goes from a lower energy level ϵ_l to a higher one ϵ_m. For such an arrangement of energies, the denominator of the second term in the square brackets will go to zero when the radiation frequency is such that

$$h\nu = \epsilon_m - \epsilon_l \qquad (27)$$

For such conditions this second term can take on large values and be of major importance in determining $a_m(t)$. On the other hand, if ϵ_m were lower than ϵ_l, the first term in the square brackets would be of major importance in determining $a_m(t)$, for then $h\nu$ equal to the energy difference would lead to a zero denominator. It follows that the first term in the square brackets is important if the transition from l to m is one of emission, whereas the second term is important if the transition is one of absorption. Since we are here investigating an absorption process, the energy of the m state is greater than that of the l state, and it is only necessary to retain the final term of Eq. (26). We have, therefore, for the assumed energy-level pattern

$$a_m(t) = |\mu_{xlm}|E_x^\circ \left[\frac{1 - e^{(2\pi i/h)(\epsilon_m - \epsilon_l - h\nu)t}}{\epsilon_m - \epsilon_l - h\nu} \right] \tag{28}$$

As the system changes from the description Ψ_l to Ψ_m, it can be described by the product $\Psi^*\Psi$, where $\Psi = a_l\Psi_l + a_m\Psi_m$ and the a's are time dependent. This quantum-mechanical description can be given as a function of time if it is integrated over all values of x. This integration, moreover, removes all the space-dependent wave functions because of their orthogonality and normalization. One is left only with

$$\int_{-\infty}^{+\infty} \Psi^*\Psi \, dx = a_l^* a_l + a_m^* a_m \tag{29}$$

The importance of the m state in the description of the system is given, therefore, by the product $a_m^* a_m$ which, according to Eq. (28), is given as a function of time by

$$\begin{aligned} a_m^*(t)a_m(t) &= |\mu_{xlm}|^2(E_x^\circ)^2 \left[\frac{2 - e^{(2\pi i/h)(\epsilon_m - \epsilon_l - h\nu)t} - e^{-(2\pi i/h)(\epsilon_m - \epsilon_l - h\nu)t}}{(\epsilon_m - \epsilon_l - h\nu)^2} \right] \\ &= 4|\mu_{xlm}|^2(E_x^\circ)^2 \left[\frac{\sin^2(\pi/h)(\epsilon_m - \epsilon_l - h\nu)t}{(\epsilon_m - \epsilon_l - h\nu)^2} \right] \end{aligned} \tag{30}$$

The above expression shows the effect of a given frequency of radiation. Integration over all frequencies, treating E_x° as a constant since the absorption will usually occur over a narrow frequency range, gives, with the definite integral

$$\int_{-\infty}^{+\infty} \frac{\sin^2 x}{x^2} \, dx = \pi$$

the result

$$a_m^*(t)a_m(t) = \frac{4\pi^2}{h^2} |\mu_{xlm}|^2(E_x^\circ)^2 t \tag{31}$$

This is the desired result except for the characterization of the radiation by its electric field strength instead of its energy density. It is the latter measure of the amount of radiation that is more convenient when comparisons are made with experimental determinations of the amount of absorption. The necessary relation, which is here given without derivation, is

$$\rho = \frac{6}{4\pi} (E_x^\circ)^2$$

Planck gives

$$P_{(\nu)} = \frac{8\pi h \nu^3}{c^3} \left(e^{h\nu/hT} - 1 \right)^{-1}$$

(32)

where ρ is the energy density, i.e., the energy per unit volume that is irradiated by the electromagnetic radiation.

Replacement of E_x° in Eq. (31) by this relation gives the rate $d(a_m^* a_m)/dt$ with which the importance of state m in the description increases as

$$\frac{d(a_m^* a_m)}{dt} = \frac{8\pi^3}{3h^2} |\mu_{xlm}|^2 \rho$$

(33)

For isotropic radiation the three components of the radiation-dipole interaction are equal, and one writes

$$\frac{d}{dt} (a_m^* a_m) = \frac{8\pi^3}{3h^2} |(\mu_{xlm})^2 + (\mu_{ylm})^2 + (\mu_{zlm})^2| \rho$$

$$= \frac{8\pi^3}{3h^2} |\mu_{lm}|^2 \rho$$

(34)

This rate of change of the system as a result of absorption of radiation under the perturbing effect of the electric field of the radiation is usually written with B_{lm}, called *Einstein's coefficient of induced absorption,* introduced so that Eq. (34) becomes

$$\frac{d}{dt} (a_m^* a_m) = B_{lm} \rho$$

(35)

with

$$B_{lm} = \frac{8\pi^3}{3h^2} |\mu_{lm}|^2$$

(36)

This expression obtained for the time dependence of the coefficient of Ψ_m for a system originally described by Ψ_l shows the factors that are responsible for the change from one stationary state to another. The rate of transition is seen to depend on the term $|\mu_{lm}|$, called the *transition moment,* and on the energy density of the radiation.

To complete the general study of the process by which radiation energy is absorbed, it remains only to compare this derived expression with the quantities usually encountered in the experimental determinations of the absorption of radiation.

Exercise 4-1. Plot the function

$$\frac{\sin^2 (2\pi/h)(\epsilon_m - \epsilon_l - h\nu)}{(\epsilon_m - \epsilon_l - h\nu)^2}$$

which must be integrated over all frequencies to obtain Eq. (31), versus frequency near $h\nu = \epsilon_m - \epsilon_l$, and see that the frequencies that contribute most to the integral are those close to the Bohr condition $\epsilon_m - \epsilon_l = h\nu$.

4-4. Comparison with Experimental Quantities

The quantities used in reporting the experimental results for the absorption of radiation can be introduced by considering the derivation of Beer's law for an absorbing solute in a nonabsorbing solvent. The decrease in intensity of the radiation as it penetrates a distance dl, as in Fig. 4-1, is, according to Beer's law, proportional to I, the radiation intensity; to C, the molar concentration; and to the path length dl. Introducing $\alpha(\nu)$, the *absorption coefficient*, as the proportionality constant allows the equation

$$-dI = \alpha(\nu)IC\,dl \tag{37}$$

to be written. The dependence of α on the frequency is here emphasized by writing $\alpha(\nu)$. Integration of this equation over the cell length l allows the absorption coefficient to be measured in terms of I_0, the incident intensity, or the intensity with no absorbing material, and I, the intensity of the radiation after passing through the cell containing the solution. The integrated form of Beer's law is obtained in this way as

$$\alpha(\nu) = \frac{1}{Cl} \ln \frac{I_0}{I} \tag{38}$$

FIG. 4-1   The absorption of radiation by a solution.

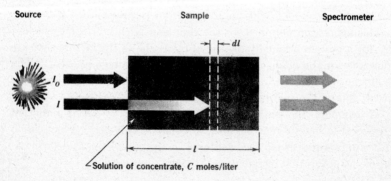

Source   Sample   Spectrometer

An absorption band for a given transition usually extends over a range of frequencies. The total intensity of the band is obtained by measuring $\alpha(\nu)$ in the region of the absorption and determining, usually by graphical integration, the integrated *absorption coefficient* A, i.e.,

$$A = \int_{\text{over band}} \alpha(\nu)\, d\nu$$

or   (39)

$$\bar{A} = \int_{\text{over band}} \alpha(\bar{\nu})\, d\bar{\nu}$$
$$= \frac{A}{c}$$

It is now necessary to relate the experimental quantities $\alpha(\nu)$, or A, to the theory of the previous section.

The theoretical result of the previous discussion is that the rate of transfer of molecules from state l to state m is

$$(B_{lm})\rho = \frac{8\pi^3}{3h^2}\,|\mu_{lm}|^2\rho \tag{40}$$

If one introduces the symbol N' to represent the number of molecules in a cubic centimeter of the sample and recognizes that an amount of energy $h\nu_{lm}$ is removed from the radiation by each transfer, the decrease in intensity, or energy, of the beam passing through a length dl of the sample is given by the theory of the previous section as

$$-dI = \frac{8\pi^2}{3h^2}\,|\mu_{lm}|^2\rho h\nu_{lm}N'\, dl \tag{41}$$

Furthermore, since I is the energy flowing through a cross-section area of 1 sq cm in 1 sec, it is related to the energy density by

$$I = c\rho \tag{42}$$

where c is the velocity of propagation of the radiation. Equation (41) can therefore be written as

$$-dI = \frac{8\pi^2}{3h^2}\,|\mu_{lm}|^2 \left(\frac{I}{c}\right) h\nu_{lm}N'\, dl \tag{43}$$

For comparison with the experimental expression, Eq. (37), it is finally necessary to relate N' to the molar concentration C. If Avogadro's number is N, this relation is

$$N' = \frac{NC}{1,000} \tag{44}$$

Substitution for N' in Eq. (43) gives

$$-dI = \frac{8\pi^3}{3h^2} |\mu_{lm}|^2 \left(\frac{I}{c}\right) h\nu_{lm} \frac{NC}{1,000} dl \tag{45}$$

Comparison with the differential form of Beer's law, Eq. (37), allows the terms corresponding to $\alpha(\nu)$ to be identified. The theory predicts, however, the total absorption for the transition rather than that for a given frequency, and the identification should be made with $A = \int\alpha(\nu)\, d\nu$. In this way we obtain

$$A = \frac{8\pi^3 N}{3hc(1,000)} \nu_{lm}|\mu_{lm}|^2 \tag{46}$$

where ν_{lm} is the center of the absorption band and, as it will be recalled,

$$|\mu_{lm}| = \int_{-\infty}^{+\infty} \psi_l^* \mu \psi_m \, dx \tag{47}$$

The important result given by Eq. (46) is that the integrated absorption coefficient, or simply the band intensity, can be calculated for a transition if the wave functions for the initial and final states are known and if the integration of Eq. (47) can be performed. Conversely, one can use the measured value of A to obtain a value of $|\mu_{lm}|^2$ and of $\pm|\mu_{lm}|$ and thereby learn, by means of Eq. (47), something about the wave functions of the states involved in the transition. In subsequent work, both procedures will be used.

4-5. The Basis of Selection Rules

The results of the previous section provide a quantitative relation between the transition moment of the absorbing species and the absorption of radiation by a given sample. From this relation, furthermore, often some very important qualitative statements can be made about which transitions can be induced by radiation, and thus lead to the absorption of radiation, and which transitions cannot be so induced, and therefore fail to absorb radiation. Such general statements are called *selection rules*, and for a given system they can be deduced by deciding for which transitions the integral $|\mu_{lm}|$ must necessarily have a zero value. The deduction of selection rules for the particle-in-a-box system will conveniently demonstrate the deduction of selection rules.

Let us consider the particle to be an electron and the balancing positive charge to be located at the mid-point of the well or, at least, to be symmetrically distributed about the mid-point. The dipole moment will then have the form

$$\mu = ey \tag{48}$$

where, as Fig. 4-2 shows, y is the distance of the electron from the center of the potential well. For a transition from a state with $n = l$ to one with $n = m$ to be induced by electromagnetic radiation, the integral

$$|\mu_{lm}| = \int_{-a/2}^{a/2} \psi_l (ey) \psi_m \, dx \tag{49}$$

must be nonzero.

The integration will be carried out in the next section when a quantitative result for the absorption intensities is desired. One can here illustrate that for the deduction of selection rules it is often sufficient to consider the symmetry of the three functions ψ_l^*, ey, and ψ_m that appear in Eq. (49).

The coordinate system, of Fig. 4-2, with y at the mid-point is convenient for the symmetry discussions that are necessary here. The coordinate y, and therefore the function ey, is clearly an odd, or anti-symmetric, function since it changes sign at the origin. All the wave

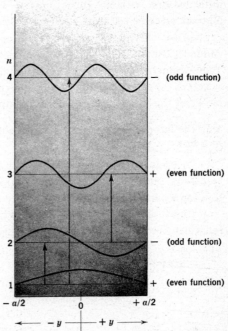

FIG. 4-2 The symmetry properties of the particle-in-a-box wave function and some of the transitions allowed by the rule $+ \leftrightarrow -$, $+ \nleftrightarrow +$, $- \nleftrightarrow -$.

functions, as was shown in Sec. 1-8, are either symmetric or antisymmetric about this origin; i.e., they are either even or odd functions. If the product of the three functions of the integral of Eq. (49) is an odd function, the result of the integration over the left half of the potential well will exactly cancel the contribution from the integration over the right half. Thus $|\mu_{lm}|$ will necessarily be zero for a transition from $n = l$ to $n = m$ if l and m are both odd numbers or both even numbers. The allowed transitions, i.e., the transitions for which $|\mu_{lm}|$ is not necessarily zero, connect a state with an even value of the quantum number to a state with an odd value.

One should recognize that the selection rule stating that transitions can occur between energy levels only if one level has an odd quantum number and the other an even quantum number is equivalent to the statement that only levels of different symmetry can combine. The selection rule can be conveniently expressed as

$$+ \longleftrightarrow -$$
$$+ \longleftrightarrow\!\!\!| + , - \longleftrightarrow\!\!\!| -$$

where $+$ indicates a state with a symmetric wave function and $-$ indicates one with an antisymmetric wave function. The transitions allowed by these selection rules are indicated in Fig. 4-2.

As for this particle-in-a-box example, it will often be possible to deduce selection rules without a detailed working out of the integrals. The symmetry of the system will be important in this regard, and the selection rules will usually have some simple direct relation to the symmetry of the wave functions corresponding to the energy levels.

4-6. The Integrated Absorption Coefficient for a Transition of a Particle in a Box

To evaluate the theoretical integrated absorption coefficient for a transition, one must work out the integral involved in $|\mu_{lm}|$. The transition for a particle in a box can be easily treated.

For the dipole moment term μ one writes, using the coordinate system for which the wave functions of the square well were given in Sec. 1-5,

$$\mu = e\left(x - \frac{a}{2}\right) = ex - \frac{ea}{2} \tag{50}$$

The wave functions are

$$\psi_n = \sqrt{\frac{2}{a}} \sin \frac{n\pi x}{a} \tag{51}$$

and the transition moment $|\mu_{lm}|$ is, therefore,

$$|\mu_{lm}| = \frac{2e}{a} \int_0^a \left(\sin \frac{l\pi x}{a} \right) \left(\sin \frac{m\pi x}{a} \right) \left(x - \frac{a}{2} \right) dx \tag{52}$$

Since the orthogonality condition eliminates the integral arising from the $a/2$ term, one is left with the expression

$$|\mu_{lm}| = \frac{2e}{a} \int_0^a x \left(\sin \frac{l\pi x}{a} \right) \left(\sin \frac{m\pi x}{a} \right) dx \tag{53}$$

Making use of the relation

$$\sin \theta \sin \phi = \tfrac{1}{2}[\cos (\theta - \phi) - \cos (\theta + \phi)] \tag{54}$$

one gets

$$|\mu_{lm}| = \frac{e}{a} \int_0^a \left[x \cos (l - m) \frac{\pi x}{a} - x \cos (l + m) \frac{\pi x}{a} \right] dx \tag{55}$$

Integration, making use of the integral $\int y \cos y \, dy = \cos y + y \sin y$, gives

$$|\mu_{lm}| = \frac{ea}{\pi^2} \left[\frac{\cos (l - m)\pi - 1}{(l - m)^2} - \frac{\cos (l + m)\pi - 1}{(l + m)^2} \right] \tag{56}$$

where the fact that $l - m$ and $l + m$ are integers has been used to elim inate the sine terms.

The selection rules deduced from symmetry considerations in the previous section can be obtained analytically by the insertion into Eq. (56) of the various even and odd combinations for l and m.

The intensity of the π-electron transition of hexatriene, for which the frequency was calculated in Exercise 1-2, can be used as a specific application of Eq. (56). The transition, as Fig. 1-2 indicates, corresponds to $l = 3$ and $m = 4$. Substitution of these values in Eq. (56) gives

$$|\mu_{lm}| = \frac{96}{49} \frac{ea}{\pi^2} \cong \frac{2ea}{\pi^2} \tag{57}$$

The integrated absorption coefficient is then given, by Eq. (46), as

$$\begin{aligned} A &= \frac{8\pi^3 N}{3hc(1,000)} \nu_{lm} \frac{4e^2 a^2}{\pi^4} \\ &= \frac{32 N e^2 a^2 \nu_{lm}}{3\pi hc 1,000} \end{aligned} \tag{58}$$

Using $\lambda_{lm} = 2,600$ A and $a = 7.3$ A, one gets

$A = 14 \times 10^{18}$ sec^{-1} cm^{-1} mole^{-1} liter

The observed value is

$$A = \int \alpha(\nu) \, d\nu = 4.3 \times 10^{18} \text{ sec}^{-1} \text{ cm}^{-1} \text{ mole}^{-1} \text{ liter}$$

In view of the simplicity of the model, the order of magnitude agreement is quite satisfactory.

Exercise 4-2. Calculate the frequency and the integrated absorption coefficient for the lowest π-electron transition of octatetraene, using the square-well potential model.

4-7. Induced Emission and Induced Absorption

In some experiments it is important to recognize, as was mentioned in Sec. 4-3, that the term for induced emission is equal to that for induced absorption. This means that, if there are the same number of molecules in the state m as in the state l, the effect of subjecting the system to electromagnetic radiation will be to cause just as many molecules to go from m to l as from l to m. No net absorption of energy will be observed. In practice, when one studies absorption spectra, one generally deals with a system where each state of lower energy has a larger population than each upper state. A net absorption of energy is then observed.

In addition to induced absorption and emission, there is the possibility of spontaneous emission. The probability of such emission is usually much less than for the induced process, and it need not be treated here.

Finally it can be mentioned that the treatment of induced absorption has been based on the interaction of the electromagnetic radiation with the dipole moment of the atom or molecule. Emission or absorption can also occur as a result of the quadrupole of the atom or molecule. The interaction of the quadrupole with the electric field of the radiation is smaller than the dipole interaction by a factor of about 10^8, and one can therefore almost always ignore these quadrupole effects.

4-8. The Integrated Absorption Coefficient for a Vibrational Transition

The treatment of vibrational energies and vibrational spectra given in Chap. 2 used the selection-rule result that for a vibrational transition to be induced by electromagnetic radiation $\Delta v = \pm 1$, where v is the vibrational quantum number. It can now be recognized that this implies that only for $\Delta v = \pm 1$ can $|\mu_{lm}|$ for a vibrational transition be nonzero. This result can be readily obtained by those familiar with the general properties of Hermite polynomials. The application to a vibrational problem of the important relations of Eqs. (46) and (47) will, however, be demonstrated. An important result will be obtained by a derivation of the relation between molecular properties and the amount of absorption caused by the fundamental $v = 0$ to $v = 1$ vibrational transition.

In Sec. 4-4 the result was obtained that the integrated absorption coefficient

$$A = \int \alpha(\nu)\, d\nu$$

$$= \frac{1}{Cl} \int \ln \frac{I_0}{I}\, d\nu \qquad \text{sec}^{-1}\ \text{cm}^{-1}\ \text{mole}^{-1}\ \text{liter}$$

is related to the transition moment according to the relation

$$A = \frac{8\pi^3 N}{3hc(1,000)}\, \nu_{lm}|\mu_{lm}|^2 \qquad \text{sec}^{-1}\ \text{cm}^{-1}\ \text{mole}^{-1}\ \text{liter}$$

In the experimental study of vibrational transitions one usually deals with frequencies $\bar{\nu}$, with units of cm^{-1}, instead of ν, with units of sec^{-1}. In terms of $\bar{\nu}$, the integrated absorption coefficient $\bar{A}$ is

$$\bar{A} = \frac{8\pi^3 N}{3hc(1,000)}\, \bar{\nu}_{lm}|\mu_{lm}|^2 \qquad \text{cm}^{-2}\ \text{mole}^{-1}\ \text{liter} \tag{59}$$

For the fundamental transition for which the values of the vibrational quantum number v are $l = 0$ and $m = 1$, the expression for $\bar{A}$ is

$$\bar{A}_{01} = \frac{8\pi^3 N}{3hc(1,000)}\, \bar{\nu}_{01}|\mu_{01}|^2 \tag{60}$$

The dipole moment, necessary for the evaluation of $|\mu_{01}|$, of a heteronuclear diatomic molecule must be expected to be some not easily determined, or even expressed, function of the internuclear distance. It is possible, however, if it is required that the dipole moment must be expressed only for small displacements of the molecule from its equilibrium configuration, to represent the dipole moment by the series expansion

$$\mu = \mu_{r=r_e} + \left(\frac{d\mu}{dr}\right)_{r=r_e} (r - r_e) + \cdots \tag{61}$$

where $\mu_{r=r_e}$ is, essentially, the quantity usually referred to as the permanent dipole moment.

In terms of the displacement coordinate

$$q = r - r_e \tag{62}$$

the dipole-moment expression is

$$\mu = \mu_{q=0} + \left(\frac{d\mu}{dq}\right)_{q=0} q + \cdots \tag{63}$$

The wave functions for the $v = 0$ and the $v = 1$ states that are involved in the fundamental transition are shown in Sec. 2-4 to be expressed in terms of the displacement coordinate as

$$\psi_0 = \left(\frac{\alpha}{\pi}\right)^{\frac{1}{4}} e^{-\alpha q^2/2}$$

and

$$\psi_1 = \left(\frac{\alpha}{\pi}\right)^{\frac{1}{4}} \sqrt{2\alpha}\, q e^{-\alpha q^2/2}$$

where

$$\alpha = \frac{2\pi\sqrt{\mu_{\text{red.}}k}}{h} = \frac{4\pi^2 \mu_{\text{red.}}\bar{\nu}c}{h}$$

and $\mu_{\text{red.}}$ is written to distinguish the reduced mass from the dipole moment μ.

With these expressions for μ, ψ_0, and ψ_1, the transition moment can be set up, if only the first two terms of Eq. (63) are retained, as

$$|\mu_{01}| = \int_{-\infty}^{+\infty} \psi_0 \left[\mu_{q=0} + \left(\frac{d\mu}{dq}\right)_{q=0} q\right] \psi_1\, dq \tag{64}$$

The orthogonality of ψ_0 and ψ_1 leads to a zero contribution from the constant term $\mu_{q=0}$ and shows that a constant dipole moment is not sufficient to lead to a vibrational transition being induced by electromagnetic radiation. A nonzero value of $|\mu_{01}|$ can, however, result from the second term of Eq. (64). This leads to the result

$$|\mu_{01}| = \left(\frac{d\mu}{dq}\right)_{q=0} \int_{-\infty}^{+\infty} \psi_0 q \psi_1\, dq$$

$$= \left(\frac{d\mu}{dq}\right)_{q=0} \sqrt{2\alpha} \left(\frac{\alpha}{\pi}\right)^{\frac{1}{2}} \int_{-\infty}^{+\infty} q^2 e^{-\alpha q^2}\, dq \tag{65}$$

The necessary integration can be performed with the tabulated integral

$$\int_0^\infty x^2 e^{-ax^2}\, dx = \frac{1}{4a}\sqrt{\frac{\pi}{a}} \tag{66}$$

One obtains

$$|\mu_{01}| = \frac{1}{\sqrt{2\alpha}} \left(\frac{d\mu}{dq}\right)_{q=0} \tag{67}$$

and with this value for the transition moment the integrated absorption coefficient $\bar{A}$ is found to be related to molecular properties according to

$$\bar{A} = \frac{\pi N}{3c^2(1,000)\mu_{\text{red.}}} \left(\frac{d\mu}{dq}\right)^2_{q=0} \tag{68}$$

or

$$\left(\frac{d\mu}{dq}\right)_{q=0} = \pm \sqrt{\frac{3c^2(1,000)\mu_{\text{red.}}\bar{A}}{\pi N}} \tag{69}$$

Equation (68) is the important result that shows how the absorption intensity of a fundamental vibrational transition is related to the properties $\mu_{\text{red.}}$ and $(d\mu/dq)_{q=0}$ of the molecule under study. The transposition given in Eq. (69) is that which is used when it is desired to obtain the dipole-moment derivative from the measured absorption intensity.

The measured value of $\bar{A}$ for the fundamental transition of BrCl at 439 cm^{-1}, for example, has been reported by W. V. F. Brooks and B. Crawford [J. Chem. Phys., **23**: 363 (1955)] to be

$$\bar{A} = 105 \pm 14 \ cm^{-2} \ mole^{-1} \ liter \tag{70}$$

From this value and the reduced mass of 4.1×10^{-23} g, one calculates

$$\left(\frac{d\mu}{dq}\right)_{q=0} = \pm 0.76 \times 10^{-10} \ esu \tag{71}$$

Although distortion of a chemical bond from its equilibrium distance is undoubtedly generally accompanied by a complicated redistribution of the electrons of the bonded atoms, the order of magnitude that is to be expected for values of $(d\mu/dq)_{q=0}$ can be obtained by assuming a constant charge of $+\delta e$ on one atom of the bond and $-\delta e$ on the other atom. With this model the bond dipole moment is

$$\mu = (\delta e)r \tag{72}$$

and, since $q = r - r_e$,

$$\left(\frac{d\mu}{dr}\right)_{r=r_e} = \left(\frac{d\mu}{dq}\right)_{q=0} = \delta e \tag{73}$$

This result suggests that values of $(d\mu/dq)_{q=0}$ should be of the order of magnitude of the electron charge, 4.8×10^{-10} esu. The result obtained for BrCl is consistent with this expectation.

It is, in fact, rather unsatisfactory to attempt to express the dipole moment of a bond, or a diatomic molecule, by means of Eq. (72). One can, however, recognize that at $r = 0$ the dipole moment μ is necessarily zero and that at $r = \infty$, since in inert solvents or gaseous media essentially all bonds are expected to break to give neutral particles, μ is also zero. The value of μ at the equilibrium distance can be determined, but even this determination does not lead directly to a determination of the sign of this equilibrium dipole moment. The information available, including a deduced value of $\pm (d\mu/dq)_{q=0}$ from the measured value of A, can be illustrated by the curves for possible dipole-moment versus bond-distance dependence shown in Fig 4-3. It is at present a difficult matter to decide whether the curve with a positive value of $(d\mu/dq)_{q=0}$ or a negative value is correct for a given molecule. Nevertheless, the measurement of values of A and the deduction of values for $\pm (d\mu/dq)_{q=0}$, according to Eq. (71), lead to the accumulation of data that are of considerable potential value in consideration of the electronic structure of molecules.

4-9. The Intensities of Absorption Bands Due to Electronic Transitions

Detailed discussion of the changes in the electronic structure of molecules that lead to the absorption of radiation, usually in the visible or ultraviolet regions, will not be given until Chaps. 10 and 11. It is, however, convenient to obtain here an often-used guide to the intensities of absorption bands that result from electronic transitions. The calculation is based on a simple model for the behavior of an electron in a molecule or ion.

One assumes that the electron that is responsible for the absorption of the radiation is attracted to the center of the molecule, here assumed to be spherical, with a Hooke's law type of force. With this model, the

FIG. 4-3 Types of μ versus r curves that can be drawn from measured values of μ and $d\mu/dq$.

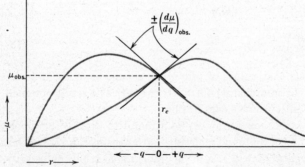

behavior of the electron is given by the harmonic oscillator wave functions used in the previous section.

Each cartesian coordinate contributes a dipole-moment integral like that of Eq. (67). Now, however, since $\mu_x = ex$, $\mu_y = ey$, and $\mu_z = ez$, one can replace $(d\mu/dx)_{x=0}$ by e, and so forth. Likewise, since the mass of the electron is much less than that of the remainder of the molecule, one replaces $\mu_{\text{red.}}$ by m, the mass of the electron. With these variations the transition moments for this simple model of a bound electron are, according to Eq. (67) and the expression for α,

$$|\mu_{01x}| = |\mu_{01y}| = |\mu_{01z}| = e\left(\frac{h}{8\pi^2 m\bar{\nu}c}\right)^{\frac{1}{2}} \tag{74}$$

Addition of the equal cartesian components then gives

$$|\mu_{01}|^2 = \frac{3e^2h}{8\pi^2 m\bar{\nu}c} \tag{75}$$

Substitution of this expression in Eq. (46) gives, for the integrated absorption coefficient predicted by this model, the result

$$A = \frac{Ne^2}{1,000cm} \text{ sec}^{-1} \text{ cm}^{-1} \text{ mole}^{-1} \text{ liter}$$

or $\qquad\qquad\qquad\qquad\qquad\qquad\qquad\qquad\qquad\qquad\qquad$ (76)

$$\bar{A} = \frac{Ne^2}{1,000c^2m} \text{ cm}^{-2} \text{ mole}^{-1} \text{ liter}$$

Insertion of numerical values gives the prediction as

$$\bar{A} = \int\alpha(\bar{\nu})\,d\bar{\nu} = 2.31 \times 10^8 \text{ cm}^{-2} \text{ mole}^{-1} \text{ liter} \tag{77}$$

This result is often used as a reference value against which the actual intensities of electronic absorption bands are compared. To do this one introduces the term *oscillator strength*. This is denoted by f and is defined as the ratio of the observed integrated absorption coefficient to the value predicted by Eq. (76). Thus one has

$$f = \frac{[\int\alpha(\bar{\nu})\,d\bar{\nu}]_{\text{obs}}}{[Ne^2/1,000c^2m]}$$
$$= 4.33 \times 10^{-9}\int\alpha(\bar{\nu})\,d\bar{\nu} \tag{78}$$

One finds, in fact, that many electronic absorption bands have f values near unity. One also finds electronic absorption bands with very much smaller values of f, and in these cases one expects to assign the absorption band to some "forbidden transition." These ideas will be enlarged upon in Chap. 11.

PRINCIPAL REFERENCES

1. Pitzer, K. S.: "Quantum Chemistry," chap. 6, Prentice-Hall, Inc., Englewood Cliffs, N.J., 1953.
2. Pauling, L., and E. B. Wilson, Jr.: "Introduction to Quantum Mechanics," chap.11, McGraw-Hill Book Company, Inc., New York, 1935.
3. Slater, J. C.: "Quantum Theory of Atomic Structure," vol. 1, chap. 6, McGraw-Hill Book Company, Inc., New York, 1960.

5 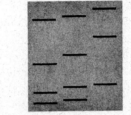 ROTATIONAL SPECTRA

Some of the principal features of the energy levels of the allowed rotational states of diatomic molecules and of the transitions between these states have been discussed in Chap. 3. The rotational energies and rotational spectra of general polyatomic molecules are conveniently treated under headings that specify the relative value of the three principal moments of inertia of the molecule. On this basis, the chapter is divided into the three principal topics: linear, symmetric-top, and asymmetric-top molecules. A number of aspects of the rotational spectra of linear molecules have already been dealt with in Chap. 3. Now the heading will be used principally to introduce a number of finer features of rotational spectra that were not mentioned in the earlier introductory chapter.

LINEAR MOLECULES

The selection rules for transitions between rotational energy levels and the multiplicity of these levels have been stated in Chap. 3. Before proceeding to molecules of general geometry, it is perhaps advisable to look in somewhat more detail at these two features for the relatively simple situation of linear molecules. These molecules also provide a convenient basis for mention of the fine structure that is observed in rotational spectra when nuclear spin, if present, interacts with the molecular rotation and for commenting on the effect that any nuclear spin has, as a result of the statistics that are followed, on the rotational states that exist.

5-1. Rotational Selection Rules for Linear Molecules

The requirement that a molecule must have a permanent dipole moment and that the rotational quantum number can change only by one unit for a rotational transition to be induced by electromagnetic radiation must first be investigated. As was shown in Chap. 4, to do this it is only necessary to investigate the value of the transition moment for the transition under consideration.

The three-dimensional nature of the problem suggests the use of the polar coordinate system of Fig. 3-2 to describe the wave functions and the dipole moment that appear in the transition-moment integral.

The rotational wave functions can be obtained by solution of the Schrödinger equation expressed in polar coordinates for a molecule freely rotating in three-dimensional space. Solution of this problem will not be given here since it is somewhat intricate and can be found in any of the standard texts on quantum mechanics. The problem is, as was mentioned in Chap. 3, generally solved when the hydrogen atom is studied. It turns out that the Schrödinger equation for the hydrogen atom can be separated into two parts. One part involves only the angular coordinates θ and ϕ of the electron considered to move about a fixed nucleus; the other involves only the distance between the electron and the nucleus. The former part is identical to the equation that would be set up for a freely rotating rigid molecule which, of course, would involve only the angles describing the orientation of the molecule as variables. The correspondence of these equations means that the rotational wave functions that are of importance here are identical to the familiar angular part of the hydrogen-atom wave functions. These are illustrated in Fig. 5-1, where both the J quantum-number notation appropriate to molecular rotation problems and the $s, p, d, \ldots$ notation appropriate to atomic problems are given.

Those familiar with the hydrogen-atom wave functions will recall that the angular part of these solutions is related to functions known as associated Legendre functions. Each solution is characterized by two quantum numbers which are here denoted by J and M and which can be assigned integral values, with the provision that M is less than, or equal to, J. The wave functions corresponding to some of the lowest energy states are given in Table 5-1.

The Schrödinger equation solution to the rotating linear molecule problem leads to allowed energies that are identical to those given in Sec. 3-2. The solution functions illustrated in Fig. 5-1 and Table 5-1

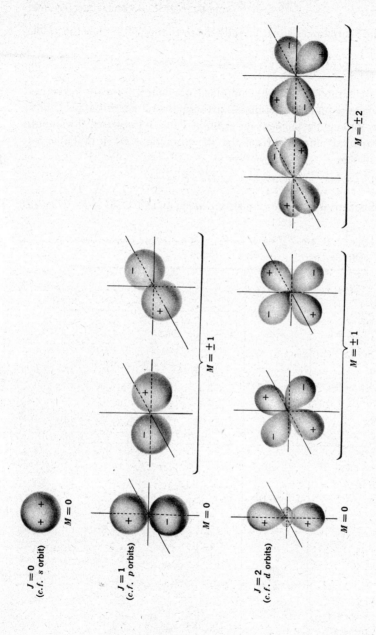

$J = 0$
(c.f. s orbit)

$M = 0$

$J = 1$
(c.f. p orbits)

$M = 0$

$M = \pm 1$

$J = 2$
(c.f. d orbits)

$M = 0$

$M = \pm 1$

$M = \pm 2$

FIG. 5-1 Diagrammatic representations of the rotational wave functions for $J = 0$, 1, and 2.

85

satisfy the Schrödinger equation only if ϵ in that equation has the values

$$\epsilon = \frac{h^2}{8\pi^2 I} J(J+1) \qquad J = 0, 1, 2, \ldots \tag{1}$$

This result is the same as that obtained previously from the quantized angular momentum restriction. Furthermore, if quantum-mechanical operators for angular momentum given in Table 1-1 are used to compute average angular momenta from the wave functions given in Table 5-1, it is found that

$$\text{Total angular momentum} = \sqrt{J(J+1)}\,\frac{h}{2\pi}$$

$$\text{Component of angular momentum along an axis} = M\,\frac{h}{2\pi} \tag{2}$$

TABLE 5-1   Some of the Wave Functions for a Rigid Rotating Linear Molecule

$J = 0$	$M = 0$	$\psi = \dfrac{1}{2\sqrt{\pi}}$
$J = 1$	$M = 0$	$\psi = \dfrac{1}{2}\sqrt{\dfrac{3}{\pi}}\cos\theta$
	$M = \pm 1$	$\psi = \dfrac{1}{2}\sqrt{\dfrac{3}{2\pi}}\sin\theta e^{\pm i\phi} \qquad \text{or}$
		$\psi = \begin{cases} \dfrac{1}{2}\sqrt{\dfrac{3}{\pi}}\sin\theta\cos\phi \\[2mm] \dfrac{1}{2}\sqrt{\dfrac{3}{\pi}}\sin\theta\sin\phi \end{cases}$
$J = 2$	$M = 0$	$\psi = \dfrac{1}{4}\sqrt{\dfrac{5}{\pi}}\,(3\cos^2\theta - 1)$
	$M = \pm 1$	$\psi = \dfrac{1}{2}\sqrt{\dfrac{15}{2\pi}}\sin\theta\cos\theta e^{\pm i\phi} \qquad \text{or}$
		$\psi = \begin{cases} \dfrac{1}{2}\sqrt{\dfrac{15}{\pi}}\sin\theta\cos\theta\cos\phi \\[2mm] \dfrac{1}{2}\sqrt{\dfrac{15}{\pi}}\sin\theta\cos\theta\sin\phi \end{cases}$
	$M = \pm 2$	$\psi = \dfrac{1}{4}\sqrt{\dfrac{15}{2\pi}}\sin^2\theta e^{\pm 2i\phi} \qquad \text{or}$
		$\psi = \begin{cases} \dfrac{1}{4}\sqrt{\dfrac{15}{\pi}}\sin^2\theta\cos 2\phi \\[2mm] \dfrac{1}{4}\sqrt{\dfrac{15}{\pi}}\sin^2\theta\sin 2\phi \end{cases}$

where

$$M = 0, \pm 1, \pm 2, \ldots, \pm J$$

The first of these is the now familiar total angular momentum stipulation, while the second corresponds to the stipulation that the angular momentum component in a direction in space be quantized.

It is sometimes convenient to illustrate the angular momentum components implied by the rotational wave functions by means of a vector diagram. The diagrams that result for quantization in terms of $\sqrt{J(J+1)}$ and M are illustrated in Fig. 5-2. The number of angular momentum components along an axis that can be obtained from a given value of J can be seen from such a diagram to be $2J + 1$.

Exercise 5-1. Apply the operator for total angular momentum to the $J = 0$ and $+1$ wave functions, and confirm that the average angular momentum is $\sqrt{J(J+1)}(h/2\pi)$ in these cases.

After the wave functions of the states involved are specified, the remaining term that is necessary for the evaluation of the transition-moment integral is the dipole moment. If the permanent dipole moment of the molecule is represented by μ_0, the components along the three axes

FIG. 5-2   The total and component angular momentum vectors for $J = 2$. For $J = 2$ an applied field reveals five components. More generally for the Jth rotational level $2J + 1$ states would be revealed.

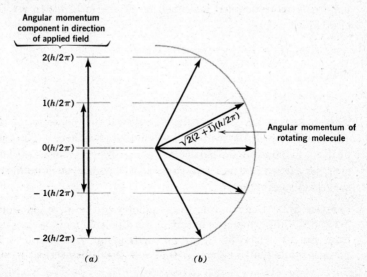

Angular momentum component in direction of applied field

$2(h/2\pi)$

$1(h/2\pi)$

$\sqrt{2(2+1)}(h/2\pi)$

Angular momentum of rotating molecule

$0(h/2\pi)$

$-1(h/2\pi)$

$-2(h/2\pi)$

(a)   (b)

of Fig. 3-2 are given, for any orientation of the molecule, by

$$\mu_x = \mu_0 \sin \theta \cos \phi$$
$$\mu_y = \mu_0 \sin \theta \sin \phi \qquad\qquad (3)$$
$$\mu_z = \mu_0 \cos \theta$$

With the rotational wave functions of Table 5-1 and the dipole-moment expressions of Eq. (3), one can investigate the contributions of the transition-moment components to the total transition moment. In this way, if a transition between a state characterized by J' and M' and one characterized by J'' and M'' is investigated, one obtains the integrals

$$\left|\mu_x^{J'M'J''M''}\right| = \mu_0 \int_0^{2\pi} \int_0^{\pi} \psi^{J'M'} \sin \theta \cos \phi \psi^{J''M''} \sin \theta \, d\theta \, d\phi$$

$$\left|\mu_y^{J'M'J''M''}\right| = \mu_0 \int_0^{2\pi} \int_0^{\pi} \psi^{J'M'} \sin \theta \sin \phi \psi^{J''M''} \sin \theta \, d\theta \, d\phi \qquad (4)$$

$$\left|\mu_z^{J'M'J''M''}\right| = \mu_0 \int_0^{2\pi} \int_0^{\pi} \psi^{J'M'} \cos \theta \psi^{J''M''} \sin \theta \, d\theta \, d\phi$$

(It will be recalled that the element of solid angle is $\sin \theta \, d\theta \, d\phi$ in polar coordinates.) These components allow the calculation of the total transition moment as

$$\left|\mu^{J'M'J''M''}\right|^2 = \left|\mu_x^{J'M'J''M''}\right|^2 + \left|\mu_y^{J'M'J''M''}\right|^2 + \left|\mu_z^{J'M'J''M''}\right|^2 \qquad (5)$$

It is immediately clear from Eq. (4) that the transition moment for rotational transitions will be zero unless μ_0 has a nonzero value. It requires a more detailed investigation of the integrals to see that they also vanish unless

$$J' = J'' \pm 1$$

that is,

$$\Delta J = \pm 1 \qquad\qquad (6)$$

The deduction of this result is outlined in "Spectra of Diatomic Molecules," by G. Herzberg, and will not be given here. The verification of this selection rule for particular values of J', M' and J'', M'' can, however, be carried out in a straightforward manner; such verifications are suggested as exercises.

Exercise 5-2. Deduce from the symmetry of the wave functions of Fig. 5-1 and the antisymmetric nature of the dipole moment, as can be verified from Eq. (3), that the transition moment for $J = 0$ to $J = 1$ will be nonzero while that for the $J = 0$ to $J = 2$ will be necessarily zero.

Since the energy of a freely rotating molecule is, according to Eq. (1), dependent only on J, the selection rule for J is of prime importance in rotational spectroscopy. When, however, as will be discussed in the next section, an external electric field imposes a direction on the rotating molecule, the states with different values of M have different energies and the selection rule for M becomes significant. It is found that the integrals of Eq. (4) vanish unless

$$\Delta M = 0 \tag{7}$$

Again, since the general proof of this requires a knowledge of the behavior of spherical harmonics, it will not be given. One can, however, verify that this selection rule operates for transitions between states described by the wave functions of Table 5-1.

Exercise 5-3. Verify the $\Delta J = \pm 1$ and the $\Delta M = 0$ selection rules for the $J = 0$ to $J = 1$ transition.

The treatments of the rotational spectra of generally shaped molecules that will be presented in the remainder of the chapter will introduce other selection rules. These will be stated, without derivation, and it is understood that they are based on the same considerations as those indicated here for linear molecules. Derivations, or reference to derivations, of these selection rules can be found in ref. 3.

5-2. The Stark Effect in Molecular Rotation Spectra

Although the rotational states of linear molecules are characterized by two quantum numbers, the energies of these states depend only on the total angular momentum quantum number J. The $2J + 1$ degeneracy of these rotational levels, due to the various values of M for a given value of J, can be made apparent if an external field is applied to the molecules while their rotational spectrum is observed. An electric field is used, and the shifting and splitting of rotational spectral lines that results is known as a *Stark effect*.

The quantum number M gives the component of the angular momentum in an applied direction, and in a Stark effect experiment this direction is that of the applied electric field. The states with different values of M correspond, therefore, in a classical picture, to different orientations of the rotating molecule relative to the applied field. Since the molecule has a dipole moment, it can be expected that these different orientations relative to the applied electric field will correspond to the different energies. The calculation of these energy shifts that the states with given J and various values of M experience is, however, not simply done. The effect of the applied field is, as will be seen, very small, and the calculation of the energy requires a second-order perturbation calculation to be made. The derivation of the expression for the energy shifts is beyond the scope of this treatment and is outlined, with references, in ref. 2.

The result of the calculation is that the energy of a state character-ized by values of J and M is shifted in an electric field of ε volts/cm by $\delta\epsilon$, where

for $J \neq 0$

$$\delta\epsilon = \frac{4\pi^2 I \mu_0^2 \varepsilon^2}{h^2(300)^2} \frac{J(J+1) - 3M^2}{J(J+1)(2J-1)(2J+3)} \qquad \text{ergs}$$

while for $J = 0$ $\hspace{4cm}$ (8)

$$\delta\epsilon = -\frac{4\pi^2 I \mu_0^2 \varepsilon^2}{3h^2(300)^2} \qquad \text{ergs}$$

These energy shifts in ergs can be converted to frequency shifts of cm^{-1} or megacycles per second, the unit usually used in microwave spectroscopy.

The effect on the energy levels given by these equations is shown for a particular case in Fig. 5-3.

These energy-level shifts show up when spectral transitions are obtained for molecules subject to an electric field. Now, both selection rules

$$\Delta J = \pm 1 \qquad \Delta M = 0 \hspace{4cm} (9)$$

or, for absorption experiments,

$$\Delta J = +1 \qquad \Delta M = 0 \hspace{4cm} (10)$$

as mentioned in the previous section, are important. With these rules the allowed transitions can be added to the energy-level diagram, and this is done in Fig. 5-3. Observation of the number of components that rotational line splits into when an electric field is applied is often a great help in deciding which J levels of the molecule are responsible for the transition. In Chap. 3 it was assumed that a simple series of equally spaced lines could be expected if a rotational spectrum of a linear molecule is obtained. While this is true for linear molecules, sufficient complexi-ties are introduced into the rotational spectrum of generally shaped molecules that a simple matching of the spectral lines with the expected pattern is seldom possible.

In addition to illustrating the space quantization effect, measurement of Stark effect splittings allow, with the aid of Eq. (8), the determination of often rather precise values of the molecular dipole moment μ_0. The first such determination was made by T. W. Dakin, W. E. Good, and

FIG. 5-3 The effect of a Stark field of 1,000 volts/cm on the rotational energy levels of HCl.

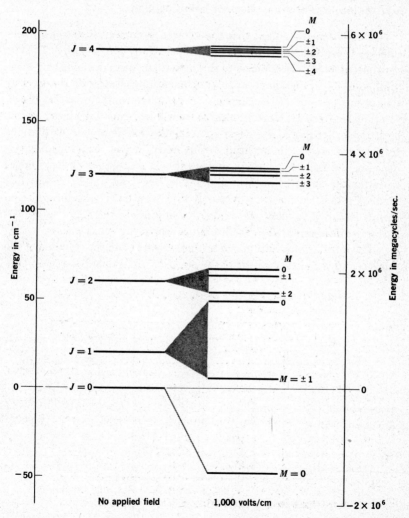

D. K. Coles [*Phys. Rev.*, **70**: 560 (1946)] for the molecule OCS. The oscilloscope pattern of the $J = 1$ to $J = 2$ line is shown for different electric field strengths in Fig. 5-4.

Some dipole-moment determinations that have been made using the Stark effect in rotational spectra are given in Table 5-2.

Exercise 5-4. (*a*) Calculate the shift in the $J = 1$, $M = 1$ energy level of N_2O as a result of an applied electric field of 5,000 volts/cm.

(*b*) Estimate from Fig. 5-4 the dipole moment of the OCS molecule.

5-3. Molecular Rotation—Nuclear-spin Coupling

It has been recognized that the allowed rotational states of a molecule are those for which the angular momentum is a $\sqrt{J(J + 1)}$ type multiple, of $h/2\pi$. In addition to this molecular rotation angular momentum, some molecules have angular momentum because of the nuclear spin of one or more of their nuclei. A complete characterization of the rotational states of such molecules, as we will see, must take into account both the molecular and nuclear-spin angular momentum contributions to the total angular momentum. One finds, in fact, experimental evidence in the hyperfine structure of rotational transitions of some molecules for the effect of nuclear spin. The basis and nature of this fine detail of rotational spectra will be only briefly outlined. Its introduction here is intended to allow the student to appreciate the many rotational spectra studies reported in the literature where this effect occurs.

The angular momentum of a nucleus results from the spinning of the nucleus and is a characteristic of the nucleus. It is quantized in units of

TABLE 5-2   Some Molecular Dipole Moments from Stark Splittings of Rotational Transitions*

Molecule	Dipole moment (Debye)	Molecule	Dipole moment (Debye)
FCl	0.88	NF_3	0.23
FBr	1.29	CHF_3	1.64
BrCl	0.57	CH_3F	1.79
OCS	0.710	CH_3Cl	1.87
HCN	3.00	CH_3Br	1.80
N_2O	0.166	CH_3I	1.65
NH_3	1.47	CH_3CCH	0.75
PH_3	0.55	B_5H_9	2.13

* From W. Gordy, W. V. Smith, and R. F. Trambarulo, "Microwave Spectroscopy," John Wiley & Sons, Inc., 1953.

$h/2\pi$, and, if the nuclear-spin quantum number is designated by I, the spin angular momentum of a particular nucleus has one of the values

$$\sqrt{I(I+1)}\ \frac{h}{2\pi} \qquad \text{where } I = 0, \tfrac{1}{2}, 1, \tfrac{3}{2}, \ldots$$

If there is no coupling, i.e., interaction between the orientation of the nucleus and that of the molecule, the molecule will rotate and leave the spinning nuclei unchanged in orientation. In such a case the energy of a given molecular rotation state, designated by J, would be unaffected by the nuclear spin I. If, on the other hand, there is an energy of interaction the energy of the system will depend on the orientation of the nuclear spin relative to that of the molecular rotation. This dependence can be expressed by introducing a quantum number for the total angular momentum of the system. This is usually denoted by F, and the total angular momentum of the system is then $\sqrt{F(F+1)}\ (h/2\pi)$. A molecu-

FIG. 5-4 The Stark splitting of the $J = 1 \rightarrow 2$ absorption line of OCS. [From T. W. Dakin, W. E. Good, and D. K. Coles, Phys. Rev., 70: 560 (1946).] The line for no field is centered at about 24,320 megacycles/sec, and the two markers on each curve are spaced 6 megacycles/sec apart.

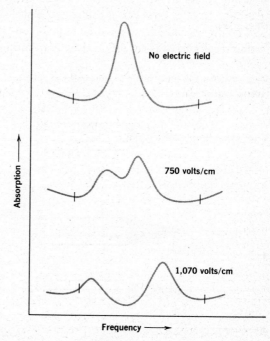

No electric field

750 volts/cm

1,070 volts/cm

Absorption ——→

Frequency ——→

lar rotation state with a given value of J can then lead to states with various values of F according to

$$F = J + I, J + I - 1, \ldots, J - I \qquad (11)$$

with the provision that the total angular momentum cannot be negative and, therefore, that the $J - I$ type terms are not always realized for states with low J numbers. The splittings of the J levels that result from a nuclear spin of $\frac{3}{2}$ are illustrated schematically in Fig. 5-5.

Something must be said about the source of the interaction between the orientation of the molecule and that of the nuclear spin. For almost all molecules, the exceptions being odd molecules such as NO, this interaction occurs between the electric field that the molecule exerts at the spinning nucleus and the quadrupole moment of the nucleus. (All nuclei lack dipole moments. Those with I greater than $\frac{1}{2}$, however, have a charge asymmetry that gives them quadrupole moments.) It is, of course, the directional asymmetry of the electric field of the molecule acting on the nucleus that is now important. Although s orbits bring their electrons close to the nucleus, they are ineffective in orienting the nucleus because of their spherical symmetry. The next most effective electron orbits in producing an electric field at the nucleus are the p orbits. Again, however, a completed p shell has spherical symmetry, and no directional effect would be imposed on the nucleus. Some interesting results have been obtained by attributing the extent of coupling,

FIG. 5-5 The hyperfine splittings (schematic) of rotational levels resulting from coupling with a nuclear spin $I = \frac{3}{2}$.

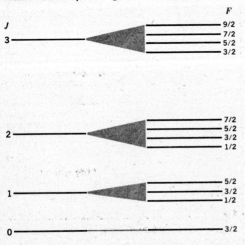

for a given nucleus with a given quadrupole moment, with the extent to which the p subshell of the atom is more or less complete in a particular molecule [2].

The spectral effect produced by the coupling of J and I to produce a resultant F can be understood with an energy-level diagram like that of Fig. 5-5 and the selection rules

$$\Delta J = \pm 1 \qquad \Delta F = 0, \pm 1 \tag{12}$$

A simple illustration is provided by the molecule DCN, in which N^{14} has a spin of unity. The energy levels and $J = 0 \rightarrow 1$ transition, observed by Simmons, Anderson, and Gordy [$Phys.\ Rev.$, **77**: 77 (1950) are shown in Fig. 5-6.

In summary: any molecule containing a nucleus with a spin greater than $\frac{1}{2}$ will, if the nucleus is embedded in an asymmetric electric field of the molecule, show such hyperfine structure due to nuclear-spin interaction. Considerable complexity can be introduced into rotational spectra by this effect. No detailed treatment of this quadrupole coupling fine structure will, therefore, be attempted in the following treatments of symmetric- and asymmetric-top molecules.

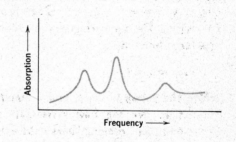

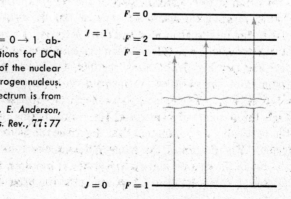

FIG. 5-6 The $J = 0 \rightarrow 1$ absorption and transitions for DCN showing the effect of the nuclear spin $I = 1$ of the nitrogen nucleus. [The absorption spectrum is from J. W. Simmons, W. E. Anderson, and W. Gordy, Phys. Rev., 77:77 (1950).]

*5-4. The Positive and Negative Character of the Wave Functions of Linear Molecules

It has been shown, in Sec. 1-8, that the wave functions for the very simple system of a particle in a box were either unchanged or changed in sign when the wave function was subjected to an inversion through the origin, i.e., when y was replaced by $-y$. On the basis of this behavior, the allowed states were labeled with a plus or a minus, depending on their behavior with regard to this symmetry operation. It was found, furthermore, that the selection rules $(+ \longleftrightarrow -, + \longleftrightarrow\!\!\!| +, - |\!\!\!\longleftrightarrow -)$ for the transitions induced by electromagnetic radiation could be deduced on the basis of the plus or minus character of the states involved in the transition. We will now see that plus and minus signs can, in an entirely analogous manner, be assigned to the wave functions that describe diatomic molecules. This positive and negative character is important in connection with selection rules and with the statistical weights of rotational levels, considered in the following section.

We now consider the effect on the total wave function ψ_{total} of a diatomic molecule when this function is inverted through the origin, i.e., when all the coordinates involved in ψ_{total} are reversed, as by the substitution $x, y, z \rightarrow -x, -y, -z$. The effect of this on ψ_{total} is best deduced by writing the approximate, but adequate for the present argument, separated function

$$\psi_{\text{total}} = \psi_e \psi_v \psi_r \tag{13}$$

where the subscripts e, v, and r stand for electronic, vibrational, and rotational. We can now investigate the effect of inversion on each factor and then combine these results to see the effect on ψ_{total}.

Inversion of the electronic part of the wave function can be accomplished by rotating the entire molecule by 180 deg about an axis perpendicular to the internuclear axis and then performing a reflection through a plane perpendicular to this rotation axis and passing through the internuclear axis (see Fig. 5-7). Since the first step in this process leaves the coordinates of the electrons unchanged with respect to the nuclei, it does not alter ψ_e. The second step reflects the electronic wave function through the designated plane, and the result of this reflection depends on the particular wave function that describes the electronic state of the molecule. The nature of the many different electronic wave functions that occur in the ground and excited states of diatomic molecules will be considered in some detail in Chap. 10. For the present it is enough to concern ourselves with the electronic wave functions that occur in the ground state of almost all diatomic and linear molecules that have even numbers of electrons. This common ground-state function is positive both above and below any plane passing through the internuclear axis. Electronic functions that are symmetric with respect to such planes are labeled with a plus sign, and one finds that most ground-state electronic wave functions are of this type. Most ground-state wave functions, in fact, are designed as Σ^+ states. The basis for the use of the letter Σ will be discussed in Chap. 10. For these often encountered Σ^+ states, therefore, we conclude that an inversion of ψ_e through the origin leaves ψ_e unchanged.

The vibrational component ψ_v of the total wave function depends, as shown in Sec. 2-4, on the magnitude of the internuclear distance. It follows that ψ_v will also be unaffected by an inversion through the origin since this operation leaves the magnitude of the internuclear distance unchanged.

The remaining factor ψ_r, discussed in Sec. 5-1, must now be considered. The polar coordinate equivalent to the inversion implied by $x, y, z \rightarrow -x, -y, -z$ is obtained by replacing $r, \theta,$ and ϕ by $r, \pi - \theta,$ and $\pi + \phi$. The effect of this inversion on ψ_r can be seen either analytically by this replacement in the expressions for ψ_r given in Table 5-1 or diagrammatically from the wave functions depicted in Fig. 5-1. On either basis, one sees that for even values of J the function ψ_r remains unchanged by inversion, while for odd values of J the function ψ_r changes sign.

With the recognition that ψ_e and ψ_v are unchanged by inversion,

FIG. 5-7 Illustration that rotation by 180 deg around an axis and reflection through a plane perpendicular to the axis correspond to inversion through the origin.

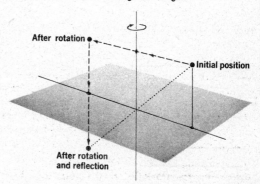

for the molecules considered here, one deduces that ψ_{total} behaves in a manner dictated by ψ_r, as shown in Fig. 5-8.

An immediate result of this assignment is the selection-rule result $(+ \longleftrightarrow -, + \longleftrightarrow\!\!\!\!| +, - \longleftrightarrow\!\!\!\!| -)$ that can be deduced for interaction with electromagnetic radiation in the same way as illustrated for the one-dimensional example in Sec. 4-5. This result can be recognized to be consistent with that of $\Delta J = \pm 1$ obtained from a more detailed analysis of the rotational wave functions.

We now will proceed to another important type of symmetry consideration and will make use of the plus and minus assignments obtained above.

*Exercise 5-5. Deduce that the interaction of a molecular dipole with electromagnetic radiation can lead only to transitions of the type $+ \longleftrightarrow -$.

*5-5. Symmetric-Antisymmetric Character and Statistical Weight of Homonuclear Linear Molecules

Another rather different type of symmetry behavior must be recognized when the molecule under consideration is a homonuclear diatomic molecule with identical nuclei, or a linear molecule with identical nuclei, such as CO_2 or $HC\equiv CH$. We are concerned now with the effect of an interchange of identical nuclei on the wave function of the molecule. This feature, which must be considered whenever a system contains like particles, is perhaps best known to a chemist in terms of an interchange of electrons. Mention of this operation for the two electrons of the

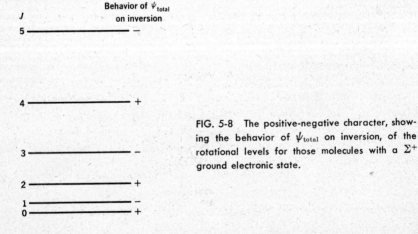

FIG. 5-8 The positive-negative character, showing the behavior of ψ_{total} on inversion, of the rotational levels for those molecules with a Σ^+ ground electronic state.

helium atom may clarify the parallel treatment that will be given for like nuclei of molecules.

For the helium atom, or any atom, the total wave function contains no vibrational and rotational factors and might be written as

$$\psi_{\text{total}} = \psi_e \tag{14}$$

Furthermore, one can write a suitable approximate expression for ψ_e for the helium atom by regarding each electron as behaving according to $1s$ hydrogenlike wave functions, properly adjusted for the increased nuclear change. Thus one would write

$$\psi_{\text{total}} = \psi_e = 1s(1)1s(2) \tag{15}$$

This function is clearly unchanged by the interchange of the two electrons; i.e., $1s(1)1s(2) = 1s(2)1s(1)$.

Thus far our discussion of the helium atom has lacked the important factor of the spin of the electrons. The electronic wave function given above describes only the orbital behavior of the electrons, and one should write the more complete expression

$$\psi_{\text{total}} = \psi_e \psi_{\text{spin}} \tag{16}$$

Each electron has a spin quantum number $\frac{1}{2}$, and since the angular momentum associated with this spin can be directed one way, designated say by the symbol α, or the other way, designated by the symbol β, one can write various possible spin functions for ψ_{spin} as

$\alpha(1)\alpha(2)$
$\beta(1)\beta(2)$
$\alpha(1)\beta(2) + \alpha(2)\beta(1)$
$\alpha(1)\beta(2) - \alpha(2)\beta(1)$

These have all been written so that ψ_{spin} will go to $\pm\psi_{\text{spin}}$ when the electrons are interchanged.

To attach correct spin functions, from these four possibilities, to the orbital functions, one must make use of the fact that the behavior of electrons in nature can be accounted for only if wave functions that are antisymmetric with respect to the exchange of any pair of electrons are used. It follows that a suitable antisymmetric ψ_{total} can be written by combining the orbital and spin factors to give

$$\psi_{\text{total}} = 1s(1)1s(2)[\alpha(1)\beta(2) - \alpha(2)\beta(1)] \tag{17}$$

One deduces by this means the familiar result, given immediately by the usual form of the Pauli exclusion principle, that the electrons of the helium atom, in its ground state, must have opposite spins.

In a similar way the total wave function for a molecule must behave, for the interchange of like nuclei, in a manner dictated by the nature of the spin of the nucleus. It turns out that the spin of the nucleus, or any particle, is the index which determines whether the wave function must be unchanged, i.e., symmetric, or must be changed in sign, i.e., antisymmetric, with respect to an exchange of identical particles. If the spin quantum number of the particle is half integral, as is that of the electron, the wave function must change sign; whereas if the spin quantum number is zero or integral, the wave function must remain unchanged. Particles of the first type, electrons and protons are the most often encountered examples, are said to follow Fermi-Dirac statistics; those of the second type, such as O^{16} (with zero spin) and H^2 (with unit spin), are said to follow Bose-Einstein statistics.

The effect of an interchange of like nuclei on ψ_{total} will now be analyzed. Then the nuclear spin, dealt with in another connection in Sec. 5-3, will be introduced in a way so that the complete wave function behaves in a manner suitable to the statistics followed by the nuclei.

It is informative to analyze the effect of an interchange of identical nuclei of a diatomic, or linear, molecule by imagining this exchange to occur as a result (1) of an inversion of all the particles, electrons and nuclei, through the origin, and then (2) of the inversion of the electrons back through the origin. The first step of this process is nothing more than the symmetry operation treated in the previous section. We therefore already know that its effect on the total wave function, for Σ^+ states, is plus or minus depending on whether J is even or odd. The second step of the process has an effect that depends only on the electronic wave function. Some electronic wave functions, such as the lowest particle-in-a-box state, are symmetric with respect to this inversion through the center of symmetry of the molecule. These symmetric electronic states, which constitute the most often encountered ground states, are labeled with a g (for the German *gerade*). Those electronic states which are antisymmetric with respect to inversion through the center of symmetry are labeled with a u (for *ungerade*). (Note that electronic functions only have g or u properties when there is a center of symmetry as there is in H_2, CO_2, and so forth. The property plus and minus assigned to electronic wave functions in the previous section depends on reflection through a plane containing the molecular axis. Such behavior can be considered even for molecules like HCl, NaCl, and so forth.)

The net effect of the two-step process is, if the electronic state is of the g type, to leave the total wave function unchanged for even values of J and to change its sign for odd values of J. For u states this conclusion is reversed. Thus, since the two-step process is equivalent to the exchange of the identical nuclei, we have found the behavior of the total wave function, exclusive of the effect of nuclear spin, as a result of this exchange. Symmetric or antisymmetric behavior with regard to this exchange is indicated by an s or an a.

For molecules, such as $O^{16}CO^{16}$, that have identical nuclei with zero spin, the above treatment is complete; i.e., no spin function is involved in the total wave function. It follows, since nuclei with zero spin behave according to Bose-Einstein statistics which require symmetric behavior as a result of nuclear interchange, that only the states with even values of J can exist. The rotational energy-level diagram should show, as illustrated in Fig. 5-9, only the states with even values of J. The absence of the odd levels cannot, of course, be observed in rotational spectra because such symmetric molecules with identical nuclei have zero dipole moments and do not give rise to rotational absorption

FIG. 5-9 The rotational energy-level diagrams for linear molecules with like nuclei. The statistical weight factor due to the nuclear spin is shown. In (a) the like nuclei have $I = 0$, in (b) they have $I = \frac{1}{2}$.

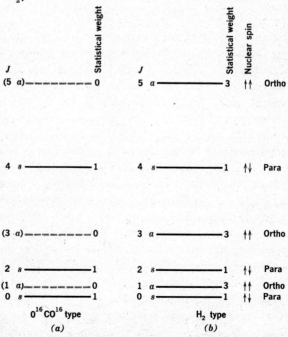

$O^{16}CO^{16}$ type
(a)

H_2 type
(b)

spectra. It should be mentioned, however, that rotational Raman spectra, which will not be discussed here, confirm the absence of the odd J levels for such molecules. Furthermore, the absence of these levels will be noticed in rotation-vibration spectra that will be studied in Chap. 7.

Let us now consider molecules, such as H_2 and $H—C\equiv C—H$, that have like nuclei with spin quantum number $\frac{1}{2}$. (The C^{12} nuclei of acetylene have zero spin and can here be ignored.) As for the two electrons of the helium atom, three symmetric spin functions $\alpha\alpha$, $\beta\beta$, and $\alpha\beta + \beta\alpha$ and one antisymmetric function $\alpha\beta - \beta\alpha$ can be written. Furthermore, nuclei with a spin quantum number of $\frac{1}{2}$ follow Fermi-Dirac statistics that require a total wave function which is antisymmetric with respect to the interchange of the nuclei. Now states with both even and odd values of J can be brought to the required antisymmetry by suitably coupling ψ_{total} with spin functions. Thus one writes, for g electronic functions, antisymmetric functions for the s states, which have J even, as

$$\psi_e\psi_v\psi_r(\alpha\beta - \beta\alpha)$$

and for the a states, which have J odd, as

$$\psi_e\psi_v\psi_r \begin{Bmatrix} \alpha\alpha \\ \beta\beta \\ \alpha\beta + \beta\alpha \end{Bmatrix}$$

Since three spin functions are available to provide the correct symmetry for the odd J levels whereas only one spin function makes the total wave function antisymmetric when J is even, the odd J levels have a statistical weight due to the spin function of 3 while the even J levels have a weight of 1. Thus, in addition to the $2J + 1$ multiplicity that all levels have, the odd J levels have an additional multiplicity factor of 3 while this factor is only 1 for even J levels. Again this alternation in multiplicities, which leads to an alternation in populations, illustrated in Fig. 5-9, cannot be observed in rotational spectra but, for molecules like $HC\equiv CH$ that will be discussed in Sec. 7-4, an alternation in the intensities of the rotational components of rotation-vibration absorption bands is observed.

One should recognize that the analysis given above has led us to recognize the *ortho states* of H_2-like molecules, which are those having parallel ↑↑ nuclear spins, and the *para states*, which have opposed ↑↓ nuclear spins. A very strong selection rule exists which prohibits, by any mechanism, transitions between s states and a states. Thus ortho and para states cannot be interconverted, unless the molecules are dissociated. One should notice that the selection rule $s \longleftrightarrow s$, $a \longleftrightarrow a$,

$s \longleftrightarrow a$, which applies to homonuclear molecules, and $+ \longleftrightarrow -$, $+ \longleftrightarrow +$, $- \longleftrightarrow -$, which applies to any diatomic molecule, eliminates the possibility of pure rotational spectra of diatomic homonuclear molecules.

A similar treatment can be applied to molecules containing like nuclei with spins of 1, $\frac{3}{2}$, and so forth. Again, one finds that all J levels can be combined with spin functions to give total wave functions with the symmetry required by the nuclei. Again, however, the s and a states, with even and odd J values, have different statistical weights.

SYMMETRIC-TOP MOLECULES

Symmetric-top molecules are defined as those having two equal principal moments of inertia, the third being different from these two. The unique moment of inertia is generally represented by I_A, while the two equal moments of inertia are $I_B = I_C$. Most symmetric-top molecules that will be treated belong to this class because of a symmetric arrangement of some of the like atoms of the molecule. A typical example is cyclobutane, which has its unique axis perpendicular to the plane of the carbon atoms, and the two axes with equal moments of inertia pass through either the carbon atoms at opposite corners of the square or through the opposite sides of the square. Benzene and the methyl halides also are symmetric-top molecules. Figure 5-10 shows the principal axes of these two examples.

The classical treatment of the rotation of such symmetric-top molecules will first be given so that the quantized angular momentum restriction can be applied to give the allowed rotational energy levels. A state-

FIG. 5-10   Examples of symmetric-top molecules, i.e., those with $I_A \neq I_B = I_C$.

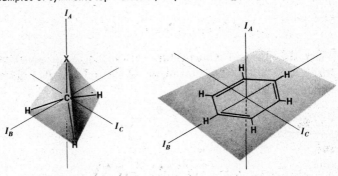

$(I_A < I_B$; prolate symmetric top$)$ $(I_A > I_B$; oblate symmetric top$)$

ment of the selection rules will then allow the spectral transitions to be drawn in and a comparison with observed spectra to be made.

5-6. The Rotational Energy of Symmetric-top Molecules

As with linear molecules, the allowed rotational energy levels can be obtained from the classical equations by the appropriate angular momentum restrictions. The rotation of a system with principal moments of inertia I_A, I_B, and I_C is written classically as

$$\epsilon = \tfrac{1}{2}I_A\omega_A^2 + \tfrac{1}{2}I_B\omega_B^2 + \tfrac{1}{2}I_C\omega_C^2$$
$$= \frac{p_A^2}{2I_A} + \frac{p_B^2}{2I_B} + \frac{p_C^2}{2I_C} \tag{18}$$

where p_A, p_B, and p_C are the angular momenta about the three axes. For a symmetric-top molecule $I_B = I_C$, and this general expression becomes

$$\epsilon = \frac{p_A^2}{2I_A} + \frac{p_B^2}{2I_B} + \frac{p_C^2}{2I_B} \tag{19}$$

The energy levels of a quantum-mechanical symmetric-top system can be obtained from Eq. (19). As for linear molecules, it is assumed that the total angular momentum is quantized and, with the quantum number J, is given by

$$\sqrt{J(J+1)}\,\frac{h}{2\pi} \qquad J = 0, 1, 2, \ldots \tag{20}$$

The correct quantum-mechanical solution for symmetric-top molecules is obtained by further assuming that the component of the angular momentum about the unique axis is quantized and that this quantization is

$$K\frac{h}{2\pi} \qquad K = 0, \pm1, \pm2, \ldots, \pm J \tag{21}$$

where the plus and minus values correspond to the possibility of clockwise and anticlockwise rotation about the unique axis. These quantum restrictions lead to

$$p_A^2 = K^2\left(\frac{h}{2\pi}\right)^2$$

and
$$\tag{22}$$

$$p_B^2 + p_C^2 = J(J+1)\left(\frac{h}{2\pi}\right)^2 - K^2\left(\frac{h}{2\pi}\right)^2$$

These relations convert Eq. (19) to the quantum-mechanical result

$$\epsilon_{JK} = K^2 \frac{h^2}{8\pi^2 I_A} + J(J+1)\frac{h^2}{8\pi^2 I_B} - K^2 \frac{h^2}{8\pi^2 I_B}$$

$$= J(J+1)\frac{h^2}{8\pi^2 I_B} + \left(\frac{h^2}{8\pi^2 I_A} - \frac{h^2}{8\pi^2 I_B}\right)K^2 \quad \text{erg}$$

and   (23)

$$\bar{\epsilon}_{JK} = \frac{h}{8\pi^2 c I_B} J(J+1) + \left(\frac{h}{8\pi^2 c I_A} - \frac{h}{8\pi^2 c I_B}\right)K^2 \quad \text{cm}^{-1}$$

It is again convenient to introduce rotational constants $\bar{B}$ and $\bar{A}$ defined by

$$\bar{B} = \frac{h}{8\pi^2 c I_B} \quad \text{cm}^{-1} \quad \text{and} \quad \bar{A} = \frac{h}{8\pi^2 c I_A} \quad \text{cm}^{-1}$$

With this notation, the energies of the allowed states of a rigid rotating symmetric-top molecule are given by

$$\bar{\epsilon}_{JK} = \bar{B}J(J+1) + (\bar{A} - \bar{B})K^2 \tag{24}$$

with $J = 0, 1, 2, \ldots$ and $K = 0, \pm 1, \pm 2, \ldots, \pm J$

This expression gives the same set of energy levels that would have been obtained if solutions to the Schrödinger equation for a rotating symmetric-top molecule had been sought. By the application of the appropriate quantum mechanical operators, one would also have found that the quantum number J determines the total angular momentum of the system while the number K determines the component of this angular momentum along the unique axis of the molecule.

It will only be mentioned here that Eq. (24) corresponds to the assumption of a rigid molecule and that additional terms must be introduced to allow for centrifugal stretching. As for linear molecules treated in Sec. 3-5, the shifting of the energy levels due to this effect is always very small.

The significance of Eq. (24) is best illustrated by a diagram of the energies that are predicted for various values of J and K. Two different situations are recognized. Molecules that have the unique moment of inertia I_A less than $I_B = I_C$ are said to be *prolate* molecules. An example is CH_3CN. For such molecules the coefficient of K^2 in Eq. (24) is positive, and for a given J value the higher the value of K, the higher the energy. Molecules that have the unique moment of inertia I_A greater than $I_B = I_C$ are said to be *oblate* molecules. An example is benzene. For this class of symmetric tops, the coefficient of K^2 is negative, and for a given value of J the higher the value of K, the lower the energy.   The energy-level diagrams for these two cases are shown schematically in Fig. 5-11.

It should be pointed out that the occurrence of K in Eq. (24) as a squared term leads to the same energy for a state with positive or negative values of K.   Thus all levels with $K \neq 0$ are doubly degenerate.

Exercise 5-6.   Given the geometry of the CH_3Cl molecule in Table 5-3, locate the center of gravity and calculate the three principal moments of inertia.   Also calculate the rotational constants and plot to scale the first few rotational energy levels.

5-7. Selection Rules and Spectra of Symmetric-top Molecules

Most symmetric-top molecules that have a dipole moment have this dipole moment in the direction of the figure, or unique, axis of the molecule.   In such cases the selection rules for the absorption or emission of electromagnetic radiation are

$$\Delta J = 0, \pm 1 \qquad \Delta K = 0 \qquad \text{for } K \neq 0$$

and   (25)

$$\Delta J = \pm 1 \qquad \Delta K = 0 \qquad \text{for } K = 0$$

For an absorption experiment, the part of the selection rule that corresponds to an increase in the energy of the system and is appropriate is

$$\Delta J = +1 \qquad \Delta K = 0 \tag{26}$$

The fact that electromagnetic radiation cannot induce a transition between different K values can be understood from the fact that, for the molecules considered here, rotation about the figure axis contributes no rotating dipole moment.   This component of the rotation cannot,

TABLE 5-3   Some Molecular Structure Results for Symmetric-top Molecules*

Molecule	Bond angle	Bond distances	
CH_3F	HCH 110°0′	CH 1.109	CF 1.385
CH_3Cl	HCH 110°20′	CH 1.103	CCl 1.782
CH_3Br	HCH 110°48′	CH 1.101	CBr 1.938
CH_3CN	HCH 109°8′	CH 1.092	CC 1.460
		CN 1.158	
$CH_3C{\equiv}CH$	HCH 108°14′	CH (methyl) 1.097	CC 1.460
		C≡C 1.207	≡CH 1.056
$CHCl_3$	ClCCl 110°24′	CH 1.073	CCl 1.767
NH_3	HNH 107° ± 2°	NH 1.016	

* From W. Gordy, W. V. Smith, and F. R. Trambarulo, "Microwave Spectroscopy," John Wiley & Sons, Inc., New York, 1953.

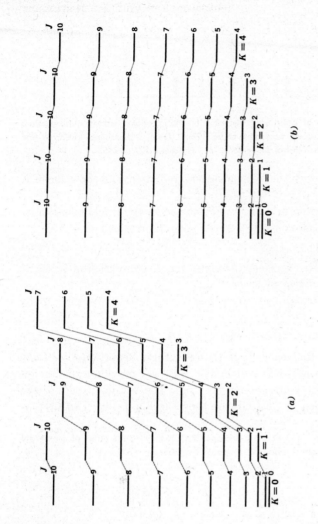

FIG. 5-11 The rotational energy-level patterns for (a) prolate and (b) oblate symmetric-top molecules. (From G. Herzberg, "Infrared and Raman Spectra," D. Van Nostrand Company, Inc., Princeton, N.J., 1945.)

$K(\Delta K = 0)$

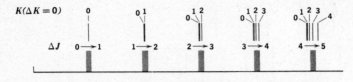

FIG. 5-12   The effect of centrifugal distortion on the rotational transition absorptions of a symmetric-top molecule according to Eq. (28).   (*From G. Herzberg, "Infrared and Raman Spectra," D. Van Nostrand Company, Inc., Princeton, N.J., 1945.*)

therefore, interact with the electromagnetic radiation, and the value of K does not change.

With the selection rule $\Delta J = +1$ and the energy-level expression of Eq. (24), the absorption spectral frequencies are obtained as

$$\bar{\nu} = 2\bar{B}(J + 1) \qquad \text{cm}^{-1} \tag{27}$$

The same pattern is expected, therefore, for a symmetric-top molecule as was found for a linear molecule.

Inclusion of centrifugal stretching effects leads, however, to the expression

$$\bar{\nu} = 2\bar{B}(J + 1) - 2\bar{D}_{KJ}K^2(J + 1) - 4\bar{D}_J(J + 1)^3 \tag{28}$$

for the transition frequencies.   If the centrifugal distortion effects are resolved, the splittings indicated in Fig. 5-12 will provide a distinction between linear and symmetric-top spectra.   The details of part of the $J = 8 \rightarrow 9$ transition of CF_3CCH are shown in Fig. 5-13.   The alterna-

FIG. 5-13   Part of the $J = 8 \rightarrow 9$ transition of CF_3CCH showing the effect of centrifugal distortion.   (The diagram is centered at about 51,800 megacycles/sec.)   [*From W. E. Anderson, R. F. Trambarulo, J. Sheridan, and W. Gordy, Phys. Rev., 82: 58 (1951).*]

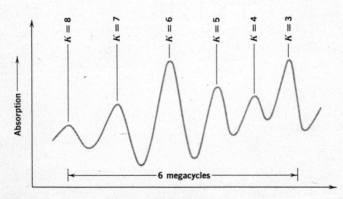

tion in intensity of the different K components is due to the different statistical weights of the levels involved.

5-8. Results from Analyses of Rotation Spectra of Symmetric-top Molecules

According to Eq. (27), measurement of the frequencies of the rotational transitions of a symmetric-top molecule leads only to information about the two equal moments of inertia about the axes of the molecule perpendicular to the figure axis. This one determined quantity is, of course, insufficient for the determination of the bond lengths and bond angles of a polyatomic molecule. Again it is possible to make use of different isotopic species to obtain further moment-of-inertia data. As we will see, however, such a procedure requires the assumption that bond lengths and angles are independent of isotopic substitution; while this would undoubtedly be true to a very good approximation if the atoms were at their equilibrium positions, it introduces some uncertainty when data for the $v = 0$ states are used. Another procedure is to make use of diffraction data, either x-ray or electron diffraction, to provide data on the internuclear distances between the heavy atoms and to supplement these data with the moment-of-inertia result from the rotational spectrum. In this way one can often deduce additional bond length and angle data and, for example, fix the positions of the hydrogen atoms of a molecule.

In spite of the inadequacy of the data provided by the rotational spectrum of a given molecule, many structures have been determined with considerable accuracy. Some of these structures are listed in Table 5-3.

ASYMMETRIC MOLECULES

A molecule with three different moments of inertia is known as an *asymmetric-top* molecule. It will be apparent that the rotational energies and, therefore, the rotational spectrum of such a molecule are expressed with much more difficulty than was encountered for linear and symmetric-top molecules.

5-9. The Energy Levels of an Asymmetric-top Molecule

The rotational energy of an asymmetric system can be expressed by the general, classical formula

$$\epsilon = \tfrac{1}{2}I_A\omega_A^2 + \tfrac{1}{2}I_B\omega_B^2 + \tfrac{1}{2}I_C\omega_C^2$$
$$= \frac{p_A^2}{2I_A} + \frac{p_B^2}{2I_B} + \frac{p_C^2}{2I_C} \tag{29}$$

Conversion to a system which obeys quantum mechanics requires the stipulation that the total angular momentum, ignoring nuclear-spin angular momentum, is quantized according to the relation

$$\text{Total angular momentum} = \sqrt{J(J+1)}\ \frac{h}{2\pi} \qquad (30)$$

Unlike the symmetric-top case, no component of this total angular momentum is quantized; therefore, no quantum number other than J is available to characterize the rotational energy states. As for symmetric-top molecules, however, it must be expected that for each value of J there will be $2J + 1$ states. We are brought to this result by the following statement. A small change of the moments of inertia from a symmetric-top system, which has, for a given value of J, the $2J + 1$ states characterized by $K = 0, \pm 1, \pm 2, \ldots, \pm J$, can be expected only to shift the energy levels and would not eliminate any of the allowed states. This "adiabatic" argument shows that, even for an asymmetric-top molecule, the $2J + 1$ states will still exist for each value of J. A difficulty in characterizing these states arises in the asymmetric-top case because there is no quantized component of this total angular momentum; i.e., K is not a "good" quantum number for an asymmetric-top molecule.

Solution of the Schrödinger equation for an asymmetric-top molecule has been accomplished, although the problem is one of some difficulty, and for each value of J it is found that there are $2J + 1$ solution functions, each with its own energy. Since these $2J + 1$ solutions for a given J are not characterized by quantum numbers, it is customary to keep track of them by adding a subscript to the J value. This index τ is given integers going from $-J$ for the lowest energy of the set to $+J$ for the highest energy.

No closed general expression is available for any but the lowest few energy levels of an asymmetric-top molecule. The nature of the energy pattern can, however, be illustrated by a diagram of the type shown in Fig. 5-14. The energy-level pattern for an oblate symmetric-top molecule, for example, with $A = B = 3$ and $C = 1$, is drawn at the left of the diagram, and the corresponding symmetric-top diagram for the prolate symmetric-top molecule, for example, with $A = 3$ and $B = C = 1$, at the right of the diagram. (Notice that this procedure violates the usual agreement to have the A axis unique.) One can now schematically connect the energy levels of the symmetric-top patterns to show what would happen if the moment of inertia along the B axis were gradually changed so that B varied from the value of 3 to the value of 1. In this way, the interconnecting lines of Fig. 5-14 are drawn. The J value of any line remains unchanged, and the index τ can be entered as a subscript to each J value as shown.

The labeling of the asymmetric-top energy levels in Fig. 5-14 suggests an alternative to the use of τ. One can notice from that figure that the value of τ is related to the K values of the symmetric-top mole-

FIG. 5-14 A correlation diagram illustrating the energy-level pattern for asymmetric-top rotors. *(From W. Gordy, W. V. Smith, and R. F. Trambarulo, "Microwave Spectroscopy," John Wiley & Sons, Inc., New York, 1953.)*

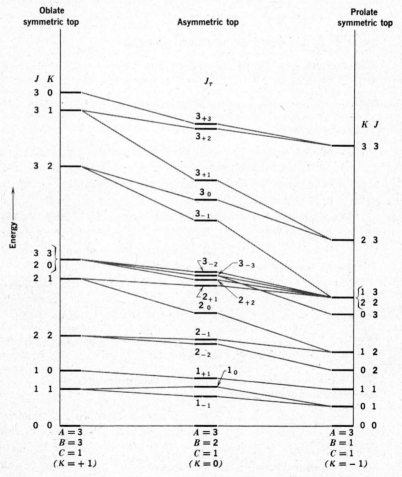

cules according to

$$\tau = K_{\text{prolate}} - K_{\text{oblate}} \tag{31}$$

With this recognition one can identify an energy level with the notation as J_τ or with the K notation as $J_{K_{\text{prolate}} \cdot K_{\text{oblate}}}$. Thus a level 3_{-2} with the τ notation is $3_{1,3}$ with the K notation. Both types of notation may be encountered.

For quantitative treatments of asymmetric-top molecules, it is convenient to have an abscissa scale to show the "degree of asymmetry." A convenient quantity is the asymmetry parameter κ defined as

$$\kappa = \frac{2[\bar{B} - \frac{1}{2}(\bar{A} + \bar{C})]}{\bar{A} - \bar{C}} \tag{32}$$

where $\bar{A}$, $\bar{B}$, and $\bar{C}$ are the rotational constants

$$\bar{A} = \frac{h}{8\pi^2 c I_A} \qquad \text{cm}^{-1} \qquad \text{etc.} \tag{33}$$

One can readily verify that for an oblate symmetric top with

$$I_A > I_B = I_C$$

and therefore $\bar{A} < \bar{B} = \bar{C}$, $\kappa = 1$; while for a prolate symmetric top with $I_A < I_B = I_C$, and therefore $\bar{A} > \bar{B} = \bar{C}$, $\kappa = -1$. For all asymmetric tops, κ lies between $+1$ and -1, and for the most asymmetric case, such as $A = 3$, $B = 2$, $C = 1$, $\kappa = 0$.

The expressions that have been obtained by B. S. Ray [Z. Physik, 78: 74 (1932)] and by G. W. King, R. M. Hainer, and P. C. Cross [J. Chem. Phys., 11: 27 (1943)] for the energy levels of some of the lower J states of asymmetric molecules are listed in Table 5-4.

For states with higher J values, energies have been tabulated for molecules of various degrees of asymmetry. See, for example, King, Hainer, and Cross [J. Chem. Phys., 11: 27 (1943); 17: 826 (1949)].

Exercise 5-7. Using the expressions of Table 5-4, plot to scale the first several correlation lines of Fig. 5-12.

5-10. Selection Rules, Spectra, and Structure Results for Asymmetric-top Molecules

The selection rule $\Delta J = 0$, ± 1 encountered with symmetric-top molecules, is applicable also to asymmetric tops. Now, even in absorption spectroscopy, it is necessary to retain all three possible changes in J since, as Fig. 5-14 shows, the energy levels are not necessarily ordered in the order of J; i.e., an energy level with a higher value of J may occur at lower energy than that corresponding to a lower value of J.

Selection rules for the τ values have also been given. These depend on the components of the dipole moment of the molecule along the directions of the principal axes. The selection rules themselves, and their derivation, are sufficiently elaborate so that it is adequate here merely to indicate that they are treated in ref. 2.

The complexity of the energy-level diagram of an asymmetric top leads, with the selection rules for induced transitions, to a corresponding complexity in the observed rotational spectrum. The assignment of each of the observed lines to the energy levels involved in the transition is now a problem of some difficulty. The most helpful aid in this work is the splitting observed when a Stark field is applied. The splittings of the lines and the relative intensities of the components are characteristic of the J and τ numbers involved in the transition.

In spite of the difficulties encountered in analyzing the rotational spectra of asymmetric-top molecules, quite a few molecules have been

TABLE 5-4   Some Closed Solutions for the Rotational Energy Levels of Asymmetric Tops

$J_{K(\kappa=-1)K(\kappa=+1)}$	Energy ϵ_{rot}
0_{00}	0
1_{10}	$A + B$
1_{11}	$A + C$
1_{01}	$B + C$
2_{20}	$2A + 2B + 2C + 2\sqrt{(B-C)^2 + (A-C)(A-B)}$
2_{21}	$4A + B + C$
2_{11}	$A + 4B + C$
2_{12}	$A + B + 4C$
2_{02}	$2A + 2B + 2C - 2\sqrt{(B-C)^2 + (A-C)(A-B)}$
3_{30}	$5A + 5B + 2C + 2\sqrt{4(A-B)^2 + (A-C)(B-C)}$
3_{31}	$5A + 2B + 5C + 2\sqrt{4(A-C)^2 - (A-B)(B-C)}$
3_{21}	$2A + 5B + 5C + 2\sqrt{4(B-C)^2 + (A-B)(A-C)}$
3_{22}	$4A + 4B + 4C$
3_{12}	$5A + 5B + 2C - 2\sqrt{4(A-B)^2 + (A-C)(B-C)}$
3_{13}	$5A + 2B + 5C - 2\sqrt{4(A-C)^2 - (A-B)(B-C)}$
3_{03}	$2A + 5B + 5C - 2\sqrt{4(B-C)^2 + (A-B)(A-C)}$
4_{41}	$10A + 5B + 5C + 2\sqrt{4(B-C)^2 + 9(A-C)(A-B)}$
4_{31}	$5A + 10B + 5C + 2\sqrt{4(A-C)^2 - 9(A-B)(B-C)}$
4_{32}	$5A + 5B + 10C + 2\sqrt{4(A-B)^2 + 9(A-C)(B-C)}$
4_{23}	$10A + 5B + 5C - 2\sqrt{4(B-C)^2 + 9(A-C)(A-B)}$
4_{13}	$5A + 10B + 5C - 2\sqrt{4(A-C)_2 - 9(A-B)(B-C)}$
4_{14}	$5A + 5B + 10C - 2\sqrt{4(A-B)^2 + 9(A-C)(B-C)}$

TABLE 5-5   Some Molecular Structure Results for Asymmetric-top Molecules*

Molecule	Bond angle		Bond distance	
SO_2	OSO	119°20′	SO	1.433
O_3	OO′O	116°49′	OO′	1.278
CH_2Cl_2	HCH	112°0′	CH	1.068
	ClCH	111°47′	CCl	1.772
CH_2—CH_2	HCH	116°41′	CH	1.082
\\/	COC	61°24′	CC	1.472
O			CO	1.436
SO_2F_2	OSO	129°38′	SO	1.370
	FSF	92°47′	SF	1.570

* From W. Gordy, W. V. Smith, and R. F. Trambarulo, "Microwave Spectroscopy," John Wiley & Sons, Inc., New York, 1953.

studied and the observed transitions identified with the participating energy levels.   When this is done, one can use the equations of Table 5-4 or the tables of King, Hainer, and Cross to deduce the three rotational constants and thus the three moments of inertia of the molecule.   These three data, especially when supplemented by isotopic studies, provide a good basis for the deduction of the structure of the molecule.   Some of the results that have been obtained from such studies are shown in Table 5-5.

PRINCIPAL REFERENCES

1. Herzberg, G.: "Spectra of Diatomic Molecules," D. Van Nostrand Company, Inc., Princeton, N.J., 1950.
2. Gordy, W., W. V. Smith, and R. F. Trambarulo: "Microwave Spectroscopy," John Wiley & Sons, Inc., New York, 1953.
3. Herzberg, G.: "Infrared and Raman Spectra," D. Van Nostrand Company, Inc., Princeton, N.J., 1945.

6   THE VIBRATIONS OF
POLYATOMIC MOLECULES

An introduction to the classical and quantum-mechanical nature of the vibrations of polyatomic molecules will now be presented. This theoretical development provides the background for an understanding of the absorption spectrum in the infrared region, like that of Fig. 2-1, of solutions and pure liquids containing polyatomic molecules. In the following chapter, simultaneous vibration and rotation of molecules will be dealt with, and the absorption spectra of gases, which show the effect of changes in both vibrational and rotational energies, will be studied.

6-1. The Number of Independent Vibrations of a Polyatomic Molecule

If a molecule containing n atoms is imagined to have these atoms held together by extremely weak bonds, the motions of the system might best be described in terms of the motion of the n, nearly independent individual atoms. If three cartesian coordinates are used to describe the position and motion of each atom, there will be a total of $3n$ such coordinates required for a description of the set of the n atoms. Each of these $3n$ coordinates represents a degree of freedom of the system in that any arbitrary displacement and velocity can be given along each of these coordinates. Any additional displacement or velocity, beyond these $3n$, that is imposed on an atom, or on the molecule, could be described in terms of the $3n$ cartesian coordinates.

For actual molecules the $3n$ cartesian coordinates are not, in fact, very convenient. One can recognize that if the bonding of the hypothetical molecule with very weak bonds were to be gradually strengthened, it would become increasingly important to recognize the existence of the molecule rather than to treat the system as consisting of n rather independent particles. One likes, for example, to use three coordinates to describe the motion of the center of mass of the molecule and, for nonlinear molecules, three coordinates to describe the rotation of the molecule about this center of mass. If one imagines a gradual strengthening of the bonds between the atoms as one goes from a set of independent atoms to the rather firmly held set that constitutes a molecule, one will see that none of the $3n$ degrees of freedom is destroyed. The degrees of freedom are merely reclassified. It follows that if three translational and three rotational degrees of freedom are recognized, there will be left a total of $3n - 6$ degrees of freedom which must be accounted for by internal coordinates of the system. Displacements and velocities in accordance with these $3n - 6$ coordinates constitute vibrations of the molecule.

If the molecule is linear; molecular rotations can occur only about the two axes that can be drawn perpendicular to the molecular axis. For such molecules, three over-all translations and two over-all rotations are subtracted from the total of $3n$ degrees of freedom, and there remain $3n - 5$ internal degrees of freedom.

The number of internal degrees of freedom of a molecule corresponds to the number of ways in which the atoms of the molecule can be given independent displacements and velocities relative to one another. They are, as will be shown in the following section, the number of vibrations of the molecule. It is now necessary to see if these $3n - 6$ or, for linear molecules, $3n - 5$ internal degrees of freedom can be further described.

6-2. The Nature of Normal Vibrations and Normal Coordinates

A collection of many mass units interconnected by springs can be expected to undergo an infinite variety of internal motions, or vibrations, depending on what initial displacements are given to the particles of the system. The general motion of such a system can be analyzed in terms of a set of internal coordinates, and, as the previous section indicates, there are $3n - 6$ (or $3n - 5$) independent internal coordinates. For any molecule there is, furthermore, a particular set of coordinates, called *normal coordinates*, which is especially convenient for the description of the vibrations of a system. The nature of normal coordinates, which are very important in vibrational problems, can be illustrated by a simple example.

Consider a particle of mass m held by springs, as in Fig. 6-1. If

x and y coordinates are set up as indicated, the motion of the particle, in the plane of the spring system, can be deduced from the potential and kinetic energies which are written as

$$U = \tfrac{1}{2}k_x x^2 + \tfrac{1}{2}k_y y^2 \qquad (1)$$
$$T = \tfrac{1}{2}m\dot{x}^2 + \tfrac{1}{2}m\dot{y}^2 \qquad (2)$$

where the springs have been assumed to obey Hooke's law and to have force constants k_x and k_y. [It should be noticed that the spring system, for small displacements, is such that the restoring force in the x direction arises only from a displacement in the x direction and, similarly, forces in the y direction only from y displacements. One can see that the potential-energy expression of Eq. (1) leads to this result by forming

$$f_x = -\left(\frac{\partial U}{\partial x}\right)_y = -k_x x$$

and

$$f_y = -\left(\frac{\partial U}{\partial y}\right)_x = -k_y y.]$$

The motion of the particle can now be deduced by applying Lagrange's equation to the coordinates of the system. For the x coordinate, the equation

$$\frac{d}{dt}\left(\frac{\partial T}{\partial \dot{x}}\right) + \frac{\partial U}{\partial x} = 0 \qquad (3)$$

gives

$$m\ddot{x} + k_x x = 0 \qquad (4)$$

This is the now familiar differential form which indicates vibrational

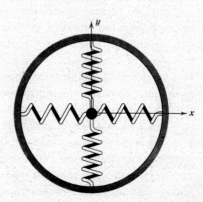

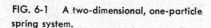

FIG. 6-1 A two-dimensional, one-particle spring system.

motion with the displacement as a function of time given by

$$x = A_x \sin (2\pi\nu_x t + \varphi_x) \tag{5}$$

where

$$\nu_x = \frac{1}{2\pi} \sqrt{\frac{k_x}{m}} \tag{6}$$

Similarly, for the y coordinate, Lagrange's equation gives

$$m\ddot{y} + k_y y = 0 \tag{7}$$

which leads to the solution

$$y = A_y \sin (2\pi\nu_y t + \varphi_y) \tag{8}$$

where

$$\nu_y = \frac{1}{2\pi} \sqrt{\frac{k_y}{m}} \tag{9}$$

Initial displacements along the x or y axis will, therefore, lead to simple sinusoidal vibrations along this axis. Displacement in any other direction will lead to a complicated motion that can be interpreted in terms of sinusoidal components in the x and y directions; i.e., Eqs. (5) and (8) will simultaneously apply, and the motion is described when the appropriate values of A_x and A_y for the displacement are used. The x and y coordinates allow the motion of the particle to be most simply described, and they are the *normal coordinates* for the system. Motion of the system along a normal coordinate consists of simple harmonic motion, and such motion is said to be a *normal vibration or normal mode.*

Similar normal coordinates and normal vibrations will exist for more complicated vibrating systems. In such cases a normal coordinate will, in general, consist of the displacement coordinates of more than one atom of the system. The normal coordinate will, therefore, often be a complicated combination of atomic displacements. In terms of this coordinate, however, the vibrational motion of the system will be simply described, and a *displacement of the system according to the normal coordinate will lead to a simple motion in which all the particles move in phase with the same frequency and, if Hooke's law is applicable, will execute simple harmonic motion.* (For some systems, as we will see, it will be necessary to modify this description of normal coordinates so that it is stated that displacement according to the normal coordinate will lead to motion for which the cartesian coordinates of all the atoms of the molecule will execute simple harmonic motion.)

Exercise 6-1. Consider a spring system like that of Fig. 6-1 with $M = 1$ atomic mass unit equivalent to a hydrogen atom, $k_x = 1 \times 10^5$ and $k_y = 2 \times 10^5$ dynes/cm, values that are of the order of magnitude encountered with chemical bonds.

(a) Calculate the classical natural frequencies of this system.

(b) Draw a diagram showing, side by side, the allowed energies for the two normal modes treated quantum mechanically. What would be the wave numbers of the radiation absorbed in the fundamental transitions of this system?

It is informative to consider also the way in which one would proceed to a description of the vibrating system of Fig. 6-1 if one did not know in advance the directions along which the springs lay and, therefore, did not know the convenient directions in which to choose coordinates. The simple calculation that is necessary will, in fact, anticipate the problems that will arise with molecular systems where one generally does not initially know what coordinates are the normal coordinates and, therefore, what atomic displacements will lead to normal modes of vibration.

Let us suppose that the spring system of Fig. 6-1 has been turned through an angle as shown in Fig. 6-2. The axes relative to this orientation of the system are labeled x' and y' as in Fig. 6-2. The essential difference between the axis choice of Fig. 6-1 and that of Fig. 6-2 can be recognized by considering the restoring force that would act for displacements along the coordinate axes. In Fig. 6-1 it is clear that displacement

FIG. 6-2 The spring system of Fig. 6-1 described by an awkward coordinate system such as might be used if the directions of the springs were not initially known.

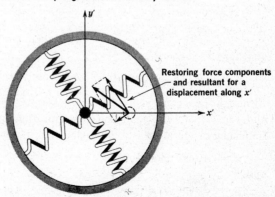

Restoring force components and resultant for a displacement along x'

along the x axis, or the y axis, results in a restoring force acting along that axis and directed toward the origin. This was the basis for the form of the potential written in Eq. (1).

For the coordinate system of Fig. 6-2, displacement along the coordinate axes will not, as the force vectors suggest, lead to restoring forces along these axis. It follows that the potential-energy function has the form

$$U = \tfrac{1}{2}k'_x(x')^2 + k'_{xy}(x')(y') + \tfrac{1}{2}k'_y(y')^2 \qquad (10)$$

This potential expression can be seen to lead to the restoring forces expected for the spring orientation of Fig. 6-2. Thus one has

$$f_{x'} = -\left(\frac{\partial U}{\partial x'}\right)_{y'} = -k'_x x' - k'_{xy}y'$$

and $\qquad (11)$

$$f_{y'} = -\left(\frac{\partial U}{\partial y'}\right)_{x'} = -k'_y y' - k'_{xy}x'$$

A restoring force in the x' direction can result, therefore, from displacements in both the x' and y' directions. Thus, a selection of coordinates, where the normal coordinate directions are not recognized in advance, will lead to a potential-energy expression which is not just the sum of squared terms but contains, in addition, cross products between the coordinates.

Let us proceed now to study the vibrations of this one-particle system, using the coordinates of Fig. 6-2. The potential is written in Eq. (10), and since the coordinates are still orthogonal, the kinetic energy is

$$T = \tfrac{1}{2}m(\dot{x}')^2 + \tfrac{1}{2}m(\dot{y}')^2 \qquad (12)$$

Lagrange's equation for the x' coordinate now gives, with Eqs. (10) and (12),

$$m\ddot{x}' - k'_x x' - k'_{xy}y' = 0 \qquad (13)$$

and, for the y' coordinate,

$$m\ddot{y}' - k'_{xy}x' - k'_y y' = 0 \qquad (14)$$

Although these equations are clearly less convenient than those of Eq. (4) and Eq. (7), we can again look for vibration-type solutions, where the frequency of vibration is ν, by trying the functions

$$x' = A'_x \sin (2\pi\nu t + \varphi)$$

and $\qquad (15)$

$$y' = A'_y \sin (2\pi\nu t + \varphi)$$

Differentiation twice with respect to time gives functions for $\ddot{x}'$ and $\ddot{y}'$ and, with Eqs. (13) and (14), leads to the expressions

$$4\pi^2\nu^2 m A_x' - k_x' A_x' - k_{xy}' A_y' = 0$$

and   (16)

$$4\pi^2\nu^2 m A_y' - k_{xy}' A_x' - k_y' A_y' = 0$$

For these equalities to hold, for other than the trivial solution with $A_x' = A_y' = 0$, the determinant of the coefficients of the amplitudes must be zero; i.e.,

$$\begin{vmatrix} 4\pi^2\nu^2 m - k_x' & -k_{xy}' \\ -k_{xy}' & 4\pi^2\nu^2 m - k_y' \end{vmatrix} = 0 \tag{17}$$

Expansion of the determinant gives

$$(4\pi^2\nu^2 m - k_x')(4\pi^2\nu^2 m - k_y') - (k_{xy}')^2 = 0 \tag{18}$$

The roots of this quadratic in ν^2 are found to be

$$\nu = \frac{1}{2\pi}\sqrt{\frac{(k_x' + k_y') \pm [(k_x' - k_y')^2 + 4(k_{xy}')^2]^{\frac{1}{2}}}{2m}} \tag{19}$$

Thus the two natural vibrational frequencies of the system can be calculated.

Finally, the roots given by Eq. (19) can be substituted into Eq. (16); or, alternatively, the appropriate minors of Eq. (17) can be calculated, and values for the ratio of A_x' to A_y' can be obtained for each vibration frequency.

Exercise 6-2. When the spring and particle system of Exercise 6-1 is rotated counterclockwise by 30 deg with respect to the axes, now labeled x' and y', the potential-energy function is

$$U = \tfrac{1}{2}(1.25 \times 10^5)(x')^2 + \sqrt{\tfrac{3}{4}} \times 10^5(x')(y') + \tfrac{1}{2}(1.75 \times 10^5)(y')^2$$

(a) Calculate the natural frequencies of the system, and see that the same values are obtained as in Exercise 6-1.

(b) Calculate the relative values of A_x' and A_y' for each vibration, and see that one can deduce, from the given potential function, the directions in which the particle moves in each vibration.

This rather detailed treatment of a very simple system will later be recognized as an illustration of the procedure that is necessary when the relation between the force constants and vibrations of a molecule is treated. The immediate purpose of the example is to illustrate that there is a convenient set of coordinates, called normal coordinates, for treating the vibrations of a system. Furthermore these coordinates are such that they allow *both the kinetic and potential energies to be written as the sum of squared terms.* Finally, even if these convenient coordinates are not initially known, solution of the problem can be carried through with any other set of coordinates, and the normal coordinates can then be deduced from the amplitudes that are obtained for the natural, or normal, vibrations of the system.

6-3. Quantum-mechanical Treatment of the Vibrations of Polyatomic Molecules

Previous applications of the Schrödinger equation have been restricted to one-dimensional problems. The equation can, however, be written for n particles, the position of each being described by three cartesian coordinates. In this way the Schrödinger equation is written as

$$-\frac{h^2}{8\pi^2}\sum_{j=1}^{n}\frac{1}{mj}\left(\frac{\partial^2\psi}{\partial x_j^2} + \frac{\partial^2\psi}{\partial y_j^2} + \frac{\partial^2\psi}{\partial z_j^2}\right) + U(x_1,y_1, \ldots ,z_r)\psi = \epsilon\psi \quad (20)$$

where the function ψ will involve the $3n$ coordinates. As in the classical discussion of the previous section, the $3n$ cartesian coordinates are not convenient for describing the molecular motions. One can, as in the classical case, treat separately the three coordinates that describe the motion of the center of mass of the system and the three (or two for a linear molecule) that describe the rotation of the system about the principal moment-of-inertia axes. The derivation that shows how this separation of external from internal coordinates is carried out will not be given here. It can be found in many texts on quantum mechanics, as, for example, "Introduction to Quantum Mechanics," by L. Pauling and E. B. Wilson (McGraw-Hill Book Company, Inc., New York, 1935).

Let us now proceed to investigate the form that the solutions of the Schrödinger equation will take when it is applied to the internal, or vibrational, coordinates of a molecule. Furthermore we will proceed, formally, with the normal coordinates, designated by Q_i, of the molecule. In general one is not initially able to describe these normal coordinates in terms of the relative motions of the atoms of the molecule. We know, however, from the simple example of the preceding section the important fact that normal coordinates are such that both the kinetic and potential energies of a system are expressed by the sum of terms each involving the square of a normal coordinate.

The correct form of the Schrödinger equation for treatment of the internal motion of a molecule in terms of the $3n - 6$ (or $3n - 5$) normal coordinates can be deduced from the fact that the kinetic-energy operator for a coordinate Q_i is given by an expression of the type

$$- \frac{h^2}{8\pi^2} \frac{\partial^2}{\partial Q_i^2}$$

The mass term that normally appears in the denominator of this kinetic-energy operator is generally absorbed in the normal coordinate Q_i. The operator for the potential energy is the potential energy function itself. Since, in terms of the normal coordinates, the kinetic energy is a function of squared terms, one can write

$$- \frac{h^2}{8\pi^2} \sum_{i=1}^{3n-6} \frac{\partial^2 \psi}{\partial Q_i^2} + U(Q_1 \cdots Q_{3n-6})\psi = \epsilon\psi \tag{21}$$

where the solution function ψ will, in general, be a function of the $3n - 6$ normal coordinates.

This many-dimensional equation is greatly simplified because of the fact that, in terms of normal coordinates, not only is the kinetic energy a sum of squared terms, but so also is the potential energy. The form of the potential-energy function can be shown by writing

$$U(Q_1 Q_2 \cdots Q_{3n-6}) = \tfrac{1}{2}\lambda_1 Q_1^2 + \tfrac{1}{2}\lambda_2 Q_2^2 + \cdots + \tfrac{1}{2}\lambda_{3n-6}Q_{3n-6}^2$$
$$= \tfrac{1}{2} \sum_{i=1}^{3n-6} \lambda_i Q_i^2 \tag{22}$$

where the λ's are coefficients that depend on the force constants of the molecule.

Equation (21) can now be written as

$$- \frac{h^2}{8\pi^2} \sum_{i=1}^{3n-6} \frac{\partial^2 \psi}{\partial Q_i^2} + \left(\frac{1}{2} \sum_{i=1}^{3n-6} \lambda_i Q_i^2 \right) \psi = \epsilon\psi \tag{23}$$

It is profitable to try to separate this equation into $3n - 6$ equations, each involving only one of the normal coordinates. We write

$$\psi = \psi_1(Q_1)\psi_2(Q_2) \cdots \psi_{3n-6}(Q_{3n-6})$$

or

$$\psi = \psi_1\psi_2 \cdots \psi_{3n-6} \tag{24}$$

and substitute Eq. (24) into Eq. (23).   When this is done and the entire equation is divided through by ψ, one gets $3n - 6$ expressions of the type

$$-\frac{h^2}{8\pi^2}\frac{1}{\psi_i}\frac{\partial^2\psi_i}{\partial Q_i^2} + \tfrac{1}{2}\lambda_i Q_i^2 = \epsilon_i$$

or   (25)

$$-\frac{h^2}{8\pi^2}\frac{\partial^2\psi_i}{\partial Q_i^2} + (\tfrac{1}{2}\lambda_i Q_i^2)\psi_i = \epsilon_i\psi_i$$

Each such expression is identical to that already encountered in one-dimensional vibrational problems.   The solution functions for each of the $3n - 6$ equations like Eq. (25) are, therefore, the harmonic oscillator wave functions listed in Sec. 2-4.   Furthermore, each normal coordinate Q_i will lead to a set of energy levels with a constant spacing, such as shown for the one-dimensional case in Fig. 2-4.

The important result has been obtained that, since normal coordinates allow both the kinetic and potential energy to be written as the sums of squared terms, the quantum-mechanical problem (cf. the classical solution at the beginning of the previous section) is separable in terms of these coordinates.   A molecule containing n atoms will have, therefore, $3n - 6$ (or $3n - 5$) vibrational energy-level patterns, each pattern corresponding to one of the classical normal vibrations of the system.

Since the wave functions written in terms of normal coordinates are the same as those discussed in Sec. 2-4, the selection rules for transitions between the vibrational states for each normal coordinate are

$$\Delta v = \pm 1 \tag{26}$$

For absorption experiments, the pertinent rule

$$\Delta v = +1 \tag{27}$$

is again obtained.   We can expect, therefore, an absorption of radiation corresponding to the transition from the $v = 0$ to the $v = 1$ level of each energy-level pattern.   (We will see that, in fact, for symmetric molecules some of these transitions are forbidden.)   The energy-level diagrams and the observed spectrum of H_2O are shown schematically in Fig. 6-3.

It perhaps should be pointed out that in general we do not know the normal coordinates of a molecule.   For some of the simpler molecules they have been deduced, but their deduction is often rather difficult. The previous derivation of the separation of the vibrational problem does not, however, require us to be able to describe the normal coordinates. It is sufficient to know that there are coordinates in terms of which T and U are both sums of squared terms.   With this knowledge one deduces that the vibrational energy of a molecule is to be treated in terms of $3n - 6$ energy-level patterns.

6-4. The Symmetry Properties of Normal Coordinates

Normal coordinates are often complicated functions in that they involve the displacement coordinates of many, or all, of the atoms of the molecule. When the molecule has some symmetry, as many do, a great simplification occurs. The consequences of symmetry in molecular spectroscopy are, in fact, widespread and profound. One way in which symmetry enters into treatments of molecular systems will here be illustrated by a discussion of the nature of the normal coordinates of a symmetric molecule.

A complete classification of the ways in which a molecule can be symmetric will be given in Chap. 8. Here it will be enough to consider a linear system, like CO_2, and to recognize that a plane perpendicular to the molecular axis is a plane of symmetry; i.e., the molecule in its

FIG. 6-3 The energy-level patterns and schematic representations of the corresponding vibrations and a schematic infrared absorption spectrum of H_2O.

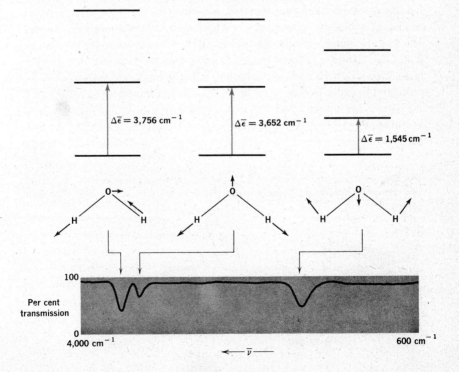

equilibrium configuration is identical on both sides of the plane. It is customary to call such a plane an *element of symmetry*.

The axis of the molecule of CO_2 is another such symmetry element of the molecule.

In vibrational spectroscopy we are concerned with displacements of the atoms of a molecule from their equilibrium positions. These displacements can be depicted by vectors, as shown for a general displacement of an oxygen atom of CO_2 in Fig. 6-4. To deal with the relation of such displacements to symmetry elements, one introduces the idea of a *symmetry operation*. Thus the symmetry operation corresponding to the plane of symmetry is a reflection through the plane. This operation transforms the displacement vector of Fig. 6-4 in the manner shown. The symmetry operation for an axis of symmetry is rotation about the axis, and this operation is also shown in Fig. 6-4. It should be pointed out that the numbering of the atoms will be kept unaltered by symmetry operations; only the displacement vectors will undergo the symmetry operation.

That symmetry and normal vibrations are related can be readily illustrated by reference to the spring system of Fig. 6-5. If one were asked to set this system vibrating according to its natural or normal modes of vibration, one would, without any detailed analysis, distort the system symmetrically, as in Fig. 6-5*a*, or antisymmetrically, as in Fig. 6-5*b*. In this simple example it is obvious, particularly if one has a model to work with, that the coordinates along which the system must be distorted in order for the particles to vibrate in phase and with the same frequency are either symmetric or antisymmetric with respect to the plane of symmetry. A similar conclusion can also be drawn for the less easily visualized normal coordinates of molecular systems.

FIG. 6-4. Two symmetry elements of CO_2: a plane and an axis of symmetry. Symmetry operations corresponding to these elements transform the solid arrows into the dashed arrows.

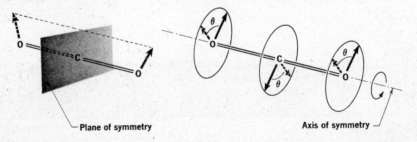

Plane of symmetry   Axis of symmetry

To do this, it is first necessary to point out that both the kinetic and potential energy of a molecule must be unaltered by a symmetry operation. If a symmetry operation is performed on a distorted molecule, which has, therefore, some higher potential energy than the equilibrium configuration, the distorted molecule that is obtained by the symmetry operation will have the same potential energy as the original distorted one. This is illustrated in Fig. 6-6a. In a similar way, if a molecule has kinetic energy as a result of motion of its atoms, a symmetry operation cannot change this energy. This is apparent in Fig. 6-6, where the velocities of the atoms are represented vectorially and the symmetry operation changes the directions of these in space but does not affect the magnitude of the velocities of atoms of given masses. It follows then that a symmetry operation, since it does not alter the potential or kinetic energy of a molecule, does not alter the total energy.

In the previous section it was shown that the vibrational energy is most simply expressed in terms of the normal coordinates of the molecules. In these coordinates both the kinetic and potential energies contain only squared terms; i.e.,

$$\epsilon = \tfrac{1}{2}\dot{Q}_1^2 + \tfrac{1}{2}\lambda_1 Q_1^2 + \tfrac{1}{2}\dot{Q}_2^2 + \tfrac{1}{2}\lambda_2 Q_2^2 + \cdots + \tfrac{1}{2}\lambda_{3n-6}Q_{3n-6}^2 \qquad (28)$$

Now, since the normal coordinates represent the displacements of the atoms during a vibration, they can be represented by displacement

FIG. 6-5 A two-particle spring system with a plane of symmetry perpendicular to the axis of the springs. Distortions are indicated that are (a) symmetric and (b) antisymmetric with respect to the plane of symmetry. The arrows indicate the initial motions of the particles that would follow such displacements.

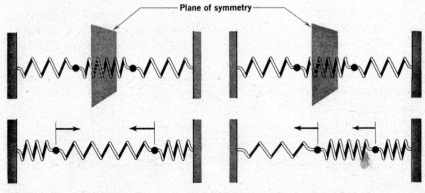

Plane of symmetry

(a)   (b)

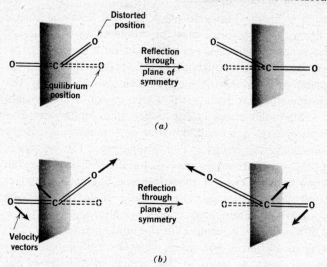

(a)

(b)

FIG. 6-6 Illustration that a symmetry operation does not change the potential or the kinetic energy of a molecule.

vectors such as those of Fig. 6-4 or 6-6. In view of Eq. (28), however, it is seen that for the energy to remain constant, in the general case where all λ_i are different, when a symmetry operation is performed, *each normal coordinate must remain unchanged or, at most, change sign.* Thus, ϵ of Eq. (28) is unchanged if as a result of a symmetry operation

$$Q_i \rightarrow \pm Q_i \qquad\qquad\qquad\qquad (29)$$

This important conclusion is that *normal coordinates are either symmetric or antisymmetric with respect to a symmetry operation.* With this result one can, for example, immediately represent two of the normal coordinates of the CO_2 molecule. One needs only to draw arrows, as in Fig. 6-7, which keep the center of gravity of the molecule fixed, lead to no

FIG. 6-7 Arrows indicating the relative motions of the atoms of CO_2 in two normal vibrations with displacements along the molecular axis.

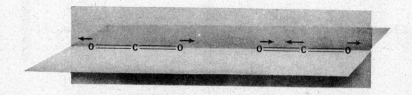

rotation of the molecule, and are such that they are left unchanged or result in a simple change of sign, i.e., of direction, when a symmetry operation is performed. For simple molecules with a high degree of symmetry, as for CO_2, one can often write down immediately the form of the normal coordinates. In general, however, the symmetry properties of a molecule can be used to classify the normal coordinates according to whether they transform symmetrically or antisymmetrically with the various symmetry operations of the molecule. In later chapters we will see that such a classification is a tremendous aid in studies of the vibrations of polyatomic molecules.

The previous discussion has been based on the general case where all the normal coordinates have different values of λ in Eq. (28). This supposition corresponds to cases in which all the normal vibrations of the molecule have different frequencies. The bending vibrations of CO_2 in the two perpendicular planes, as shown in Fig. 6-8, provide an illustration of normal coordinates that have equal values of λ. The frequency expected for each vibration is therefore identical. Such vibrations are said to be *degenerate*, and in this case, since 2 degrees of freedom are involved and, quantum mechanically, two identical sets of energy levels will exist, the vibration is said to be *doubly degenerate*.

When such degeneracy occurs, the requirement that the energy remain unchanged during a symmetry operation does not lead, according to Eq. (28), to the restriction that $Q_i \rightarrow \pm Q_i$. If the normal coordinates of the degenerate vibration are Q_1 and Q_2, one has

$$\epsilon = \tfrac{1}{2}\dot{Q}_1^2 + \tfrac{1}{2}\lambda_1 Q_1^2 + \tfrac{1}{2}\dot{Q}_2^2 + \tfrac{1}{2}\lambda_1 Q_2^2 + \cdots \tag{30}$$

where the equal potential energy coefficients have been designated λ_1. Rearrangement of Eq. (30) gives

$$\epsilon = \tfrac{1}{2}(\dot{Q}_1^2 + \dot{Q}_2^2) + \tfrac{1}{2}\lambda_1(Q_1^2 + Q_2^2) + \cdots \tag{31}$$

Now the energy remains constant, as far as Q_1 and Q_2 are concerned, as long as the symmetry operation does not change the value of $Q_1^2 + Q_2^2$.

FIG. 6-8 The two components of the doubly degenerate bending vibration of CO_2.

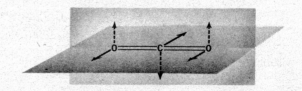

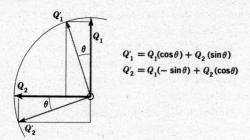

$$Q'_1 = Q_1(\cos\theta) + Q_2(\sin\theta)$$
$$Q'_2 = Q_1(-\sin\theta) + Q_2(\cos\theta)$$

FIG. 6-9 The behavior of degenerate motions under a symmetry operation. (The figure corresponds to an end view of Fig. 6-8 with only the arrows on the oxygen atoms shown.)

Within this restriction, it is allowed that a symmetry operation produce the transformations

$$Q_1 \rightarrow aQ_1 + bQ_2$$

and   (32)

$$Q_2 \rightarrow cQ_1 + dQ_2$$

An illustration of this behavior is given in Fig. 6-9 where the symmetry operation consisting of a rotation of CO_2 about its axis by an angle θ is considered.

In summary, the behavior of normal coordinates with respect to symmetry operations can be stated as

1. For nondegenerate vibrations, the normal coordinates remain unchanged or change sign.

2. For degenerate vibrations, each normal coordinate of the set can be transformed, by the operation, into combinations of the coordinates of the set, subject to a restriction imposed by the particular symmetry operation.

Exercise 6-3.   Draw, *to the extent that one can* on the basis of symmetry and zero translation and rotation, arrows showing the relative displacements of the atoms of the linear molecule CS_2 and the bent molecule H_2S in the normal vibrations of each molecule.

PRINCIPAL REFERENCES

1. Herzberg, G.: "Infrared and Raman Spectra," chap. 2, D. Van Nostrand Company, Inc., Princeton, N.J., 1945.
2. Wilson, E. B., Jr., J. C. Decius, and P. C. Cross: "Molecular Vibrations," McGraw-Hill Book Company, Inc., New York, 1955.

7 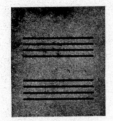 ROTATION-VIBRATION SPECTRA

When the infrared radiation absorbed by a pure liquid or by a material in solution is measured, well-defined regions of absorption which can, for the most part, be attributed to the $v = 0$ to $v = 1$ transitions in the various vibrational energy patterns are observed. Typical liquid-phase spectra of fairly simple molecules are shown in Figs. 2-1 and 7-1a. In the previous chapter it was indicated that each absorption band can be associated with a fundamental transition in an energy-level pattern corresponding to a specific normal mode of vibration of the molecule.

The infrared absorption spectrum of a simple molecule in the gas phase does not, if the resolution of the instrument is adequate, show such smooth, structureless absorption bands, but rather, as Fig. 7-1b illustrates, absorption regions of considerable complexity. The structure of such absorption bands can be attributed to changes in the rotational energy of the molecule accompanying the vibrational transition. In the liquid phase no well-defined rotational energy levels exist, and rotational structure is not observed on a vibrational absorption band.

We will now investigate in some detail the nature of rotation-vibration bands, and we will see that molecular-structure information can be deduced from an analysis of the structure of such bands. Furthermore, the nature of the rotational structure of a rotation-vibration absorption band will be seen to reveal much about the type of vibration that is occurring, and this information will be of great aid when we attempt to match up the observed vibrational absorption bands with the normal vibrations of polyatomic molecules. The general features of the rota-

131

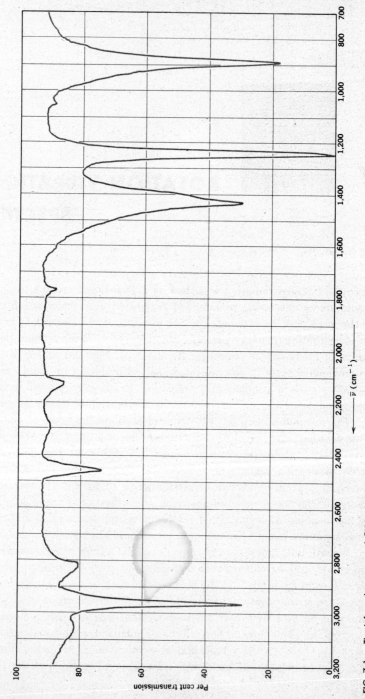

FIG. 7-1a The infrared spectrum of CH₃I as a liquid.

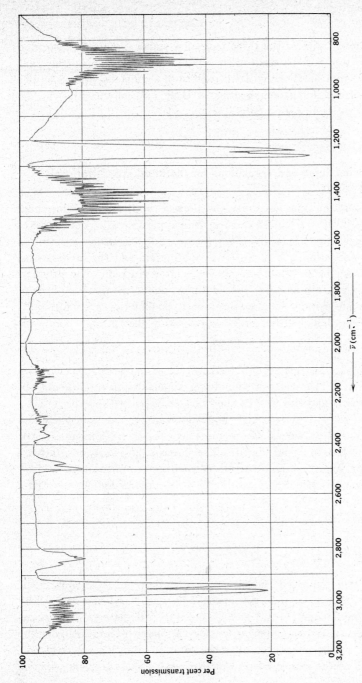

FIG. 7-1b The infrared spectrum of CH₃I as a vapor.

133

tion-vibration bands of the three molecular types, diatomic, linear, and symmetric top, will be dealt with separately. The complexities that arise in the rotational energy-level pattern of asymmetric-top molecules lead to corresponding complexities in their rotation-vibration bands. These will not be analyzed here.

DIATOMIC MOLECULES

7-1. Selection Rules and Transitions for the Rigid Rotor–Harmonic Oscillator Model

The selection rules governing the allowed rotational and vibrational transitions, given in Chaps. 2 and 3, remain applicable when both types of energy are changed in a given transition. For absorption spectra, as before, the selection rule $\Delta v = +1$ is appropriate and the fundamental transition, from $v = 0$ to $v = 1$, is again often studied. The selection rule for J was given as $\Delta J = \pm 1$, and now, unlike the situation in pure rotational absorption spectroscopy, both possibilities are important. Thus the selection rules for a rotation-vibration absorption band are

$$\Delta v = +1 \qquad \Delta J = \pm 1 \tag{1}$$

(Exceptions to this rule are provided by molecules like NO that have an odd electron. This electron contributes angular momentum about the molecular axis, and this in turn allows $\Delta J = 0$ transitions to occur.)

These rules, together with an expression for the rotational and vibrational energy levels, allow the energies, or frequencies, of the absorption lines to be calculated. The simplest, and fairly satisfactory, energy-level expression is obtained by treating the molecule as a rigid-rotor, harmonic-oscillator system. With this approximation, one writes

$$\bar{\epsilon}_{v,J} = (v + \tfrac{1}{2}) \frac{1}{2\pi c} \sqrt{\frac{k}{\mu}} + \frac{h}{8\pi^2 I c} J(J + 1)$$

$$= (v + \tfrac{1}{2}) \frac{1}{2\pi c} \sqrt{\frac{k}{\mu}} + \bar{B} J(J + 1) \tag{2}$$

The two improved models treated earlier, i.e., the anharmonic oscillator and the nonrigid rotor, could be introduced and would lead to terms involving $(v + \tfrac{1}{2})^2$ and $[J(J + 1)]^2$. These correction terms are, however, of less importance than a rotation-vibration coupling term that will be introduced after the rotation-vibration spectrum corresponding to the simple rigid-rotor, harmonic-oscillator energy expression is deduced.

It is convenient to replace, as was done in Sec. 2-4, the factor $1/2\pi \sqrt{k/\mu}$ by the symbol ω and $1/2\pi c \sqrt{k/\mu}$ by the symbol $\bar{\omega}$. With this notation, the energy-level expression of Eq. (2) and the selection rules of Eq. (1) give the allowed transition frequencies $\bar{\nu} = \Delta\bar{\epsilon}$ for the $v = 0 \rightarrow v = 1$ transitions as

For $\Delta J = +1$, i.e., $J \rightarrow J + 1$,

$$\begin{aligned}
\bar{\nu} &= \bar{\omega} + \bar{B}[(J + 1)(J + 2) - J(J + 1)] \\
&= \bar{\omega} + 2\bar{B}(J + 1) \qquad \text{where } J = 0, 1, 2, \ldots
\end{aligned} \qquad (3)$$

For $\Delta J = -1$, i.e., $J \rightarrow J - 1$,

$$\begin{aligned}
\bar{\nu} &= \bar{\omega} + \bar{B}[(J - 1)(J) - J(J + 1)] \\
&= \bar{\omega} - 2\bar{B}(J) \qquad \text{where } J = 1, 2, \ldots
\end{aligned} \qquad (4)$$

One should note that in these expressions the value to be inserted for J is the rotational quantum number for the lower vibrational state.

These transitions, and the resulting absorption lines, are best shown on a diagram such as that of Fig. 7-2. There it is clear, as the above expressions show, that there should be a set of absorption lines, spaced by the constant amount $2\bar{B}$, on the high-frequency side of the band center, which occurs at $\bar{\nu} = \bar{\omega}$, and a corresponding set on the low-frequency side with a similar constant spacing. There should, furthermore, be a gap in the band center corresponding to the absent $\Delta J = 0$ transitions, all of which would have had a frequency $\bar{\omega}$. It is customary to label the low-frequency set of lines as the P branch of the rotation-vibration band and the high-frequency side as the R branch. (For some molecules, as we will see, the central $\Delta J = 0$ branch is allowed, and it is known as the Q branch.)

The infrared absorption spectrum of HBr shows the absorption, given in Fig. 7-3, that can be attributed to the $v = 0$ to $v = 1$ transition. The general shape of this experimental curve is, in fact, that predicted on the basis of Eqs. (3) and (4) or Fig. 7-2. It is clear that the frequency of the $v = 0$, $J = 0$ to $v = 1$, $J = 0$ transition can be deduced from the central gap in the band and that this value gives the spacing of the vibrational energy levels of the molecule. Furthermore, the separation of the components of the P and R branches can be identified with the molecular quantity $2\bar{B}$. From this quantity, values for the moment of inertia and the bond length of the molecule can be deduced as they were when the spacing of pure rotational lines was determined from studies in the microwave region.

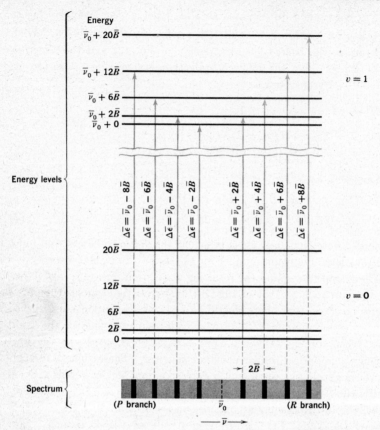

FIG. 7-2 The transitions that lead to rotational structure in a vibrational band for a linear molecule based on the assumption that B is independent of v.

Two features illustrated by the HBr example in Fig. 7-3 have not yet been accounted for and must now be considered. First, the relative intensities of the components remain to be investigated and, second, the fact that the spacings of the components are not found to be exactly constant must be dealt with.

7-2. The Relative Intensities of the Components of a Rotation-Vibration Absorption Band

The relative intensities of the components of bands such as that of Fig. 7-3 can be understood on the basis of the population of the various rotational energy levels of the ground vibrational state. The approximation can be made that the intensities of the components of the rotation-

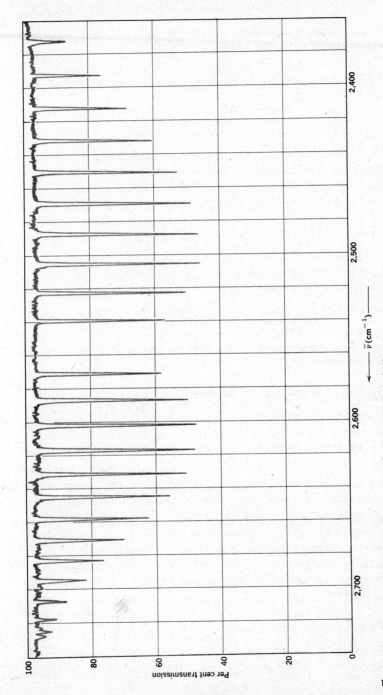

FIG. 7-3 The rotational structure of the $v = 0$ to $v = 1$ transition of HBr gas.

137

vibration band are proportional to the populations of the rotational energy levels from which the components originate. As was shown in Sec. 3-3, the multiplicity of the Jth rotational energy level is $2J + 1$, and it follows that, according to the Boltzmann distribution, the population of the Jth level is

$$N_J = (2J + 1)N_0 e^{-J(J+1)h^2/8\pi^2 IkT} \qquad (5)$$

The moment-of-inertia value for the molecule being studied and the temperature of the experiment can be substituted into this expression, and the value of N_J/N_0 can be calculated for various J values. The intensities of the components starting from various J values will be proportional to the values of N_J/N_0. The absorption band predicted on this basis, with the rigid-rotor approximation, will correspond rather closely to that observed.

Exercise 7-1. Calculate the relative populations of the $J = 0, 2, 4, 6, 8,$ and 10 energy levels of HBr at 25°C, and compare these results with the relative values of $\log \dfrac{I_0}{I}$ for the components of the P and R branches shown in Fig. 7-3. (Much of the disagreement that will be found is because of the experimental problems that arise when very sharp absorption lines are measured.)

7-3. Coupling of Rotation and Vibration

The energy-level expression of Eq. (2) is based on the assumption that the energy of a molecule can be treated in terms of separate contributions from the rotation of the molecule and the vibration of the molecule. The fact that the spectral transitions derived on this basis are not in complete accord with the observed bands, i.e., the spacing of the components is not constant, can be attributed to coupling between the rotation and the vibration of the molecule. This coupling introduces a cross term in the energy expression for a rotating-vibrating molecule that involves a term of the type $(v + \frac{1}{2})J(J + 1)$. This term is usually introduced by recognizing that $\bar{B}$ depends, since it involves the effective bond length r, on the vibrational energy. Thus one usually treats the coupling by writing

$$\bar{\epsilon}_{v,J} = (v + \tfrac{1}{2})1/2\pi c \sqrt{k/\mu} + \bar{B}_v J(J + 1) \qquad (6)$$

where $\bar{B}_v$ implies that the rotational term is a function of the vibrational quantum number. One finds, in fact, that the dependence is pretty well represented by an expression of the type

$$B_v = B_e - \alpha_e(v + \tfrac{1}{2}) \tag{7}$$

where B_e is the rotational term corresponding to the equilibrium bond length and α_e is a small, positive constant.

With this energy expression the selection rules give the allowed transition frequencies $\bar{\nu} = \Delta\bar{\epsilon}$ for the $v = 0$ to $v = 1$ transition as

R branch, $J \to J + 1$

$$\begin{aligned}\bar{\nu}_R &= \bar{\omega} + [\bar{B}_1(J + 1)(J + 2) - \bar{B}_0 J(J + 1)] \\ &= \bar{\omega} + 2\bar{B}_1 + (3\bar{B}_1 - \bar{B}_0)J + (\bar{B}_1 - \bar{B}_0)J^2 \end{aligned} \tag{8}$$

P branch, $J \to J - 1$

$$\begin{aligned}\bar{\nu}_P &= \bar{\omega} + [\bar{B}_1(J - 1)(J) - \bar{B}_0 J(J + 1)] \\ &= \bar{\omega} - (\bar{B}_1 + \bar{B}_0)J + (\bar{B}_1 - \bar{B}_0)J^2 \end{aligned} \tag{9}$$

Since the higher energy vibrational state has a greater vibrational amplitude, it will have a larger effective value of r. It follows that $I_1 > I_0$ and that $\bar{B}_1 < \bar{B}_0$. The coefficients of the J^2 terms in the expressions for the P and R branches are therefore negative. It is these terms that are primarily responsible for the nonconstant spacing of the components of a rotation-vibration band and for the asymmetry of the band that is apparent in the band of Fig. 7-3. The high J components of the P branch are at frequencies that are lower than would be expected on the basis of $\bar{B}_1 = \bar{B}_0 = \bar{B}$, and as a consequence this branch extends farther down to the low-frequency side. The high J components of the R branch are similarly at somewhat lower frequencies than would be expected for $\bar{B}_1 = \bar{B}_0 = \bar{B}$, and the high J components of the R branch tend, therefore, to bunch up. (It can be mentioned that this effect can become sufficiently important so that the components of the R branch start moving back to lower frequencies for very high J values. The band is then said to have a *band head*. Such behavior is observed only in electronic-vibration-rotation bands.)

Analysis of the rotation-vibration band can, as Fig. 7-4 suggests, lead to values of $\bar{B}_1$ and $\bar{B}_0$. It should be clear from Fig. 7-4 that the difference in the frequency of the component of the R branch and that of the P branch that start from the same value of J gives information on the rotational spacing in the upper vibrational level. Similarly, the difference in the frequency of the component of the R branch and that of the P branch that end at the same value of J in the $v = 1$ level gives information on the rotational spacing in the lower vibrational level. From the rotational spacings in the $v = 0$ and $v = 1$ levels, one can deduce values of $\bar{B}_0$ and $\bar{B}_1$. Furthermore, values of $\bar{B}_0$ and $\bar{B}_1$ can be obtained, from various pairs of transitions as a function of J, and any effect of centrifugal distortion can be recognized.

The combinations that lead to values of $\bar{B}_0$ and $\bar{B}_1$ can be deduced by considering Fig. 7-4 or, analytically, by taking the appropriate differences between the frequencies of the P and R branch components.

FIG. 7-4 An illustration that the rotational spacing and, therefore, the moment of inertia in the $v = 1$ and $v = 0$ states can be deduced from the rotational structure of a vibration-rotation absorption band. The difference in frequency of the components shown as heavy solid lines gives the spacing in the $v = 1$ state, while the difference in the frequency of the dashed lines gives the spacing in the $v = 0$ state.

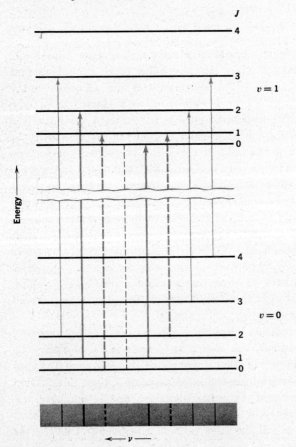

Thus for P and R components that start from the same J value, one has

$$\bar{\nu}_R(J) - \bar{\nu}_P(J) = 2\bar{B}_1(2J + 1) \tag{10}$$

from which $\bar{B}_1$ can be evaluated. An R component starting from the J level and a P component starting from the $J + 2$ level end on the same J level in the upper state. One then can obtain, by writing J in the expression for the R components and $J + 2$ in the expression for the P components and performing the subtraction,

$$\bar{\nu}_R(J) - \bar{\nu}_P(J + 2) = 2\bar{B}_0(2J + 3) \tag{11}$$

From these differences, values of $\bar{B}_0$ can be obtained.

The dependence of $\bar{B}$, and therefore of I and r, on the vibrational level turns out to be appreciable. Some results for diatomic molecules are given in Table 7-1. Also shown in the table are values for $\bar{B}_e$ and r_e which are deduced, by means of the formula $\bar{B}_v = \bar{B}_e - \alpha_e(v + \frac{1}{2})$ and the measured values of $\bar{B}_v$, for at least two vibrational levels. These results correspond to the equilibrium bond length, i.e., the bond length corresponding to the minimum in the potential-energy curve. One should particularly notice that r_e is significantly different from r_0. This difference makes itself known when one uses isotopic substitution, as was mentioned in Chap. 5, to obtain additional moment-of-inertia data for polyatomic molecules from which additional bond lengths or angles can be determined. The assumption of constant bond length with isotopic substitution would appear to be valid to a very good approximation for the equilibrium bond length. For the $v = 0$ state, which is usually what is studied in pure rotational spectral studies, a substitution of, for example, D for H lowers the $v = 0$ energy level in the potential curve and moves the effective bond length part way from the value r_0

TABLE 7-1 Dependence of $\bar{B}$ and the Bond Distance on the Vibrational State of a Molecule
[Values of α_e are for the formula $\bar{B}_v = \bar{B}_e - \alpha_e(v + \frac{1}{2})$]

Molecule	$\bar{B}_e$ (cm^{-1})	α_e (cm^{-1})	r_e (A)	r_0 (A)	r_1 (A)
H_2	60.809	2.993	0.7417	0.7505	0.7702
HD	45.655	1.993	0.7414	0.7495	0.7668
D_2	30.429	1.049	0.7416	0.7481	0.7616
HCl	10.5909	0.3019	1.27460	1.2838	1.3028
DCl	5.445	0.1118	1.275	1.282	1.295
CO	1.9314	0.01748	1.1282	1.1307	1.1359
N_2	2.010	0.0187	1.094	1.097	1.102

for the H-containing compound to r_e If rotation-vibration bands can be analyzed, as discussed here, results for r_e can be obtained for different isotopic species, and these can be safely assumed to remain constant with isotopic substitution.

Exercise 7-2.   The molecule DCl has a reduced mass of 3.14×10^{-24} g, an equilibrium bond length of about 1.27 A, and a force constant of 4.8×10^5 dynes/cm.

(a) Draw to scale an energy-level diagram showing the first five rotational levels of the $v = 0$ and $v = 1$ vibrational states.

(b) Draw vertical arrows to represent the transitions that would occur in an absorption study of the fundamental band.   (Place the arrows so that the one corresponding to the lowest energy change is at the left and the highest one is at the right, as is done in Fig. 7-2.)

(c) Pick out two transitions, and therefore absorption lines, that could be used to calculate $\bar{B}_0$ and two that could be used to calculate $\bar{B}_1$.

LINEAR MOLECULES

Two principal types of rotation-vibration bands occur for linear molecules.   If the vibration is such that the oscillating dipole moment connected with the vibration is parallel to the molecular axis, a certain set of selection rules, which will be discussed in the following section, apply and the rotation-vibration band is said to be a *parallel band*.   If the vibration is such that the oscillating dipole moment is perpendicular to the molecular axis, a different set of selection rules apply and the rotation-vibration band is said to be a *perpendicular band*.

7-4. Parallel Bands of Linear Molecules

When the vibration of a linear molecule results in an oscillating dipole moment that is parallel to the molecular axis, the situation, as far as rotation-vibration selection rules and resulting band shapes are concerned, is in no way different from the simpler linear molecules, the diatomic molecules.   Thus the selection rules are $\Delta v = \pm 1$ and $\Delta J = \pm 1$, and the rotation-vibration band has the same appearance, i.e., P and R branches and no Q branch, as that observed for diatomic molecules.   This is illustrated in Fig. 7-5.   The treatment of the previous section can also be applied to the bands of linear molecules and leads, for the fundamental vibrational transition, to values of $\bar{B}_1$ and $\bar{B}_0$. (Values of $\bar{B}_1$ and $\bar{B}_0$ would be expected to depend somewhat on the particular vibration being studied; the value deduced for $\bar{B}_e$ should be

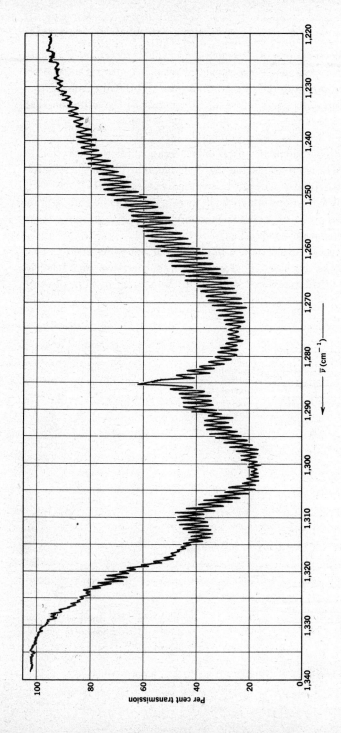

FIG. 7-5 A parallel band of the linear molecule N_2O. The P and R branches are partly resolved. (An underlying band occurs at about 1,315 cm^{-1}.)

143

the same for all vibrations of the molecule.) The problem of deducing bond lengths from the single experimental result, $\bar{B}$ or I, is, of course, the same as that encountered in studies of pure rotational spectra.

It is of interest to point out that, in contrast to the situation that exists in pure rotational spectroscopy, linear symmetric molecules can exhibit rotation-vibration absorption bands even if the molecule possesses no permanent dipole moment. It is only necessary for the vibration to be such that there is an oscillating dipole moment. The antisymmetric stretching vibration of CO_2, $O=C=O$, and that of acetylene, $H-C\equiv C-H$, are examples of vibrations which lead to rotation-vibration absorption bands. From analysis of such bands, moment-of-inertia data for these nonpolar molecules can be obtained.

The statistics followed by the like atoms of molecules such as CO_2 and C_2H_2 lead, as discussed in Sec. 5-5, to the decrease in statistical weight of some of the rotational levels or to the absence of some of these

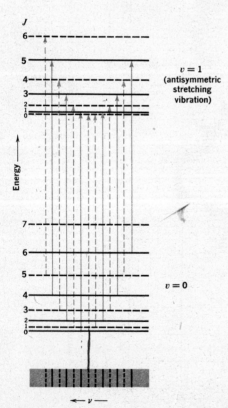

FIG. 7-6a The energy-level diagram and transitions of a molecule like CO_2.

levels. The appropriate energy-level diagram for CO_2^{16}, an example in which the like atoms have zero spin and obey Bose-Einstein statistics, is shown in Fig. 7-6a. The absorption band that results from the asymmetric stretching vibration is also shown in Fig. 7-6b. Although the appearance of the band does not immediately indicate the effect of the missing rotational levels, one finds that the spacing of the components is twice $2\bar{B}$ and that the central gap is half again as large as the spacing in the P and R branches.

The molecule acetylene illustrates the case where Fermi statistics apply since the hydrogen nuclei have spin $\frac{1}{2}$. (The carbon nuclei have no spin and, therefore, do not have an effect.) The alternation in statistical weight of the rotational levels is like that of H_2, and this

FIG. 7-6b A parallel band of the linear molecule CO_2 which has a center of symmetry and like atoms which obey Bose-Einstein statistics.

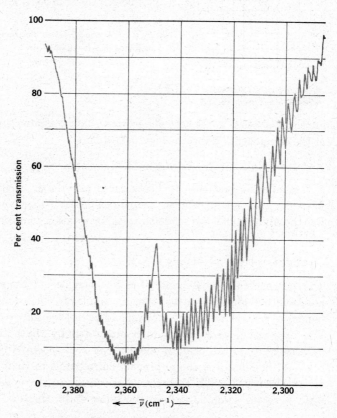

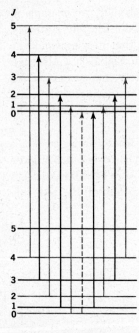

FIG. 7-7a The energy-level diagram and transitions of a molecule like H—C≡C—H.

alternation leads, in the case of acetylene, to the alternation in intensity of the components shown in Figs. 7-7a and b.

7-5. Perpendicular Bands of Linear Molecules

Bending vibrations of linear molecules have oscillating dipole moments that are in a direction perpendicular to the molecular axis. For these vibrations the selection rules for rotation-vibration transitions are

$$\Delta v = \pm 1 \qquad \Delta J = 0, \pm 1 \tag{12}$$

The perpendicular-type band of a linear molecule has, therefore, in addition to P and R branches that are similar to those found in parallel bands, a central Q branch corresponding to the $\Delta J = 0$ transitions. The appearance of such bands is illustrated by the absorption band corresponding to the bending vibration of N_2O shown in Fig. 7-8. The principal new feature, the Q branch, corresponds to the overlap of the $\Delta J = 0$ transitions. If the rotational spacing in the upper vibrational state were the same as that in the lower state, the $J \rightarrow J$ transitions

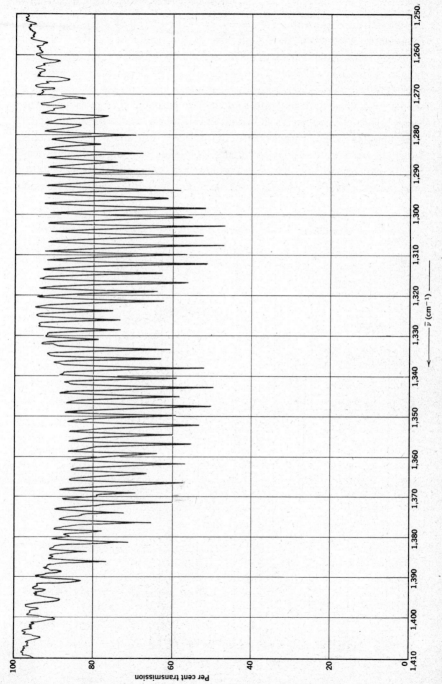

FIG. 7-7b A parallel band of the linear molecule H—C≡C—H which has a center of symmetry and like atoms that obey Fermi-Dirac statistics.

Per cent transmission

$\bar{\nu}$ (cm^{-1}) ⟶

would all have the same frequency $\bar{\nu}_0$. The fact that $\bar{B}_1$ is somewhat smaller than $\bar{B}_0$ leads to a slight decrease in frequency of the Q components with high J values. The Q branch usually, therefore, has a slight asymmetry.

The perpendicular vibrations of a linear molecule are, as mentioned in Sec. 6-4, doubly degenerate, and the two perpendicular motions of the molecule can be coupled to show that in this vibrational state the molecule has angular momentum as a result of this vibrational motion. This angular momentum about the figure axis leads to some additional features of perpendicular bands. The lowest J value for the $v = 1$ state, for example, is $J = 1$ because the one unit of angular momentum that

FIG. 7-8 A perpendicular band of the linear molecule N_2O. (The two satellite Q branches can be attributed to N_2O molecules that are in a vibrationally excited state.)

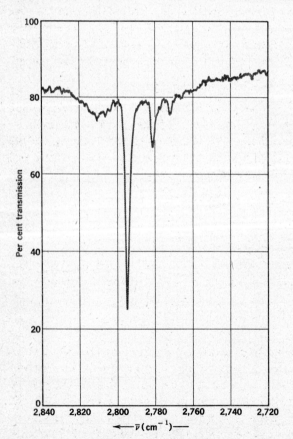

the vibration contributes disallows the total angular momentum value of zero. The angular momentum, furthermore, couples with the over-all rotation of the molecule in such a way that each J level of the $v = 1$ state is split and the two levels that result can be attributed to rotation of the molecule in opposite directions. These finer details can, however, best be passed over here. They will occur again in our study of the rotation-vibration spectra of symmetric-top molecules and will be discussed at greater length there.

SYMMETRIC-TOP MOLECULES

The infrared active normal vibrations of molecules like CH_3Cl and benzene, which are symmetric tops because of the symmetric arrangement of the atoms, have their oscillating dipole moment either parallel to the unique axis of the molecule or perpendicular to this axis. As for linear molecules, these two types of vibrations have different rotation-vibration selection rules and therefore different rotation-vibration band shapes.

7-6. Parallel Bands of Symmetric-top Molecules

Vibrations that lead to parallel bands can be illustrated by the displacements indicated in Fig. 7-9a. All these vibrations have an oscillating dipole moment along the unique axis, the figure axis of the molecule. For such vibrations the selection rules for the rotational changes in a rotation-vibration transition are

$$\Delta K = 0 \qquad \Delta J = 0, \pm 1 \qquad \text{if } K \neq 0$$

and (13)

$$\Delta K = 0 \qquad \Delta J = \pm 1 \qquad \text{if } K = 0$$

These rules can be combined with the energy-level expression, Eq. (14) in Chap. 5, for the rotational energies of a symmetric-top molecule

$$\bar{\epsilon}_{J K} = \bar{B} J(J + 1) + (\bar{A} - \bar{B})K^2 \qquad J = 0, 1, 2, \ldots \qquad (14)$$
$$K = 0, \pm 1, \pm 2, \ldots, \pm J$$

where J and K are quantum numbers, $\bar{A}$ is the rotational constant for the unique axis, and $\bar{B}$ is the rotational constant for the axes perpendicular to the figure axis. The transitions that constitute the parallel band can then be represented on the energy diagram of Fig. 7-10. If the dependence of the moments of inertia on the value of K is small, the spacing within each set of levels with a given value of K will be almost

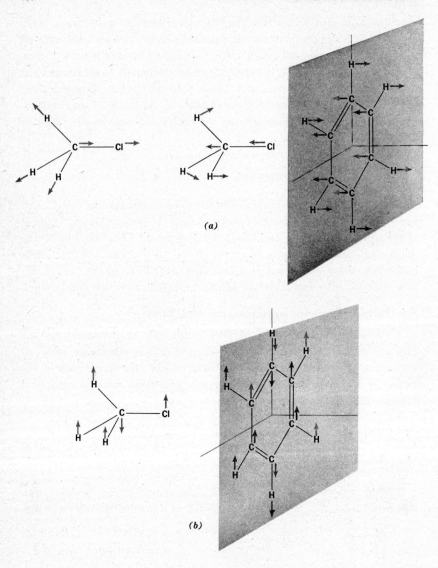

(a)

(b)

FIG. 7-9 Vibrations of symmetry-top molecules that lead to (a) parallel absorption bands and (b) perpendicular absorption bands.

the same since they are governed by the same term, i.e., the $J(J + 1)\bar{B}_1$ and $J(J + 1)\bar{B}_0$ terms of the energy expression. The contributions to the total band from the transitions within each set of levels with a given value of K can be shown as in Fig. 7-11. One should notice, as both Figs. 7-10 and 7-11 show, that for the higher K values the low values of J do not occur. This follows from the requirement that, since K determines a component of the angular momentum while J determines

FIG. 7-10 The energy levels of a symmetric-top molecule and the transitions that are allowed for a parallel band.

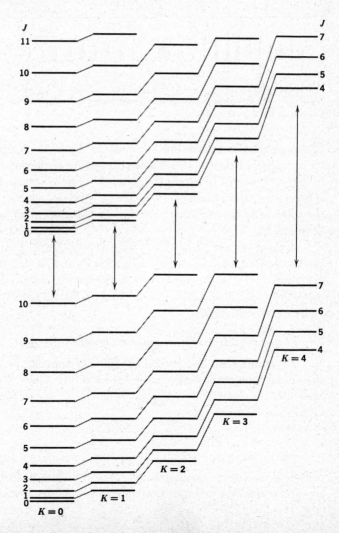

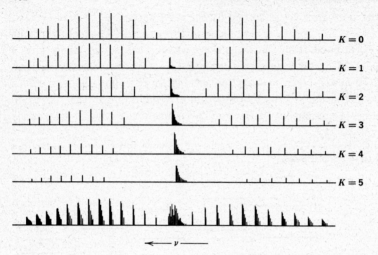

FIG. 7-11 The components of a parallel band showing the contributions from each of the K levels of the v = 0 state.

the total angular momentum, J must be equal to or greater than K for any allowed state. Outside of this feature each contribution shown in Fig. 7-11 consists of simple P, Q, and R branches (except for the $K = 0$ contribution which shows no Q branch). The appearance expected for the total band is seen to be borne out by the absorption band of CH_3Br shown in Fig. 7-12.

If the components of the P and R branches of the parallel band can be resolved, one can deduce values for $\bar{B}_1$ and $\bar{B}_0$, or at least an average value of $\bar{B}$, in the same way as previously indicated for diatomic molecules. With such data the moment of inertia perpendicular to the figure axis is obtained.

7-7. Perpendicular Bands of Symmetric-top Molecules

Vibrations that have oscillating dipole moments perpendicular to the unique axis of the molecule are shown in Fig. 7-9b. For such vibrations, the selection rule for rotational transitions accompanying the vibrational transition is

$$\Delta K = \pm 1 \qquad \Delta J = 0, \pm 1 \tag{15}$$

The energy-level diagram of Fig. 7-13 shows the transitions that can occur in a perpendicular band. The complete band can be understood in terms of a summation of subbands. These subbands consist of

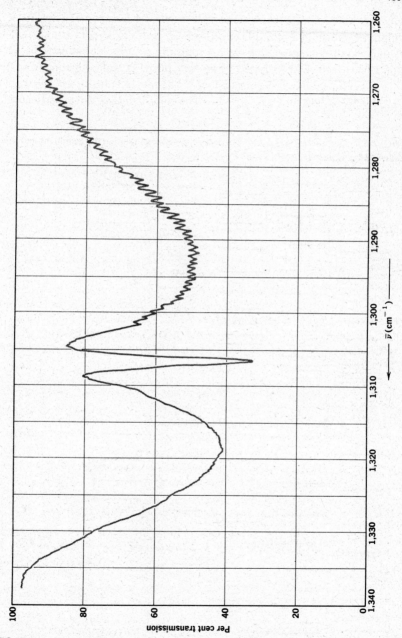

FIG. 7-12 A parallel absorption band of the symmetry-top molecule CH_3Br. The P branch is partly resolved, while only the contour of the R branch is obtained.

all the $\Delta J = 0,\ \pm 1$ transitions that occur for a given change in K. Thus, as shown in Fig. 7-14, for $K = 0 \rightarrow 1$, the P, Q, and R type sub-bands result from the $\Delta J = 0,\ \pm 1$ transitions. Similar subbands occur for $K = 1 \rightarrow 0$, and so forth. For each initial K value, except $K = 0$, one gets two subbands corresponding to the sets of transitions that occur within $\Delta K = +1$ and $\Delta K = -1$. The total band, as the experimental

FIG. 7-13 The energy levels of a symmetry-top molecule showing the transitions that are allowed for a perpendicular band.

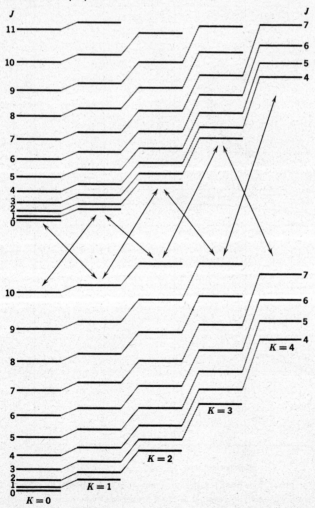

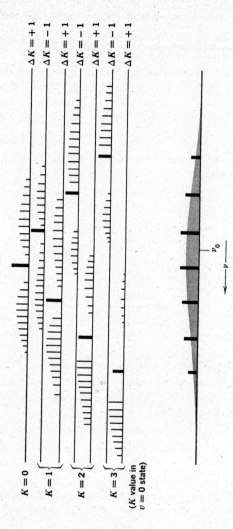

$\Delta K = +1$
$\Delta K = -1$
$\Delta K = +1$
$\Delta K = -1$
$\Delta K = +1$
$\Delta K = -1$
$\Delta K = +1$

$K = 0$
$K = 1$
$K = 2$
$K = 3$

(K value in
$v = 0$ state)

ν_0

$\longleftarrow \nu \longrightarrow$

FIG. 7-14 The components of a perpendicular band showing the contributions from each of the K levels of the $v = 0$ state.

curve of Fig. 7-15 shows, usually reveals the Q branches of the subbands superimposed on an unresolved background.

The spacing of these Q branches can be calculated from the energy-level expression

$$\bar{\epsilon}_{J,K} = \bar{B}J(J + 1) + (\bar{A} - \bar{B})K^2 \tag{16}$$

and the changes $\Delta K = \pm 1$, $\Delta J = 0$ that result in the Q branches. If $\bar{A}$ and $\bar{B}$ are taken as independent of v and if one again designates the band origin by $\bar{\omega}$, one has

For $\Delta K = +1$

$$\begin{aligned}
\bar{\nu}_{Q\text{branches}} &= \bar{\omega} + (\bar{A} - \bar{B})[(K + 1)^2 - K^2] \\
&= \bar{\omega} + (\bar{A} - \bar{B}) + 2(\bar{A} - \bar{B})K \qquad \text{for } K = 0, 1, 2, \ldots
\end{aligned} \tag{17}$$

For $\Delta K = -1$

$$\begin{aligned}
\bar{\nu}_{Q\text{branches}} &= \bar{\omega} + (\bar{A} - \bar{B}) \quad (K - 1)^2 - K^2 \\
&= \bar{\omega} + (\bar{A} - \bar{B}) - 2(\bar{A} - \bar{B})K \qquad \text{for } K = 1, 2, 3, \ldots
\end{aligned} \tag{18}$$

The spacing of the Q branches of a perpendicular band can, according to this result, be identified with $2(\bar{A} - \bar{B})$. For molecules like the methyl halides, where $\bar{A}$ is larger than $\bar{B}$, the Q branches are well separated and, as Fig. 7-15 shows, easily resolved.

The alternation in intensity of the Q branches of the CH_3Cl band of Fig. 7-15 can be attributed to the different statistical weights of the levels with different K values. The basis for the strong, weak, weak, strong variation and the intensity ratio of $2:1$ is the same as that discussed for linear molecules in Sec. 5-5. Detailed analysis of the situation in which there are three rather than two identical nuclei will, however, not be given here. (See ref. 1, page 406.)

Exercise 7-3. The rotational constants of CH_3Br are $\bar{A} = 5.08$ cm^{-1} and $B = C = 0.31$ cm^{-1}.

(a) Make two energy-level diagrams, like that of Fig. 7-9, for CH_3Br. (Draw the rotational spacings to scale for both the $v = 0$ and $v = 1$ states, but reduce the $v = 0$ to $v = 1$ energy difference.)

(b) On one diagram, indicate the transitions that occur in a vibration in which the dipole-moment oscillation is along the figure axis.

(c) On the other diagram, indicate the transitions that lead to the Q branches in a perpendicular type band.

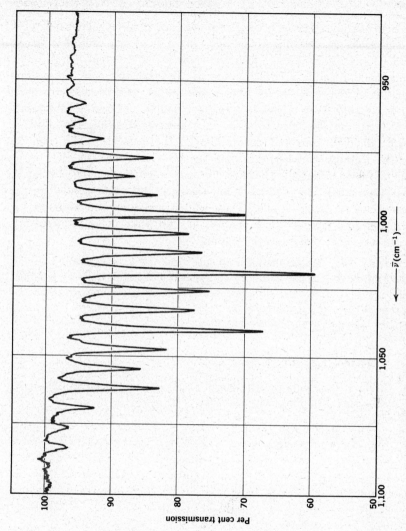

FIG. 7-15 A perpendicular band of the symmetry-top molecule CH₃Cl.

157

If one investigates in detail a number of perpendicular bands of a given molecule, one might find the rather disturbing fact that the Q branch spacing is nowhere near the same in the different bands. The treatment given here, which leads to the expectation of a constant spacing of $2(\bar{A} - \bar{B})$, is, for some molecules, in error because of neglect of a coupling that occurs between the doubly degenerate vibrations, which can be combined to show an angular momentum, that lead to perpendicular bands and the rotation of the molecule. The coupling occurs through *Coriolis forces*, and the basis and effect of such forces are discussed in ref. 1. The effect of Coriolis coupling can be calculated, but the calculation requires a knowledge of the form of the normal vibrations of the molecule. Only simple molecules can therefore be handled, and in general the analysis of a perpendicular band does not yield molecular structure information.

Exercise 7-4. Obtain the infrared spectrum of a gaseous methyl halide. Determine $\bar{A} - \bar{B}$ for as many of the perpendicular bands as possible, and see that the values obtained are not identical. Compare with the value of $\bar{A} - \bar{B}$ calculated from values of the bond lengths and bond angles reported in the literature.

PRINCIPAL REFERENCES

1. Herzberg, G.: "Infrared and Raman Spectra," chap. 4, D. Van Nostrand Company, Inc., Princeton, N.J., 1945.

8

MOLECULAR SYMMETRY
AND GROUP THEORY

The previous two chapters have suggested the importance of molecular symmetry for spectroscopy. It has been shown that for nondegenerate vibrations each normal coordinate, or vibration, of the molecule must be either symmetric or antisymmetric with respect to any symmetric element. Furthermore, the previous chapter has shown that, for a symmetric-top molecule, the appearance of a rotation-vibration absorption band is determined by the symmetry nature of the vibration. In Chap. 11, moreover, we will see that the wave functions that describe the behavior of the electrons of a molecule must conform to the symmetry of the molecule and that the symmetry properties of the electronic states of a molecule provide an important and helpful characterization of the states.

A systematic study of the symmetry properties of molecules will now be undertaken. To avoid a rather abstract treatment, applications of general methods and results will continually be made to the study of the vibrations of symmetric molecules. It should be emphasized, in this connection, that deductions based on the methods presented here are applicable to many areas of molecular spectroscopy and molecular-structure studies. Vibrational modes merely provide, in view of our studies of the previous chapters, convenient illustrations of the application of symmetry arguments.

This study can be divided into two major parts. First, the ways in which symmetry elements of a molecule are described and the ways in which the symmetry nature of molecular motions is determined and tabulated will be given. Second, it will be shown that the symmetry operations of a molecule form what is known in mathematics as a "group." The mathematical treatment that can be given for a general, or abstract, group is then developed to the extent that it is needed for application to problems of molecular spectroscopy, and some of these applications are illustrated.

SYMMETRY PROPERTIES OF MOLECULES

8-1. Symmetry Elements, Symmetry Operations, and Point Groups

It is apparent that some molecules, such as CO_2 and H_2O, are "symmetric." To proceed with a systematic study of the consequences of such symmetry, it is necessary to be able to describe in more detail the nature of the symmetry of a given molecule. The symmetry of a molecule is discussed in terms of the *symmetry elements* that the molecule has in its equilibrium configuration. All molecular symmetries can be treated in terms of the five symmetry elements listed, along with the symbols used to denote them, in Table 8-1. These symmetry elements are best explained in terms of *symmetry operations*. Each symmetry element has a symmetry operation associated with it, and Table 8-1 includes a brief statement of these operations. (The distinction between symmetry elements, such as a plane of symmetry, and symmetry operations, such as a reflection through a plane of symmetry, is necessary for an orderly treatment of the consequences of symmetry.) Various molecules drawn so as to exhibit symmetry elements are shown in Figs. 8-1 and 8-2. Illustration of the symmetry element E, which all molecules have, would be trivial. Its inclusion as an element of symmetry is

TABLE 8-1   The Symmetry Elements and Symmetry Operations

Symmetry elements		Symmetry operations
Symbol	Description	
E	Identity	No change
σ	Plane of symmetry	Reflection through the plane
i	Center of symmetry	Inversion through the center
C_p	Axis of symmetry	Rotation about the axis by $360/p$ deg
S_p	Rotation-reflection axis of symmetry	Rotation about the axis by $360/p$ deg followed by reflection through the plane

dictated by considerations that will become apparent later. The only further comment that need be made about the symmetry elements is that, in diagrams such as those of Fig. 8-1, it is customary to set up the principal axis of symmetry vertically and, if a coordinate system is used, to have the z axis in this vertical direction. In a case such as benzene, where there is a sixfold axis and also twofold axes perpendicular to it, the sixfold axis is considered to be the principal axis.

It is worth while to memorize the symbols used for the various symmetry elements.

If a great variety of molecules is investigated, it will be found that only a few different combinations of symmetry elements occur. Each combination of symmetry elements that can occur is known as a *point group*. (The term point group is used because, as we will see, the symmetry operations that are associated with the symmetry elements of the molecule leave a point of the molecule fixed in space. This is in contrast to a *space group*, as is found in a crystal, where some of the symmetry operations result in a translation of a molecule, or a unit cell, to a new location in the crystal.)

FIG. 8-1 Some of the symmetry elements in terms of the examples *trans*-dichloroethane, carbon dioxide, and allene.

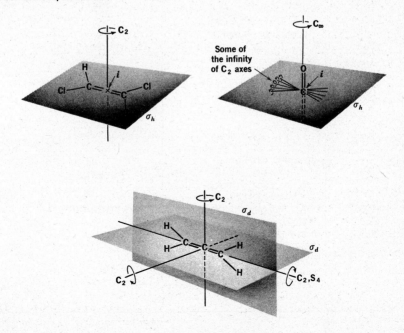

A summary of the important combinations of symmetry elements that can occur, i.e., the possible point groups, and the symbols used to denote these are given in Table 8-2. It will be noticed that the boldface symbols used for the point group are based, for the most part, on the principal symmetry element of the group and that the subscripts added to some of the point-group symbols further tie in the symbol with the elements in the group.

It is not necessary to commit to memory the symbols and symmetry

TABLE 8-2 Some of the Point Groups That Are Important in Molecular Problems
(The number of times a symmetry element occurs is indicated by a number before the symbol for that symmetry element)

Point group	Symmetry elements	Examples
C_1	E	CH_3—$CHClBr$
C_2	E, C_2	H_2O_2
C_i	E, i	CH_3—$CHCl$—$CHCl$—CH_3 (trans.)
C	E, σ	$NOCl$
C_{2v}	$E, C_2, 2\sigma_v$	H_2O, CH_2Cl_2
C_{3v}	$E, C_3, 3\sigma_v$	$NH_3, HCCl_3$
$C_{\infty v}$	$E, C_\infty, \infty\sigma_v$	HCN, OCS
C_{2h}	E, C_2, σ_h, i	$ClHC$=$CHCl$ (trans.)
D_{2d}	$E, 3C_2$ (mutually perp.), S_4 (coincident with one of the C_2), $2\sigma_d$ (through the S_4 axis)	H_2C=C=CH_2
D_{3d}	$E, C_3, 3C_2$ (perp. to the C_3 axis), S_6 (coincident with the C_3 axis), $i, 3\sigma_d$	C_6H_{12} (cyclohexane)
$D_{2h}\equiv V_h$	$E, 3C_2$ (mutually perp.), 3σ (mutually perp.), i	H_2C=CH_2
D_{3h}	$E, C_3, 3C_2$ (perp. to the C_3 axis), $3\sigma_v, \sigma_h$	BCl_3
D_{4h}	$E, C_4, 4C_2$ (perp. to the C_4 axis), $4\sigma_v, \sigma_h, C_2$ and S_4 (both coincident with C_4), i	C_4H_8 (cyclobutane)
D_{6h}	$E, C_6, 6C_2$ (perp. to the C_6 axis), $6\sigma_v, \sigma_h, C_2$ and C_3 and S_6 (all coincident with the C_6 axis), i	C_6H_6 (benzene)
$D_{\infty h}$	$E, C_\infty, \infty C_2$ (perp. to the C_∞ axis), $\infty\sigma_v, \sigma_h, i$	H_2, CO_2, HC≡CH
T_d	$E, 3C_2$ (mutually perp.), $4C_3, 6\sigma$, $3S_4$ (coincident with the C_2 axes),	CH_4
O_h	$E, 3C_4$ (mutually perp.), $4C_3, 3S_4$ and $3C_2$ (coincident with the C_4 axes), $6C_2, 9\sigma, 4S_6$ (coincident with the C_3), i	$[PtCl_6]^-$ $[Co(NH_3)_6]^{3+}$

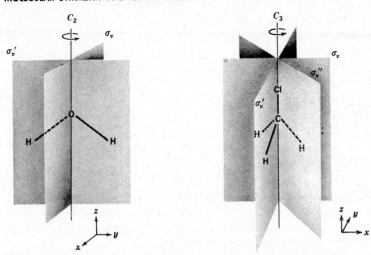

FIG. 8-2 The symmetry elements of H_2O, point group C_{2v}, and CH_3Cl, point group C_{3v}. (The coordinate systems are drawn in ways that will be convenient for later treatments.)

elements for all the point groups. It is, at this stage, sufficient to notice particularly those of the C_{2v} and C_{3v} groups since molecules of the type H_2O and CH_3Cl, which belong to these point groups, will be used in later illustrations. These molecules, and the symmetry elements they contain, are illustrated in Fig. 8-2. It should be pointed out that the C_3 axis of symmetry implies two different symmetry operations. One is a counterclockwise rotation by a third of a revolution, and the other is a counterclockwise rotation by two-thirds of a revolution, or a clockwise one of one-third of a revolution. The operation symbol C_3 designates the first of these and C_3^2 the second.

8-2. Symmetry Operations on Molecular Motions

The symmetry elements of a molecule are determined by the geometry of a molecule in its equilibrium configuration. Displacements of the atoms of a molecule, such as occur in a translation or rotation of the molecule, or a vibration of the atoms of the molecule, can be related to these symmetry elements by means of the symmetry operation associated with each element.

Application of a symmetry operation to a molecular motion is best done by first describing the motion by means of arrows along the cartesian coordinates associated with each atom of the molecule. One of the rotations and one of the translations of the H_2O molecule are so described

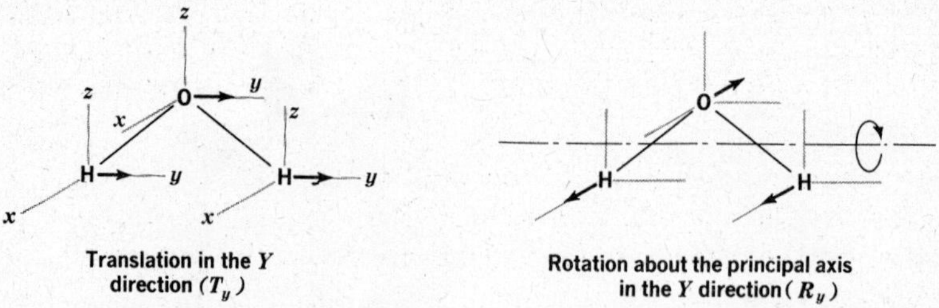

Translation in the Y direction (T_y)

Rotation about the principal axis in the Y direction (R_y)

FIG. 8-3   Representation of the translation T_y and the rotation R_y of the H_2O molecule by means of displacement vectors.

in Fig. 8-3. Also, since the features associated with degenerate vibrations are then encountered, the molecule CH_3Cl is also used as an illustration and the three translational motions are represented by vectors along the atomic cartesian coordinates in Fig. 8-4.

Let us first consider the effect of the symmetry operations on the molecular motions of the H_2O molecule, which is an example of a molecule with no degenerate motions. The symmetry operations corresponding to the various symmetry elements can be performed on the displacement vectors such as those of Fig. 8-3. When this is done for the illustrated motions T_y and R_y for H_2O, one sees that the displacement arrows either are left unchanged or are reversed in direction. These two possibilities are represented by +1 for the symmetric result of no change or −1 for the antisymmetric result of a reversal in direction. In a similar manner, a +1 or −1 can be associated with the result of each symmetry operation acting on the displacement vectors that correspond to the remaining translations and rotations of the H_2O molecule. (As the

FIG. 8-4   Representation of the translational motions of CH_3Cl by means of displacement vectors.   (Note that the coordinate system of Fig. 8-2 is used.)

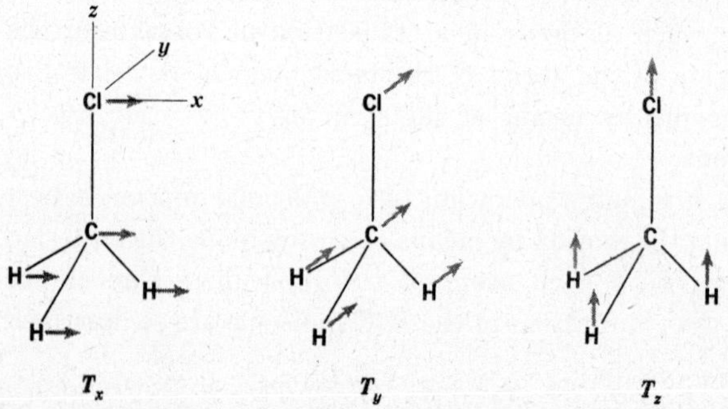

T_x

T_y

T_z

discussion of normal coordinates in Chap. 6 indicated, the vibrations of the H_2O molecule will similarly transform. The vectors of Fig. 8-5 represent displacements that have suitable symmetry behavior for molecular vibrations.)

The results of such diagrammatic analyses can be put in a form that is more convenient for mathematical extension by writing the operation of a symmetry operation on a molecular displacement as, for example, for the motions of Fig. 8-3,

$$C_2(T_y) \quad \text{and} \quad C_2(R_y)$$

These symbols are to be interpreted as "the operation corresponding to the C_2 symmetry element acting on the molecular displacements T_y and R_y."

The result, that the vectors change direction as a result of the operation, can then be indicated by writing

$$C_2(T_y) = (-1)(T_y) \tag{1}$$

and

$$C_2(R_y) = (-1)(R_y) \tag{2}$$

With this procedure one recognizes the reason for the use of $+1$ and -1 to represent symmetric and antisymmetric behavior. When degenerate motions are considered, it will be recognized that the $+1$ and -1 transformation factors that appear in the H_2O example are in fact one-by-one matrices and are examples of what are known as *transformation matrices*.

Exercise 8-1. Draw the cartesian displacement vectors that correspond to translation of the H_2O molecule in the x and z directions and show that the symmetry operations corresponding to the symmetry elements of the molecule result in either no change or a simple reversal of these vectors. Do the same for rotations about axes in the x and z directions and for the vibrations of Fig. 8-5.

When molecules have a threefold or higher axis of symmetry, it is found that degenerate motions occur; and these introduce a number of complications. In CH_3Cl, for example, one recognizes that rotations about the x axis and the y axis will lead to identical sets of rotational

FIG. 8-5   Displacements that correspond to possible vibrations of the H_2O molecule.

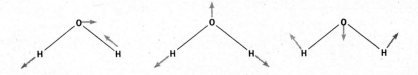

energy levels because the moments of inertia about the axes in these two directions must be identical. Similarly, certain vibrations of such molecules will necessarily have, as a result of the molecular symmetry, identical energy-level patterns. It follows, as we will now see, that such degenerate motions must be treated as a set and that, when symmetry properties are considered, they cannot be treated separately. This behavior can be illustrated by considering the effect of the symmetry operations of the CH_3Cl molecule on the degenerate set T_x and T_y.

A vector displacement indicating the motion of the C, or Cl, atom in the translation T_x and T_y is shown in projection in Fig. 8-6. (Similar arrows can be drawn on the H atoms. These will behave in an identical manner to the vectors located on the axial atoms, and since the effect of operations on them is a little harder to imagine and draw, they are not included.) Let us now consider the operations $C_3(T_x)$ and $C_3(T_y)$. The

FIG. 8-6 The effect of the symmetry operations on the translations T_x and T_y of the C_{3v} molecule CH_3Cl. The diagrams here correspond to end views, from the top, of Fig. 8-2.

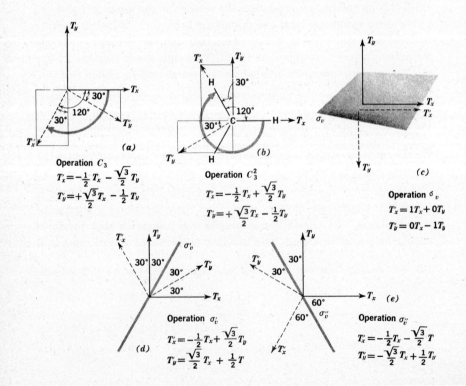

C_3 operation consists of a rotation by 120 deg, and when the operation acts on the vectors of T_x and T_y, the vector displacements shown by dashed vectors in Fig. 8-6a are obtained. Now, and this is the characteristic feature of degenerate motions, the vectors of T_x are not simply unchanged or reversed in direction. As the geometry of Fig. 8-6 shows, the result of the transformation can be described in terms of the vectors of T_x and T_y by

$$C_3(T_x) = -\frac{1}{2}(T_x) - \frac{\sqrt{3}}{2}(T_y) \tag{3}$$

Similarly, the result of rotating the T_y vector by 120 deg can be described as

$$C_3(T_y) = +\frac{\sqrt{3}}{2}(T_x) - \frac{1}{2}(T_y) \tag{4}$$

One sees that T_x and T_y cannot be kept separate. It is therefore convenient to treat their transformation properties together and write the result of the operation corresponding to the symmetry element C_3 on the pair of motions T_x and T_y by the matrix equation*

$$C_3\begin{pmatrix} T_x \\ T_y \end{pmatrix} = \begin{pmatrix} -\dfrac{1}{2} & -\dfrac{\sqrt{3}}{2} \\ +\dfrac{\sqrt{3}}{2} & -\dfrac{1}{2} \end{pmatrix}\begin{pmatrix} T_x \\ T_y \end{pmatrix} \tag{5}$$

In a similar way one can describe the effect of the symmetry operations corresponding to the remaining symmetry elements of the $\mathbf{C}_{3v}$ group by transformation matrices. Thus one writes, with the aid of Fig. 8-6, for all the operations of the $\mathbf{C}_{3v}$ group

$$E\begin{pmatrix} T_x \\ T_y \end{pmatrix} = \begin{pmatrix} 1 & 0 \\ 0 & 1 \end{pmatrix}\begin{pmatrix} T_x \\ T_y \end{pmatrix}$$

$$\sigma_v\begin{pmatrix} T_x \\ T_y \end{pmatrix} = \begin{pmatrix} 1 & 0 \\ 0 & -1 \end{pmatrix}\begin{pmatrix} T_x \\ T_y \end{pmatrix} \qquad \sigma_v'\begin{pmatrix} T_x \\ T_y \end{pmatrix} = \begin{pmatrix} -\dfrac{1}{2} & +\dfrac{\sqrt{3}}{2} \\ +\dfrac{\sqrt{3}}{2} & +\dfrac{1}{2} \end{pmatrix}\begin{pmatrix} T_x \\ T_y \end{pmatrix}$$

$$\sigma_v''\begin{pmatrix} T_x \\ T_y \end{pmatrix} = \begin{pmatrix} -\dfrac{1}{2} & -\dfrac{\sqrt{3}}{2} \\ -\dfrac{\sqrt{3}}{2} & +\dfrac{1}{2} \end{pmatrix}\begin{pmatrix} T_x \\ T_y \end{pmatrix}$$

* Only a few features of matrix methods are necessary for the treatments given in this chapter. The student with no background in this subject should be able to follow the developments if he learns matrix multiplication enough to understand equations like Eq. (5).

and, including for completeness the C_3 operation given above,

$$C_3 \begin{pmatrix} T_x \\ T_y \end{pmatrix} = \begin{pmatrix} -\dfrac{1}{2} & -\dfrac{\sqrt{3}}{2} \\ +\dfrac{\sqrt{3}}{2} & -\dfrac{1}{2} \end{pmatrix} \begin{pmatrix} T_x \\ T_y \end{pmatrix}$$

$$C_3^2 \begin{pmatrix} T_x \\ T_y \end{pmatrix} = \begin{pmatrix} -\dfrac{1}{2} & +\dfrac{\sqrt{3}}{2} \\ -\dfrac{\sqrt{3}}{2} & -\dfrac{1}{2} \end{pmatrix} \begin{pmatrix} T_x \\ T_y \end{pmatrix}$$

The transformation matrices will play an important role in later work. For the present it is enough to recognize that they allow the effect of the symmetry operation to be represented in mathematical rather than diagrammatic forms.

8-3. Symmetry Species and Character Tables

A brief introduction can now be given to the ways in which the behavior of molecular motions with respect to symmetry operations is usually tabulated. Some of the reasons for setting up the system that is actually used will, however, not be completely understandable until later material is studied.

The transformation matrices that arise when the motions of a molecule belonging to a given point group are investigated can be arranged in tabular form. The behavior of the motions of H_2O, or in fact any C_{2v} molecule, with respect to symmetry operations, is given in Table 8-3.

This table summarizes the fact that the transformation matrices for T_z are $+1$ for each symmetry element; for R_z they are $+1$ for the symmetry elements E and C_2, but -1 for σ_v and σ_v'; and so forth.

Since, as we will see later, a number of different molecular motions,

TABLE 8-3 Summary of the Transformation Matrices for the Symmetry Operations for the Translations and Rotations of the C_{2v} Molecule H_2O

C_{2v}	E	C_2	σ_v	σ_v'	Rot. and trans.
1	1	1	1	T_z
1	1	-1	-1	R_z
1	-1	1	-1	R_y, T_x
1	-1	-1	1	R_x, T_y

including vibrations as well as translations and rotations, and also the various electron orbitals for the molecule, transform with the transformation matrices given in one row of such a table, it is convenient to introduce symbols for each row. The procedure is to designate a row by A if the transformations are symmetric with respect to the principal axis of symmetry and B if antisymmetric with respect to this axis. Thus the first two rows of Table 8-3 would be labeled A and the second two B. In order to distinguish the two A rows one labels the first row, where the completely symmetric set of transformations is written, as A_1 and the second row as A_2. Similarly, the two B rows are distinguished by B_1 and B_2. Thus, with this added notation, the sets of transformation matrices of a molecule with C_{2v} symmetry are given in Table 8-4.

The rows of such a table are said to be symmetry species to which motions of a molecule or electron orbitals of a molecule belonging to the point group of the table can be assigned.

A slightly different notation is used if the molecule contains a center of symmetry. Then one uses, instead of the subscripts 1 and 2, a subscript g for a symmetry species that is symmetric with respect to inversion at the center of symmetry and u if it is antisymmetric with respect to this operation.

The transformation matrices that are found for the C_{3v} point group, a group which, as illustrated for T_x and T_y in the previous section, leads to degenerate sets of translations and rotations, are summarized in Table 8-5. It turns out, as we will see later, to be sufficient for most purposes to tabulate, not the complete transformation matrices, but merely the sums of the diagonal elements of the transformation matrices. This procedure leads, as can be readily checked from the matrices of Table 8-5, to the summary of the symmetry behavior for C_{3v} molecules shown in Table 8-6. A doubly degenerate symmetry species is generally labeled as E, not to be confused with the identity symmetry element, and a

TABLE 8-4   The Transformation Matrices for C_{2v} Molecule with Symbols for the Different Behaviors with Regard to Symmetry Operations

C_{2v}	E	C_2	σ_v	σ_v'	Rot. and trans.
A_1	1	1	1	1	T_z
A_2	1	1	-1	-1	R_z
B_1	1	-1	1	-1	R_y, T_x
B_2	1	-1	-1	1	R_x, T_y

TABLE 8-5   The Transformation Matrices for the Translations and Rotations of the Point Group C_{3v}

C_{3v}	E	C_3	C_3^2	σ_v	σ_v'	σ_v''	Rot. and trans.
	$\begin{array}{c}1\\1\end{array}$	$\begin{array}{c}1\\1\end{array}$	$\begin{array}{c}1\\1\end{array}$	$\begin{array}{c}1\\-1\end{array}$	$\begin{array}{c}1\\-1\end{array}$	$\begin{array}{c}1\\-1\end{array}$	T_z R_z
	$\begin{pmatrix} +1 & 0 \\ 0 & +1 \end{pmatrix}$	$\begin{pmatrix} -\frac{1}{2} & +\frac{\sqrt{3}}{2} \\ -\frac{\sqrt{3}}{2} & -\frac{1}{2} \end{pmatrix}$	$\begin{pmatrix} -\frac{1}{2} & -\frac{\sqrt{3}}{2} \\ +\frac{\sqrt{3}}{2} & -\frac{1}{2} \end{pmatrix}$	$\begin{pmatrix} +1 & 0 \\ 0 & -1 \end{pmatrix}$	$\begin{pmatrix} -\frac{1}{2} & +\frac{\sqrt{3}}{2} \\ +\frac{\sqrt{3}}{2} & +\frac{1}{2} \end{pmatrix}$	$\begin{pmatrix} -\frac{1}{2} & -\frac{\sqrt{3}}{2} \\ -\frac{\sqrt{3}}{2} & +\frac{1}{2} \end{pmatrix}$	T_x, T_y and R_x, R_y

TABLE 8-6 The Sums of the Diagonal Elements of the Transformation Matrices of a C_{3v} Molecule

C_{3v}	E	C_3	C_3^2	σ_v	σ_v'	σ_v''	Rot. and trans.
A_1	1	1	1	1	1	1	T_z
A_2	1	1	1	-1	-1	-1	R_z
E	2	-1	-1	0	0	0	(R_x, R_y), (T_x, T_y)

triply degenerate set as F or T. (It will, in fact, be seen later that each entry for the nondegenerate species in tables such as Tables 8-4 and 8-5 is really to be interpreted as the sum of the diagonal elements of the transformation matrix. If the matrix is a one-by-one matrix, this is, of course, identical with the transformation matrix, +1 or -1, itself.)

The identical transformation matrices for the two rotation elements and for the three planes of symmetry that can be noted in Table 8-5 are typical. It is therefore possible to abbreviate such tables by showing only one column for each type of symmetry element. The number of symmetry elements in the class is then indicated at the top of the column. Thus for the C_{3v} point group one abbreviates Table 8-6 and writes the information as in Table 8-7.

The basis, properties, and uses of tabulations such as Tables 8-4 and 8-7 will be the subject of the remainder of the chapter. Their introduction here is intended principally to establish the notation that is used. One will notice in many advanced texts on spectroscopy and quantum mechanics that such tables are given for all possible point groups. (See, for example, G. Herzberg, "Infrared and Raman Spectra," D. Van Nostrand Company, Inc., Princeton, N.J., 1945; E. B. Wilson, J. C. Decius, and P. C. Cross, "Molecular Vibrations," McGraw-Hill Book Company, Inc., New York, 1955; and H. Eyring, J. Walter, and G. K. Kimball, "Quantum Chemistry," Wiley & Sons, Inc., New York,

TABLE 8-7 The Sums of the Diagonal Elements of the Transformation Matrices of a C_{3v} Molecule in Condensed Form

C_{3v}	E	$2C_3$	$3\sigma_v$	Rot. and trans.
A_1	1	1	1	T_z
A_2	1	1	-1	R_z
E	2	-1	0	(R_x, R_y), (T_x, T_y)

1948.   The first of these references also gives a detailed discussion, with many examples, of symmetry elements and point groups.)

It can also be mentioned here that, since the sum of the diagonals of a transformation matrix is known as the *character* of the transformation matrix, these tables summarizing symmetry behavior are known as the *character tables* for the symmetry point groups.

The character table for any point group can be deduced by finding the transformation matrices for various motions of a molecule belonging to that point group.   Little difficulty will be encountered in checking some of the smaller, nondegenerate character tables by this method.   A number of general properties of character tables will, however, be developed later, and it will then be easier to understand the larger character tables containing degenerate types.

The introductory summary of molecular symmetry has now been completed.   Before making use of the quantities introduced here, an extensive digression into some of the general mathematical properties of the transformation matrices and character tables will be made.   We will then see how the character table can be used to deduce some results that are of great importance in molecular spectroscopy.

GROUP THEORY

An apparently rather abstract mathematical subject called group theory turns out to be directly applicable to investigations of a number of properties of symmetric molecules.   The theory can, for example, deal with the symmetry operations that have been treated in the preceding section and can be used to draw a number of important deductions regarding the nature of the vibrations of symmetric molecules and the electronic properties and electronic transitions of such molecules. Some of the mathematical features that can be ascribed to general, or abstract, groups will be pointed out, and deductions of properties of such groups, which are important for molecular spectroscopy, will be made.   The previous treatment of symmetry elements and symmetry operations provides material with which some of the general group-theory results can be illustrated.

8-4. The Nature of a Group

To be a mathematically useful term, the word group must be given a more precise definition than the meaning, a collection of items, usually associated with it.   To be a mathematical group, a set of elements, which can be objects, quantities, operations, and so forth, must conform to four requirements. It should, perhaps, be pointed out immediately that these requirements may appear "unreal." That they make the term group a useful mathematical concept will be apparent as our study of the theory that can be built up for groups develops.

A set of elements P, Q, R, S, . . . is said to form a group if the following conditions are satisfied:

1. There is a rule for combining any two elements of the group; and the combination of any two elements according to this rule leads to the formation of one of the elements of the group. Commonly one calls the combination procedure multiplication although, as we will see, the procedure need not be the familiar multiplication. When the elements P and Q are combined one writes PQ. The first requirement for a group is that there be a rule which makes the combination PQ meaningful and, moreover, makes PQ equal to an element of the group.

2. The associative law must hold for the combination of elements. Thus if $P(QR)$ means that Q and R are multiplied, i.e., combined according to the appropriate rule, and then P multiplies the element formed from QR, the associative law requires

$$P(QR) = (PQ)R \qquad (6)$$

The right-hand side implies that P and Q are first combined and that the element they form is then combined with R.

(It should here be mentioned that the commutative law will *not* be stipulated as a requirement for a group. Thus PQ will not necessarily be equal to QP. One must, therefore, be careful to preserve the order in which elements are written.)

3. The set must contain an identity element, which we will designate by E. An identity element E is an element with the properties such that

$$EP = PE = P$$
$$EQ = QE = Q \qquad (7)$$
$$ER = RE = R$$

and so forth, for all elements of the group. (Note that the element E does commute with all elements of the group.)

4. For every element of the group there must exist an inverse which is also an element of the group. An inverse is defined so that if S, for example, is the inverse of Q

$$QS = SQ = E \qquad (8)$$

The inverse of the element Q will sometimes be designated as Q^{-1} and, for the set of elements of which Q is a member to be a group, Q^{-1} must be one of the elements of the group. (Notice that an element and its inverse do commute.)

8-5. The Symmetry Operations as a Group

The rules that must be obeyed by a set of elements if they are to constitute a group can now be illustrated by the symmetry operations for a molecule of a particular symmetry, i.e., belonging to a given point group.

The H_2O molecule was seen to have the symmetry C_{2v}, and the symmetry operations for such a molecule are those corresponding to the symmetry elements E, C_2, σ_v, and σ_v'. These operations will be recognized as forming a group if the rule of combination is successive operation on the molecule by the symmetry operations. (One generally agrees if, for example, the combination $C_2\sigma_v$ is written to operate first with the element on the right, i.e., σ_v, and then with the element on the left, i.e., C_2.) Let us now see if the symmetry operations conform to the requirements of a group.

1. One can verify, by operating on various rotational and translational motions of H_2O, that successive operations are always equivalent to the single operation of one of E, C_2, σ_v, or σ_v'. Thus

$$EC_2 = C_2 \qquad \sigma_v\sigma_v' = C_2$$
$$C_2\sigma_v = \sigma_v' \tag{9}$$
$$C_2\sigma_v' = \sigma_v \qquad \text{etc.}$$

2. The associative law is tested by investigating such combinations as

$$\sigma_v'(C_2\sigma_v) \,?\, (\sigma_v'C_2)\sigma_v$$

We find

$$\text{Left side} = \sigma_v'(C_2\sigma_v) = \sigma_v'(\sigma_v') = E$$
$$\text{Right side} = (\sigma_v'C_2)\sigma_v = (\sigma_v)\sigma_v = E \tag{10}$$

In a similar manner it can be verified that various ways of associating the elements in a sequence of operations lead to the same element; i.e., they obey the associative law.

3. The identity operation, in which no change is imposed on the molecule, has been included in the set of symmetry operations so that these operations will constitute a group. It is apparent that

$$EC_2 = C_2E = C_2 \qquad \text{etc.} \tag{11}$$

4. To satisfy the inverse requirement, every element must be such that there is some other element of the group which, written before or after the first element, produces the identity. For the C_{2v} point group we see that

$$C_2C_2 = E$$
$$\sigma_v\sigma_v = E \qquad (12)$$
$$\sigma_v'\sigma_v' = E$$

Thus, and this will not generally be so, each element of the C_{2v} group is its own inverse, and the fourth requirement is satisfied.

Exercise 8-2. Verify by drawing the appropriate displacement diagrams that two successive symmetry operations on a translation or rotation of the H_2O molecule are equivalent to a single symmetry operation of the molecule and that this single symmetry operation is a member of the C_{2v} point group.

We have shown, therefore, that the set of symmetry operations conforms to the requirements for a group, i.e., they are a group. In a similar manner, the symmetry operations associated with other point groups can be tested. It will be found that these sets of symmetry operations similarly obey the group requirements.

Exercise 8-3. Using T_z as a basis on which to apply the group operations, verify that the elements of the C_{3v} group do, in fact, obey the group postulates.

Exercise 8-4. Using T_x and T_y as a basis, verify that the elements of the C_{3v} group obey the group postulates.

Any deduction that can be made about the elements of a group is, therefore, binding on the symmetry operations of a molecule. It is this result that ties abstract group theory to problems involving molecular symmetry.

8-6. Representations of a Group

Of particular importance for the purposes to which group theory is to be put is the fact that the elements of a group, such as the symmetry operations of a molecule, can be represented by numbers, or more generally matrices, and these can then be combined by ordinary multiplication. *For the representation to be true, or faithful, the multiplication of the numbers representing elements P and Q of the group must, if PQ = R, lead to the number which represents the element R.* A set of numbers, or matrices, which can be assigned to the elements of a group and can properly represent the multiplications of the elements of the group is said to constitute a *representation* of the group.

Again the symmetry operations of the C_{2v} point group can be used to illustrate this feature. Customarily, representations are designated by Γ and the components of a particular Γ are written under the group elements that they represent. An apparently trivial but, in fact, important representation of the C_{2v} group of symmetry operations can be constructed by assigning $+1$ to each element. Thus one would write

	E	C_2	σ_v	σ_v'
Γ_1	(1)	(1)	(1)	(1)

(The parentheses are placed about each number because, as we will see, they are one-by-one matrices.) Since any combination of symmetry operations leads to one of the symmetry operations of the group, this is properly represented by the multiplication

$$(1)(1) = (1) \tag{13}$$

Three other one-by-one representations (the way in which they were deduced will be shown shortly) can also be written and a table of representations can be constructed. Thus the representations Γ_1, Γ_2, Γ_3, and Γ_4 can be given as

	E	C_2	σ_v	σ_v'
Γ_1	(1)	(1)	(1)	(1)
Γ_2	(1)	(1)	(−1)	(−1)
Γ_3	(1)	(−1)	(1)	(−1)
Γ_4	(1)	(−1)	(−1)	(1)

It can easily be verified that these representations all properly represent the set of the symmetry operations of the point group C_{2v}. To do this one writes, for example,

$$C_2\sigma_v = \sigma_v'$$

and investigates the ways in which the various representations of the group correspond to this equality. Thus

For the Γ_1 representation: $(1)(1) = (1)$
For the Γ_2 representation: $(1)(-1) = (-1)$
For the Γ_3 representation: $(-1)(1) = (-1)$
For the Γ_4 representation: $(-1)(-1) = (1)$

The result of the four multiplications is seen, in each case, to give the number which that representation attaches to σ_v'. A similar test of other combinations will show that multiplication of the symmetry operations is always faithfully represented.

Exercise 8-5. Test that the representations of the C_{2v} group faithfully represent the multiplication of several pairs of symmetry operations.

While these simple representations might have been discovered by trial and error, it is interesting to see that they are nothing more than the transformation matrices discovered for H_2O in Sec. 8-3. We must now see why such transformation matrices should form a representation of the group of symmetry operations.

It is necessary to show, for example, that the transformation matrix for $C_2\sigma_v$ is equal to the simple product of the transformation matrices for C_2 and σ_v. To do this, one might investigate the operation equation

$$C_2\sigma_v(T_x) = \sigma_v'(T_x) \tag{14}$$

The operation of σ_v on T_x will give $(+1)T_x$, and one can write

$$C_2\sigma_v(T_x) = C_2(+1)T_x \tag{15}$$

The operation C_2 acts only on T_x and cannot affect the pure number $(+1)$. This implies that $(+1)$ and C_2 can be written in either order, i.e., they commute, and one can write

$$C_2\sigma_v(T_x) = (+1)C_2(T_x) = (+1)(-1)(T_x) = (-1)T_x \tag{16}$$

In this way one sees that, if C_2 is represented by (-1) and σ_v by $(+1)$, the combination $C_2\sigma_v$ is represented by the simple multiple

$$(+1)(-1) = (-1)$$

Furthermore, since as Table 8-4 shows, the operation σ_v' on T_x changes the direction of the T_x displacement vectors, one represents $\sigma_v'(T_x)$ by $(-1)T_x$. This example shows that, if C_2 and σ_v are represented by transformation matrices, the product $C_2\sigma_v = \sigma_v'$ will be properly represented by the product of the transformation matrices of C_2 and σ_v. It follows, therefore, and this is an illustration of a general result, that the combination of symmetry operations corresponds to simple multiplication of the corresponding transformation matrices and that this combination is faithfully represented by transformation matrices.

Although the transformation matrices dealt with so far do form representations of the group, they do not form the only representations. There are, in fact, an infinite number of representations. These generally are square matrices of various orders. Some of these that might be built up from those of the previous table are

E	C_2	σ_v	σ_v'
$\begin{pmatrix} 1 & 0 \\ 0 & 1 \end{pmatrix}$	$\begin{pmatrix} 1 & 0 \\ 0 & 1 \end{pmatrix}$	$\begin{pmatrix} 1 & 0 \\ 0 & 1 \end{pmatrix}$	$\begin{pmatrix} 1 & 0 \\ 0 & 1 \end{pmatrix}$
$\begin{pmatrix} 1 & 0 & 0 \\ 0 & 1 & 0 \\ 0 & 0 & 1 \end{pmatrix}$	$\begin{pmatrix} 1 & 0 & 0 \\ 0 & 1 & 0 \\ 0 & 0 & 1 \end{pmatrix}$	$\begin{pmatrix} 1 & 0 & 0 \\ 0 & 1 & 0 \\ 0 & 0 & 1 \end{pmatrix}$	$\begin{pmatrix} 1 & 0 & 0 \\ 0 & 1 & 0 \\ 0 & 0 & 1 \end{pmatrix}$
$\begin{pmatrix} 1 & 0 \\ 0 & 1 \end{pmatrix}$	$\begin{pmatrix} 1 & 0 \\ 0 & 1 \end{pmatrix}$	$\begin{pmatrix} 1 & 0 \\ 0 & -1 \end{pmatrix}$	$\begin{pmatrix} 1 & 0 \\ 0 & -1 \end{pmatrix}$

and so forth. Again one can verify that these form faithful representations of the group $\mathbf{C}_{2v}$.

Other large matrix representations can be found. A particularly important one for a given molecule is that based on the $3n$ cartesian displacement coordinates that can be associated with the atoms of the molecule. Such a representation can be set up by writing the $3n$ cartesian coordinates as a column matrix and deducing, by looking at a diagram of the molecule and the $3n$ displacement vectors, the $3n \times 3n$ transformation matrix for the particular operation. For example, in view of Fig. 8-7, the operation σ_v on H_2O can be seen to lead to the trans-

FIG. 8-7 The effect of the σ_v symmetry operation on the $3n$ cartesian displacement coordinates of H_2O. One sees, for example, that x_H transforms as shown into $x_{H'}$ and that $x_H' = x_{H'}$.

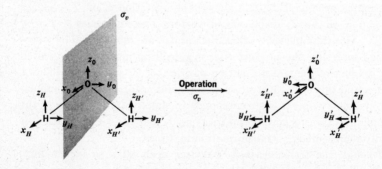

formation matrix

$$\sigma_v \begin{pmatrix} x_H \\ y_H \\ z_H \\ x_{H'} \\ y_{H'} \\ z_{H'} \\ x_0 \\ y_0 \\ z_0 \end{pmatrix} = \begin{pmatrix} 0 & 0 & 0 & 1 & 0 & 0 & 0 & 0 & 0 \\ 0 & 0 & 0 & 0 & -1 & 0 & 0 & 0 & 0 \\ 0 & 0 & 0 & 0 & 0 & 1 & 0 & 0 & 0 \\ 1 & 0 & 0 & 0 & 0 & 0 & 0 & 0 & 0 \\ 0 & -1 & 0 & 0 & 0 & 0 & 0 & 0 & 0 \\ 0 & 0 & 1 & 0 & 0 & 0 & 0 & 0 & 0 \\ 0 & 0 & 0 & 0 & 0 & 0 & 1 & 0 & 0 \\ 0 & 0 & 0 & 0 & 0 & 0 & 0 & -1 & 0 \\ 0 & 0 & 0 & 0 & 0 & 0 & 0 & 0 & 1 \end{pmatrix} \begin{pmatrix} x_H \\ y_H \\ z_H \\ x_{H'} \\ y_{H'} \\ z_{H'} \\ x_0 \\ y_0 \\ z_0 \end{pmatrix}$$

The corresponding transformation matrices for the other operations of the group can similarly be found. In this way one would obtain a representation of the C_{2v} group consisting of four $3n \times 3n$ matrices.

Exercise 8-6. Verify that the transformation matrices for a given molecular motion provide faithful representations of the symmetry operations of the C_{3v} group. Do this for the one-by-one matrices that are obtained when T_z or R_z is considered and also for the two-by-two matrices that are obtained on the basis of (T_x, T_y) or (R_x, R_y).

8-7. Reducible and Irreducible Representations

In the preceding section it was shown that representations of small dimension, such as those involving one-by-one matrices, could be built up to give any number of representations involving matrices of larger dimension. Of much more importance is the process by which a large-dimension matrix representation, such as the $3n \times 3n$ one based on cartesian displacements, is broken down into representations which consist of matrices with as small a dimension as possible. Representations that can be so broken down are said to be *reducible representations*, and those which involve matrices whose dimensions cannot be further decreased are said to be *irreducible representations*. We will find that for any given group, although there are an infinite number of reducible representations, there will be only a few irreducible representations.

Suppose that the set of large-dimension matrices $E, A, B, C, \ldots$ forms a representation of the group. New matrices can be obtained from these by what are called similarity transformations. Thus, if there is a square matrix β, with an inverse β^{-1}, matrix multiplications can be performed to give

$$A' = \beta^{-1}A\beta$$
$$B' = \beta^{-1}B\beta \tag{17}$$
$$C' = \beta^{-1}C\beta \quad \text{etc.}$$

The new matrices will now be shown to be also a representation of the group with A' representing the group element that A did, B' the element that B did, and so forth. It is necessary to show that if $AB = D$, then $A'B' = D'$. To do this we substitute the expressions which led to A', B', and D' into the equation

$$A'B' = D' \tag{18}$$

and obtain

$$\beta^{-1}A\beta\beta^{-1}B\beta = \beta^{-1}D\beta \tag{19}$$

Now since β and β^{-1} are the inverse of each other, i.e.,

$$\beta\beta^{-1} = E = \begin{pmatrix} 1 & 0 & 0 & \cdots \\ 0 & 1 & 0 & \cdots \\ 0 & 0 & 1 & \cdots \\ \cdots\cdots\cdots\cdots \end{pmatrix} \tag{20}$$

and since $EB = B$, one has, from Eq. (19),

$$\beta^{-1}AB\beta = \beta^{-1}D\beta \tag{21}$$

Now we can multiply both sides of this equation, on the left by β and on the right by β^{-1}. Since $\beta\beta^{-1} = \beta^{-1}\beta = E$, one has

$$AB = D \tag{22}$$

Thus $A'B' = D'$ is equivalent to $AB = D$, and the new matrices, connected to the old ones by a similarity transformation, also form a representation of the group.

Now it might be possible to find a transformation matrix such that all the matrices A', B', . . . are of the form

$$A' = \begin{pmatrix} (a_1) & 0 & 0 & \cdots \\ 0 & (a_2) & 0 & \cdots \\ 0 & 0 & (a_3) & \cdots \\ \cdots\cdots\cdots\cdots\cdots\cdots \end{pmatrix} \tag{23}$$

$$B' = \begin{pmatrix} (b_1) & 0 & 0 & \cdots \\ 0 & (b_2) & 0 & \cdots \\ 0 & 0 & (b_3) & \cdots \end{pmatrix} \quad \text{etc.}$$

where $a_1, b_1, c_1, \ldots$ are square matrices of the same dimension, a_2, b_2, c_2 are square matrices of the same dimension, and so forth. If such transformations can be performed, the previous multiplication result

$$AB = D \quad \text{or} \quad A'B' = D'$$

becomes, since matrices are equal only if their corresponding elements are equal,

$$a_1b_1 = d_1$$
$$a_2b_2 = d_2 \qquad\qquad\qquad (24)$$
$$a_3b_3 = d_3$$

It follows that $a_1, b_1, c_1, \ldots$; $a_2, b_2, c_2, \ldots$; and so forth, also form representations of the group. Since they are composed of matrices of smaller dimension than $A, B, C, \ldots$ or $A', B', C', \ldots$, the representation is said to have been reduced by the similarity transformation. If it is not possible to find a matrix β that will further reduce all the matrices of a given representation, the representation is said to be irreducible.

The transformation matrices deduced for the C_{2v} and C_{3v} point groups in Sec. 8-3 are irreducible representations. They are, as will be shown later, the only irreducible representations for these groups. Any other matrix representation can be reduced to one or more of these irreducible representations by a suitable similarity transformation.

8-8. The Irreducible Representations as Orthogonal Vectors

We come now to some of the most important properties common to all irreducible representations. Before proceeding to a general statement of these properties, it might be helpful to illustrate these properties by reference to the irreducible representations of the C_{2v} and C_{3v} point groups.

First it is necessary to define the *order of a group* as the number of elements in the group. The symbol g will be used to represent the order of a group. From the treatment of the C_{2v} and C_{3v} groups in Sec. 8-3, it should be apparent that their orders are 4 and 6, respectively.

As the heading of this section suggests, the elements of the irreducible representations behave like the components of orthogonal vectors. The orthogonality property requires that, if $\Gamma_i(R)$ is the matrix which represents the Rth symmetry operation of the group in the ith irreducible representation,

$$\sum_R \Gamma_1(R)\Gamma_2(R) = 0$$
$$\sum_R \Gamma_1(R)\Gamma_3(R) = 0 \qquad \text{etc.} \qquad\qquad (25)$$

Inspection of the irreducible representation table for C_{2v} confirms this property which, in general, can be represented as

$$\sum_R \Gamma_i(R)\Gamma_j(R) = 0 \qquad \text{for } i \neq j \tag{26}$$

Furthermore, each representation of the C_{2v} group corresponds to the components of a vector normalized to a value equal to the order of the group, i.e.,

$$\sum_R \Gamma_1(R)\Gamma_1(R) = 4$$
$$\sum_R \Gamma_2(R)\Gamma_2(R) = 4 \qquad \text{etc.} \tag{27}$$

Let us now see if these orthogonality and normalization properties also apply to the C_{3v} group where degeneracy occurs and one of the irreducible representations is a two-by-two matrix. One can test the orthogonality condition for all the representations only by treating separately each component of the two-by-two matrix. Thus one can notice that if the elements of the first representation listed in Table 8-5, which we will now label as Γ_1, multiply, for example, the first row, first column elements of the third representation Γ_3, the sum of the products is again zero. Likewise the sum of the squares of the elements of Γ_1 or of Γ_2 gives the value 6, the order of the group. However, the sum of the squares of any component of the matrices of Γ_3, the entries in the first row, first column, for example, gives the value 3, the order of the group divided by 2, for any component.

These results for the C_{2v} and C_{3v} groups are examples of an important general property of irreducible representations. If $\Gamma_i(R)_{mn}$ designates the mnth component of the ith representation for the R symmetry operation and $\Gamma_j(R)_{m'n'}$ designates the $m'n'$ component of the jth representation for the R symmetry operation, the general properties, which have been illustrated, can be expressed as

$$\sum_R \Gamma_i(R)_{mn}\Gamma_j(R)_{m'n'} = 0 \qquad i \neq j$$
$$\sum_R \Gamma_i(R)_{mn}\Gamma_i(R)_{m'n'} = 0 \qquad m \neq m', \, n \neq n' \tag{28}$$

and

$$\sum_R \Gamma_i(R)_{mn}\Gamma_i(R)_{mn} = \frac{g}{l_i} \tag{29}$$

where g is the order of the group and l_i is the dimension of the ith irreducible representation.

The proof that these relations are always obeyed by irreducible representation will not be given here. It is presented in some detail in Appendix II of ref. 1.

One important characteristic of the set of irreducible representations that exist for a point group can be immediately drawn from the fact that the irreducible representations, or their components if they are two-by-two or three-by-three matrices, behave as orthogonal vectors in a g dimensional space. By analogy with two- and three-dimensional space, it is apparent that one can have only as many orthogonal vectors as one has dimensions in space. Thus in g dimensional space there can only be g orthogonal vectors. The four one-by-one representations of the $\mathbf{C}_{2v}$ group given in Table 8-4 form, therefore, a complete set for this fourth-order group. Likewise, for the sixth-order $\mathbf{C}_{3v}$ group, the two one-by-one and one two-by-two matrices, the latter contributing four "vectors," given in Table 8-5, form a complete set. One sees that we now have a proof that there are no irreducible representations other than those that have already been reported for these point groups. One has a way of determining when one has found all the irreducible representations of a group.

Exercise 8-7. Verify that the elements of the transformation matrix representations of the $\mathbf{C}_{2v}$ group behave like orthogonal vectors. Do the same for the matrices of the representations of the $\mathbf{C}_{3v}$ group.

8-9. Characters of Representations

The characters of the matrices of a representation are defined as the sums of the diagonal terms of the matrices. It turns out that the characters rather than the complete matrices can be used for many important deductions. This fact introduces a considerable simplification into the applications of group theory.

The character of a representation of the Rth symmetry operation is denoted by $\chi(R)$. The definition of the character can then be written as

$$\chi(R) = \sum_m \Gamma(R)_{mm} \tag{30}$$

where Γ without a subscript implies a representation that is not necessarily irreducible. If Γ_i is the ith irreducible representation, one writes

$$\chi_i(R) = \sum_m \Gamma_i(R)_{mm} \tag{31}$$

We have already seen, in Sec. 8-7, that if a set of matrices that constitutes a representation is subjected to a similarity transformation the new set of matrices that is obtained is also a representation for the group. Now we will show that, although the similarity transformation changes the matrices, it leaves, if the similarity transformation matrices are orthogonal and normal, the characters of the matrices unaltered. [The derivation, involving more matrix manipulation than previous work, need not be followed through. The student can proceed directly to the result, Eq. (38).]

We wish to show that if P and Q are matrices related by the similarity transformation

$$Q = \beta^{-1}P\beta \tag{32}$$

then

$$\chi_Q = \chi_P \tag{33}$$

If the process of matrix multiplication involved in $\beta^{-1}P\beta$ is written out explicitly, one expresses the ith diagonal element of Q by

$$Q_{ii} = \sum_{kl} (\beta^{-1})_{ik} P_{kl} (\beta)_{li} \tag{34}$$

Now, since β is presumed to be an orthonormal matrix,

$$(\beta^{-1})_{ik} = (\beta')_{ik} = (\beta)_{ki} \tag{35}$$

where β' indicates the transposed β matrix. Equation (34) can now be written as

$$Q_{ii} = \sum_{kl} (\beta)_{ki}(\beta)_{li}P_{kl} \tag{36}$$

Finally, the sum of the diagonal elements of Q is obtained as

$$\begin{aligned}
\sum_i Q_{ii} &= \sum_{i,k,l} (\beta)_{ki}(\beta)_{li}P_{kl} \\
&= \sum_{kl} \sum_i [(\beta)_{ki}(\beta)_{li}]P_{kl} \\
&= \sum_k \delta_{kl}P_{kl} \\
&= \sum_k P_{kk}
\end{aligned} \tag{37}$$

[The Kroeniker δ, defined such that δ_{kl} equals 1 for $k = l$ and 0 for $k \neq l$, has been used to express the result of $\sum_i (\beta)_{ki}(\beta)_{li}$ which corresponds to the product of two rows of the orthonormal matrix β].

We have now reached the desired result

$$\chi_Q = \chi_P \tag{38}$$

This important result will be used when we investigate the irreducible representations that can be obtained from a reducible one. We see that if the breaking down of the large reducible representation is depicted by

$$\begin{pmatrix} & & & \\ & & & \\ & & & \\ & & & \end{pmatrix} \rightarrow \begin{pmatrix} (\ ) & 0 & 0 & 0 \\ 0 & (\ ) & 0 & 0 \\ 0 & 0 & (\ ) & 0 \\ 0 & 0 & 0 & (\ ) \end{pmatrix}$$

the character of the partially diagonalized matrix will be the same as that of the original matrix. Alternatively, one can say that *the sum of the characters of the irreducible representations that can be obtained from a reducible representation will be the same as the character of the reducible representation*. This result will be of great value.

Inspection of the characters of the representations of the C_{2v} and C_{3v} groups will show that the characters, like the representation matrices themselves, behave as orthogonal vectors. The general expression for their behavior can be written as

$$\sum_R \chi_i(R)\chi_j(R) = 0 \qquad \text{for } i \neq j \tag{39}$$

and

$$\sum_R \chi_i(R)\chi_i(R) = g \tag{40}$$

The proof of these character relations is easily given. We have, from the results on irreducible representations,

$$\sum_R \Gamma_i(R)_{mm}\Gamma_j(R)_{m'm'} = 0 \qquad \text{for } i \neq j \tag{41}$$

$$\sum_R \Gamma_i(R)_{mm}\Gamma_i(R)_{mm} = \frac{g}{l_i} \tag{42}$$

where l_i is the order of the matrices of the ith representation. If the sums of the diagonal elements are now taken, one maintains the orthogonality result of the first expression because of the orthogonality of the components that are summed when the characters are formed. Similarly, the product of the characters of one representation by itself can be written out, in view of Eq. (29), in terms of the diagonal components that are involved as

$$\sum_{m=i}^{l_i} \left[\sum_R \Gamma_i(R)_{mm}\Gamma_i(R)_{mm} \right] = l_i \left(\frac{g}{l_i} \right) = g \qquad (43)$$

In this way the result of Eq. (40) is obtained.

The expressions of Eqs. (39) and (40) give properties of the characters of two representations as one goes across a character table, i.e., one sums over the various operations of the group. It is interesting to notice also that one can relate the number of irreducible representations to the characters that appear in the column under the identity element of the group. This follows from the fact that the character of the representation of the identity operation is equal to the order of the representation. The square of this number gives the number of "vectors," as discussed in Sec. 8-8, that the representation contributes. In view of the discussion at the end of Sec. 8-8, one can write, therefore,

$$\chi_1^2(E) + \chi_2^2(E) + \cdots + \chi_c^2(E) = g \qquad (44)$$

where c is the number of representations in the group.

In almost all group-theory applications, as we will see, it will be possible to make use of the characters of the representations and the relations involving the characters that have been obtained here rather than the representations themselves.

Exercise 8-8. Verify that the characters of the C_{2v} and C_{3v} groups, given in Tables 8-4 and 8-6, behave in the manner indicated by Eqs. (39) and (40).

Exercise 8-9. Verify that the C_{2v} and C_{3v} group characters behave according to Eq. (44).

8-10. Classes

One further concept, that of classes of symmetry operations, simplifies group-theory applications. Inspection of the character table for the C_{3v} group shows that the characters of the representations for C_3 and C_3^2 are identical and those for σ_v, σ_v', and σ_v'' are also identical. The operations C_3 and C_3^2 are said to belong to one class of symmetry operations, and the operations σ_v, σ_v', and σ_v'' are said to belong to another class. The identity operation, having characters unlike that of any other operation, belongs to a class by itself. Similarly, since all four symmetry operations of the C_{2v} group have different columns of characters, each belongs to a class by itself.

In abstract group theory a class consists of a set of elements, say P and Q, of the group which, when subjected to the operation

$$X^{-1}PX \quad \text{and} \quad X^{-1}QX$$

where X is in turn all the elements of the group, gives a result which is a member of the set, i.e., is P or Q.

This general definition can be applied to C_3 and C_3^2 to show that they constitute a class in the group $\mathbf{C}_{3v}$. The following combinations are investigated, and the operation to which they are equivalent is noted:

$$E^{-1}C_3E = C_3 \qquad E^{-1}C_3^2E = C_3^2$$
$$C_3^{-1}C_3C_3 = C_3 \qquad C_3^{-1}C_3^2C_3 = C_3$$
$$(C_3^2)^{-1}C_3C_3^2 = C_3^2 \qquad (C_3^2)^{-1}C_3^2C_3^2 = C_3^2$$
$$\rho_v^{-1}C_3\sigma_v = C_3^2 \qquad \sigma_v^{-1}C_3^2\sigma_v = C_3$$
$$(\sigma_v')^{-1}C_3\sigma_v' = C_3^2 \qquad (\sigma_v')^{-1}C_3^2\sigma_v' = C_3$$
$$(\sigma_v'')^{-1}C_3\sigma_v'' = C_3^2 \qquad (\sigma_v'')^{-1}C_3^2\sigma_v'' = C_3$$

We see that, when C_3 and C_3^2 are subject to a similarity type operation by all the elements of the group, the result is either C_3 or C_3^2. Thus C_3 and C_3^2 constitute a class. In a similar way one could verify that E by itself and σ_v, σ_v', and σ_v'' form classes.

When the multiplication of the representation matrices replaces the corresponding combinations of symmetry operations, the previous result *that a similarity transformation leaves the character of a matrix unchanged can be used to deduce that the representations of all members of a class have the same characters.* The matrix of each member of a class is transformed into another member of the class by at least one of the transformation matrices. It follows that these two matrices must have the same character. *In this way all members of a class can be seen to have the same characters for all irreducible representations.*

It is this result that allows character tables to include only typical elements of each class rather than all the elements of the class. The number of elements in the class is, however, indicated as was done in the $\mathbf{C}_{2v}$ and $\mathbf{C}_{3v}$ character tables.

The detailed working out of the combination $X^{-1}PX$ is not usually necessary in order to decide which symmetry operations belong to a class. Geometric consideration will usually be sufficient, and one will find that rotations such as C_3 and C_3^2 and reflections through similar planes such as σ_v, σ_v', σ_v'' constitute classes.

When the character table is written with the characters for the different classes exhibited rather than the character for all symmetry operations exhibited, the character table is a square array. That this must be so can be shown from the fact that, if allowance is made for the number of elements, say n, in each class, the characters behave as orthogonal vectors in a space with dimension equal to that of the number of different classes. If R now denotes a typical symmetry element of its class, Eqs. (39) and (40) can be written as

$$\sum_{\substack{\text{Over} \\ \text{all classes}}} [\sqrt{n_R}\chi_i(R)][\sqrt{n_R}\chi_j(R)] = 0 \qquad \text{for } i \neq j \tag{45}$$

and

$$\sum_{\substack{\text{Over} \\ \text{all classes}}} [\sqrt{n_R}\chi_i(R)][\sqrt{n_R}\chi_i(R)] = g \tag{46}$$

Thus the $\sqrt{n_R}\chi_i(R)$ terms behave as components of orthogonal vectors, and there can be only as many such vectors as the dimensionality of the space allows. Thus we conclude that there can be only as many representations as there are classes. This conclusion is parallel, it should be recalled, to the previous one that there can be only as many representation vectors, counting one for a one-by-one representation, four for a two-by-two, and so forth, as there are symmetry elements. It should also be mentioned that the factors n_R are usually placed at the top of the character table rather than as part of the characters themselves, but this does not alter the argument given here.

8-11. Analysis of a Reducible Representation

The final aspect of abstract group theory that must be dealt with before we can proceed to some applications is the question as to whether, given a reducible representation, there is any convenient way to deduce what irreducible representations make up the reducible one. In Sec. 8-7 it was pointed out that, in principle, one could find a similarity transformation to convert the reducible representation to a form in which the irreducible representations appeared explicitly. In practice there is no convenient way of finding the transformation matrix that accomplishes this. There is, however, a simple and important procedure for discovering how many times each of the irreducible representations occurs in a given reducible representation.

Since any reducible representation can, in principle, be reduced to the irreducible representations that it contains by a similarity transformation, which leaves the character unchanged, one can write

$$\chi(R) = \sum_{j=1}^{c} a_j\chi_j(R) \tag{47}$$

where $\chi(R)$ is a reducible representation, $\chi_j(R)$ are the c irreducible representations of the group, and the a_j's are the number of times the jth irreducible representation occurs in the reducible representation. We first multiply both sides of this equation by $\chi_i(R)$ and then sum over all symmetry operations R.   In this way we obtain

$$\sum_R \chi(R)\chi_i(R) = \sum_R \sum_{j=1}^{c} a_j\chi_{j(R)}\chi_{i(R)} \tag{48}$$

Now the results of Eqs. (39) and (40), that

$$\sum_R \chi_i(R)\chi_j(R) = \begin{cases} 0 & \text{for } i \neq j \\ g & \text{for } i = j \end{cases} \tag{49}$$

can be used on the right side of Eq. (48) to convert Eq. (48) to

$$\sum_R \chi(R)\chi_i(R) = a_i g$$

or

$$a_i = \frac{1}{g} \sum_R \chi(R)\chi_i(R) \tag{50}$$

Thus, if the characters of a reducible representation are known, and the characters of the irreducible representations are available from a character table, the number of times each irreducible representation occurs in the reducible representation can be readily calculated.

The above expression requires the summation over all symmetry operations.   It is more convenient to have the corresponding expression where the summation is over all classes of symmetry operations.   For this one writes

$$a_i = \frac{1}{g} \sum_{\substack{\text{Over} \\ \text{all classes}}} n_R \chi(R)\chi_i(R) \tag{51}$$

where n_R is the number of elements in the class for which a typical operation is R.

We now have the basic results from abstract group theory and can proceed to apply them to problems in molecular spectroscopy and molecular structure.

The methods of application will be illustrated in the remainder of the chapter with problems based on molecular vibrations.   Similar applications to electronic structure and electronic spectra will be made in Chap. 11 when these subjects are studied.

Exercise 8-10. The characters of a reducible representation of the C_{2v} group are 4, 0, -2, $+2$ for the classes of E, C_2, σ_v, and σ_v'. Deduce the irreducible representations that the reducible representation is made up of.

Exercise 8-11. Deduce the irreducible representations contained in the reducible representation of the C_{3v} group which has the characters 7, 1, and -1 for the classes of E, C_3, and σ_v.

8-12. The Characters for the Reducible Representation of Molecular Motion

The effect of the symmetry operations on the motions of a molecule could be represented by the transformation matrices that show how the $3n$ normal coordinates (including translations and rotations) are changed when the various symmetry operations are performed. These transformation matrices would constitute a reducible representation. The $3n$ normal coordinates are said to form a basis for the representation of the group. Since each normal coordinate must transform according to an irreducible representation, or a degenerate set must transform according to two, three, etc., dimensional representations, the irreducible representations that make up the $3n$ dimensional representation are of particular interest. It follows that it is only necessary to see how many times the various irreducible representations occur in the reducible representation to discover how many of the $3n$ normal coordinates belong to the various symmetry species, i.e., transform according to the various irreducible representations.

We cannot, however, construct the reducible representation on the basis of the normal coordinates because these are generally initially unknown (except for the translations and rotations). A helpful result that overcomes this difficulty is that which states: if two representations of a group differ only in their basis coordinates and if the coordinates of one base are linear combinations of those of the other base, the two representations are said to be equivalent and the characters of the two representations are equal. (The result is based on the fact that two such representations can be shown to be related by a similarity transformation.) With this theorem one can resort to the much simpler procedure of constructing the reducible representation on the basis of the $3n$ cartesian displacement coordinates. Such transformation matrices were deduced for the H_2O molecule in Sec. 8-6. The character of this representation, which is found rather easily, will be the same as that for the representation based on the $3n$ normal coordinates.

To obtain the character of the $3n$ dimensional representation for the molecule being studied, it is not necessary to write out the complete matrices. It is only necessary to deduce the elements that appear on the diagonals of these matrices. To show how this can easily be done, we again consider the transformation matrices, which constitute the reducible representation, for H_2O. The $3n$ cartesian coordinate vectors are indicated as

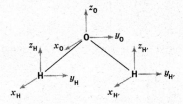

The matrices which describe the transformations by equations of the type

$$
\begin{pmatrix} x'_H \\ y'_H \\ z'_H \\ x'_{H'} \\ y'_{H'} \\ z'_{H'} \\ x'_0 \\ y'_0 \\ z'_0 \end{pmatrix} = \begin{pmatrix} & & \\ & \text{Transformation matrix} & \\ & & \end{pmatrix} \begin{pmatrix} x_H \\ y_H \\ z_H \\ x_{H'} \\ y_{H'} \\ z_{H'} \\ x_0 \\ y_0 \\ z_0 \end{pmatrix}
$$

can be found by inspection of diagrams such as that shown for the symmetry operation σ_v in Fig. 8-7. The four transformation matrices for the H_2O molecule are found to be

$$
E
$$

$$
\begin{pmatrix}
1 & 0 & 0 & 0 & 0 & 0 & 0 & 0 & 0 \\
0 & 1 & 0 & 0 & 0 & 0 & 0 & 0 & 0 \\
0 & 0 & 1 & 0 & 0 & 0 & 0 & 0 & 0 \\
0 & 0 & 0 & 1 & 0 & 0 & 0 & 0 & 0 \\
0 & 0 & 0 & 0 & 1 & 0 & 0 & 0 & 0 \\
0 & 0 & 0 & 0 & 0 & 1 & 0 & 0 & 0 \\
0 & 0 & 0 & 0 & 0 & 0 & 1 & 0 & 0 \\
0 & 0 & 0 & 0 & 0 & 0 & 0 & 1 & 0 \\
0 & 0 & 0 & 0 & 0 & 0 & 0 & 0 & 1
\end{pmatrix}
$$

$$C_2$$

$$\begin{pmatrix}
0 & 0 & 0 & -1 & 0 & 0 & 0 & 0 & 0 \\
0 & 0 & 0 & 0 & -1 & 0 & 0 & 0 & 0 \\
0 & 0 & 0 & 0 & 0 & 1 & 0 & 0 & 0 \\
-1 & 0 & 0 & 0 & 0 & 0 & 0 & 0 & 0 \\
0 & -1 & 0 & 0 & 0 & 0 & 0 & 0 & 0 \\
0 & 0 & 1 & 0 & 0 & 0 & 0 & 0 & 0 \\
0 & 0 & 0 & 0 & 0 & 0 & -1 & 0 & 0 \\
0 & 0 & 0 & 0 & 0 & 0 & 0 & -1 & 0 \\
0 & 0 & 0 & 0 & 0 & 0 & 0 & 0 & 1
\end{pmatrix}$$

$$\sigma_v$$

$$\begin{pmatrix}
0 & 0 & 0 & 1 & 0 & 0 & 0 & 0 & 0 \\
0 & 0 & 0 & 0 & -1 & 0 & 0 & 0 & 0 \\
0 & 0 & 0 & 0 & 0 & 1 & 0 & 0 & 0 \\
1 & 0 & 0 & 0 & 0 & 0 & 0 & 0 & 0 \\
0 & -1 & 0 & 0 & 0 & 0 & 0 & 0 & 0 \\
0 & 0 & 1 & 0 & 0 & 0 & 0 & 0 & 0 \\
0 & 0 & 0 & 0 & 0 & 0 & 1 & 0 & 0 \\
0 & 0 & 0 & 0 & 0 & 0 & 0 & -1 & 0 \\
0 & 0 & 0 & 0 & 0 & 0 & 0 & 0 & 1
\end{pmatrix}$$

$$\sigma_v'$$

$$\begin{pmatrix}
-1 & 0 & 0 & 0 & 0 & 0 & 0 & 0 & 0 \\
0 & 1 & 0 & 0 & 0 & 0 & 0 & 0 & 0 \\
0 & 0 & 1 & 0 & 0 & 0 & 0 & 0 & 0 \\
0 & 0 & 0 & -1 & 0 & 0 & 0 & 0 & 0 \\
0 & 0 & 0 & 0 & 1 & 0 & 0 & 0 & 0 \\
0 & 0 & 0 & 0 & 0 & 1 & 0 & 0 & 0 \\
0 & 0 & 0 & 0 & 0 & 0 & -1 & 0 & 0 \\
0 & 0 & 0 & 0 & 0 & 0 & 0 & 1 & 0 \\
0 & 0 & 0 & 0 & 0 & 0 & 0 & 0 & 1
\end{pmatrix}$$

One should first notice that *diagonal elements occur only if the symmetry operation leaves the position of an atom unchanged.* One can deduce the character of the representation matrix, therefore, by concerning oneself only with the cartesian displacement vectors of the atoms that do not change positions as a result of the symmetry operation. With this recognition and the fact that the vectors of unchanged atoms in molecules like H_2O are left unchanged or are reversed and that these effects lead to $+1$ and -1, respectively, along the diagonal, one can write down, by inspection of the displacement vector diagram, the result

C_{2v}	E	C_2	σ_v	σ_v'
x	9	-1	1	3

The sums of the diagonal elements of the complete transformation matrices given above confirm these values.

One might further notice that simple, general statements can be made about such characters. When an atom is unchanged in position as a result of a C_2 operation, it will contribute a net -1 contribution to the C_2 character. Similarly, if any atom is unchanged in position by a reflection through a plane, it will contribute a $+1$ to the appropriate σ character. Furthermore, if a molecule has a center of symmetry and an atom is situated at this center, its position will be unchanged by inversion at the center of symmetry, all three cartesian coordinate vectors will be reversed, and a contribution of -3 will be made to the character. Slightly more difficult to visualize are the characters contributed by atoms when, as a result of a C_3, C_4, and so forth, rotation their positions are unchanged. Figure 8-8 shows the geometry that leads to the transformation matrices and the contributions to the character in such cases.

FIG. 8-8   The contributions for each unshifted atom, i.e., each atom on the axis, to the character of the $3n$ dimensional representation for the operations C_n and S_n.

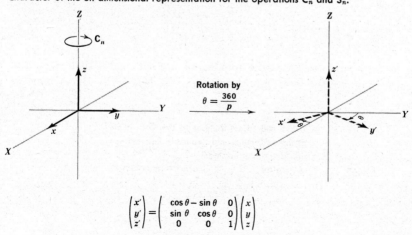

$$\begin{pmatrix} x' \\ y' \\ z' \end{pmatrix} = \begin{pmatrix} \cos\theta & -\sin\theta & 0 \\ \sin\theta & \cos\theta & 0 \\ 0 & 0 & 1 \end{pmatrix} \begin{pmatrix} x \\ y \\ z \end{pmatrix}$$

$x_{\text{(Rotation by }\theta)} = (1 + 2\cos\theta)$

$x_{\text{(Rotation by }\theta\text{ and reflection through plane perpendicular to axis)}} = (-1 + 2\cos\theta)$

With these generalizations we can summarize the contributions that unshifted atoms make to the characters of the reducible representation of order $3n$. This is done in Table 8-8. With these recipes, one can readily write down the characters of the reducible representation without making the cartesian displacement diagram and visualizing the effect of the various symmetry operations.

Exercise 8-12. Deduce the characters of the $3n$ dimension representation for molecules of the type CH_3X.

8-13. Number of Normal Modes of Various Symmetry Types

In the previous section it was shown that the $3n$ dimensional representation for a molecule could easily be set up, and in Sec. 8-11 it was shown that the number of times the various irreducible representations are contained in a reducible representation could be deduced. These results, along with the fact that each normal mode, including translation and rotation as well as vibration, transforms according to one of the irreducible representations, allow the number of normal modes of the different symmetry types, i.e., belonging to the different reducible representations, to be determined.

The H_2O example can again be used. The characters of the irreducible representations are given in the character table, Table 8-4.

The characters of the reducible representation were given in the previous section as

	E	C_2	σ_v	σ_v'
χ	9	-1	1	3

Now one calculates the number of normal modes that transform according to the first representation, i.e., belong to the symmetry

TABLE 8-8 Contributions to the Characters of the $3n$ Dimensional Reducible Representation per Unshifted Atom

Operation	Character contribution
E	3
σ	1
i	-3
C_2	-1
C_3^1, C_3^2	0
C_4^1, C_4^3	1
C_6^1, C_6^5	2

type A_1, by application of Eq. (51).   Thus

$$a_1 = \frac{1}{g} \sum_{\substack{\text{Over} \\ \text{all classes}}} n_R \chi(R) \chi_1(R)$$

$$= \tfrac{1}{4}[9 - 1 + 1 + 3] = 3$$

Similarly,

$$a_2 = \tfrac{1}{4}[9 - 1 - 1 - 3] = 1$$
$$a_3 = \tfrac{1}{4}[9 + 1 + 1 - 3] = 2$$

and   (52)

$$a_4 = \tfrac{1}{4}[9 + 1 - 1 + 3] = 3$$

These results can be summarized by saying that the reducible representation contains representations of the symmetry types according to

$$\Gamma = 3A_1 + A_2 + 2B_1 + 3B_2 \tag{53}$$

If the assigned translations and rotations, indicated in the last column of Table 8-4, are removed, one has

$$\Gamma_{\text{vib}} = 2A_1 + B_2 \tag{54}$$

There are, therefore, two vibrations of the symmetry type A_1 and one of the symmetry type B_2.   One can verify that the displacements displayed for H_2O in Fig. 6-3 do, in fact, transform according to these symmetry types.

In a similar way one can classify the normal modes of any molecule. The importance of such classifications is perhaps more apparent for molecules of the type CH_3X because of the previous discussion of rotation-vibration band contours which pointed out the great difference, i.e., parallel and perpendicular bands, of the different types of vibrations.

Exercise 8-13.   Determine the number of normal vibrations of the various symmetry types for the molecule CH_3Cl.

8-14. The Infrared Active Fundamentals

It is apparent that some vibrations of symmetric molecules, such as the symmetric stretching mode of CO_2, i.e., $\leftarrow O{=}C{=}O \rightarrow$, have no oscillating dipole moment and therefore cannot interact with electromagnetic radiation.   Furthermore, the necessarily zero oscillating dipole moment is a result of the symmetry of the molecule and the symmetry type of the vibration.   It is possible, as we will now see, to decide for which symmetry types the fundamental transition will be active, i.e., for which symmetry type the oscillating dipole moment will not necessarily be zero.

As was pointed out in Sec. 4-5, a fundamental vibrational transition, from $v = 0$ to $v = 1$, can occur with the absorption of electromagnetic radiation in the vibrational energy-level pattern corresponding to the normal coordinate Q_i only if one of the integrals

$$\int \psi_0(Q_i)\mu_x\psi_1(Q_i)\, d\tau$$
$$\int \psi_0(Q_i)\mu_y\psi_1(Q_i)\, d\tau$$
or
$$\int \psi_0(Q_i)\mu_z\psi_1(Q_i)\, d\tau$$

is nonzero. A nonzero integral leads to a nonzero value for integrated absorption coefficient, as indicated by Eq. (4-46). Since this band intensity is an observable quantity, it must have the same value for all indistinguishable orientations of the molecule. It follows that for any of the three transition moment integrals to have a nonzero value, *the value of the integral must be unchanged for all symmetry operations on the molecule.* It is now necessary to see the effect of symmetry operations on the quantities in the integrals and then on the complete integrals.

The dipole components can be represented by the charge separations shown in Fig. 8-9. It should be clear that these dipole components will transform under the various symmetry operations in exactly the same way as do the displacement arrows representing T_x, T_y, and T_z. It follows that the representations Γ_{μ_x}, Γ_{μ_y}, and Γ_{μ_z} will be the same as the representations Γ_{T_x}, Γ_{T_y}, and Γ_{T_z}.

The vibrational wave function for a molecule can be described as

$$\psi_{\text{vib}} = \varphi(Q_1)\varphi(Q_2)\varphi(Q_3) \cdots \varphi(Q_{3n-6}) \tag{55}$$

For the ground state, where all vibrational quantum numbers are zero,

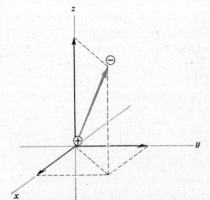

FIG. 8-9 The dipole-moment vector of a molecule and its components along the cartesian axes.

one has

$$\psi_{(v=0)} = \varphi_0(Q_1)\varphi_0(Q_2)\varphi_0(Q_3) \cdot \cdot \cdot \varphi_0(Q_{3n-6}) \tag{56}$$

For harmonic oscillator wave functions this total wave function has the form, in view of the wave functions of Eq. (2-45),

$$\psi_{(v=0)} = \text{const} \, [e^{-\gamma_1 Q_1{}^2} e^{-\gamma_2 Q_2} \cdot \cdot \cdot e^{-\gamma_{(3n-6)} Q^2{}_{(3n-6)}}] \tag{57}$$

where $\gamma_k = 2\pi\nu_k/h$. Now the effect of a symmetry operation on $\psi_{v=0}$ can be investigated. For nondegenerate vibrations $Q_i \rightarrow \pm Q_i$, and since only the squares of Q's occur in the expression, the nondegenerate terms in $\psi_{v=0}$ are unchanged by the symmetry operation. Degenerate vibrations, a doubly degenerate pair, for example, have the same value of ν_k and therefore of γ_k. A degenerate pair contributes terms of the type $e^{-\gamma_k Q_k{}^2} e^{-\gamma_k Q_l{}^2} = e^{-\gamma_k(Q_k{}^2 + Q_l{}^2)}$. In Sec. 6-4 it was shown that a symmetry operation on a degenerate set of vibrations left the value of $Q_k^2 + Q_l^2$ unchanged. It follows, therefore, that all symmetry operations on $\psi_{v=0}$ lead to $\psi_{v=0}$, i.e., *the ground vibrational state is invariant under all symmetry operations.*

The wave functions for a molecule in which the wave function corresponding to Q_i is excited to the $v = 1$ state is of the form

$$\psi_{v_i=1} = (\text{const})(Q_i)(\psi_{v=0}) \tag{58}$$

which follows because the $v = 1$ wave function is of the form

$$\varphi_{v_i=1} = (\text{const})'Q_i e^{-\gamma_i Q_i{}^2}$$

In this case, where $v_i = 1$, the wave function for the molecule transforms according to the normal coordinate Q_i. Similarly, if a degenerate pair of vibrations are excited to the $v = 1$ level, the vibrational wave function of the molecule will transform as does the degenerate pair of normal coordinates.

These results can now be summarized according to the effect of the symmetry operation R as

$$\begin{aligned}
\mu_x &\xrightarrow{R} \Gamma_{T_x}(R)\mu_x \\
\mu_y &\xrightarrow{R} \Gamma_{T_y}(R)\mu_y \\
\mu_z &\xrightarrow{R} \Gamma_{T_z}(R)\mu_z \\
\psi_{v=0} &\xrightarrow{R} \psi_{v=0} \\
\psi_{v_i=1} &\xrightarrow{R} \Gamma_{Q_i}(R)\psi_{v_i=1}
\end{aligned} \tag{59}$$

The result of the R symmetry operation on the transition-moment integrals can, therefore, be written as

$$\int \psi_{v=0}\mu_x\psi_{v_i=1} \, d\tau \xrightarrow{R} \Gamma_{T_x}(R)\Gamma_{Q_i}(R)\int \psi_{v=0}\mu_x\psi_{v_i=1} \, d\tau \qquad (60)$$

and so forth.   The previous result that all symmetry operations must leave the integral unchanged if it has a nonzero value means that $\Gamma_{T_x}(R)\Gamma_{Q_i}(R)$ must be unity for each and every symmetry operation.

The normalization and orthogonality characteristics of representations show that only if Γ_{T_x} and Γ_{Q_i} are identical representations can the product of $\Gamma_{T_x}(R)$ and $\Gamma_{Q_i}(R)$ be unity for every R.   It follows that *the transition moment integral for the $v = 0$ to $v = 1$ transition for a given normal coordinate can be different from zero only if the normal coordinate belongs to the same symmetry species as T_x, T_y, or T_z.*

With this result and an analysis of how many normal coordinates belong to the various symmetry species, one can determine the number of infrared active fundamental transitions that can occur for a molecule of a given symmetry.   The argument can, it should be mentioned, sometimes be turned around so that the geometry, and therefore the symmetry, of a molecule is determined from the number of infrared absorption bands that are observed.

(It will only be mentioned that whether or not a fundamental transition can lead to a Raman shift can be deduced in a similar manner. The requirement for a Raman shift is that at least one of the integrals of the type

$$\int \psi_0(Q_i)\alpha_{xx}\psi_1(Q_i) \, d\tau \qquad \int \psi_0(Q_i)\alpha_{xy}\psi_1(Q_i) \, d\tau \qquad \text{etc.}$$

be nonzero.   Furthermore, the polarizability components α_{xx}, α_{xy}, etc., can be shown to transform as the product of the representations for the translations indicated in the subscript on α.   It is for this reason that character tables sometimes show the symmetry species of T_xT_x, T_xT_y, etc. In a manner similar to that used to investigate transition-moment integrals one can show that for a fundamental transition to be Raman active the normal coordinate must belong to the same symmetry species as one of T_xT_x, T_xT_y, and so forth.)

Exercise 8-14.   Which of the CH_3Cl vibrations will lead to absorption bands corresponding to fundamental transitions, and which of these will be parallel and which perpendicular vibrations?

8-15. The Symmetry of Group Vibrations

Many molecules have groups of atoms that vibrate rather independently of the remainder of the molecule.   The hydrogen atoms, since their mass is usually so much less than that of the other atoms of the molecule, often lead to such vibrations. It turns out that in such a case the vibrations of the molecule can be treated, or at least visualized, in terms of separate vibrations of the molecular skeleton and vibrations of the hydrogen atoms of the molecule. This separation is of great aid in assigning the observed infrared absorption bands to normal vibrations of a molecule. A discussion of the molecule CCl_3—CH_2—CCl_3 will illustrate the procedure.

The molecule probably belongs to the C_{2v} point group. Let us first calculate the types of the vibrations of the molecule without the two hydrogen atoms. The characters of the reducible representation for this nine-atom residue can be worked out, with the aid of Table 8-4, to be

	E	C_2	σ_v	σ_v'
χ	27	-1	1	5

The number of vibrations of the different symmetry types of this heavy-atom fragment can now be calculated as

$$
\begin{aligned}
a_1 &= \tfrac{1}{4}[27 - 1 + 1 + 5] = 8 \\
a_2 &= \tfrac{1}{4}[27 - 1 - 1 - 5] = 5 \\
a_3 &= \tfrac{1}{4}[27 + 1 + 1 - 5] = 6 \\
a_4 &= \tfrac{1}{4}[27 + 1 - 1 + 5] = 8
\end{aligned}
\tag{61}
$$

Removal of the translations and rotations shows that the representation for the vibrations is composed of

$$\Gamma_{\text{vib}} = 7A_1 + 4A_2 + 4B_1 + 6B_2 \tag{62}$$

The same treatment with the entire molecule, i.e., including the two hydrogen atoms, gives

$$\Gamma_{\text{vib}} = 9A_1 + 5A_2 + 6B_1 + 7B_2 \tag{63}$$

The additional two hydrogen atoms introduce, therefore, vibrations of the types

$$\Gamma_{\text{H atoms}} = 2A_1 + A_2 + 2B_1 + B_2 \tag{64}$$

(This same result could have been obtained by writing down the contributions to the reducible representation that the two hydrogen atoms make and then resolving this representation into the irreducible representations that it contains.)

Pictures can now be drawn to represent the six hydrogen vibrations. Exact indications of how the atoms move in the normal coordinates cannot be made without the lengthy calculations that will be introduced in the following chapter. It is, however, helpful to recognize that each hydrogen atom introduces one vibration that is essentially a C—H stretching vibration and two vibrations that are essentially bending ones. With this approach the six diagrams of Fig. 8-10 can be drawn for the methylene vibrations. These vibrations can be expected to occur, more or less disturbed and altered, in any molecule that contains a CH_2 group. In a similar manner one can represent the vibrations characteristic of a CH_3 group. When such *group vibrations* are recognized, it is often possible to reach an initial understanding of some of the absorption bands of the absorption spectrum of quite complicated molecules containing CH_2 and CH_3 groups.

FIG. 8-10 Vibrations of the CH_2 group classified according to symmetry. The form of the actual vibrations and the frequencies of the fundamental absorption bands depend somewhat on the nature of the molecule containing the CH_2 group.

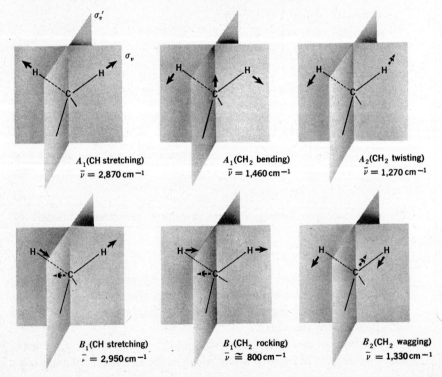

A_1(CH stretching)
$\bar{\nu} = 2{,}870 \, \text{cm}^{-1}$

A_1(CH$_2$ bending)
$\bar{\nu} = 1{,}460 \, \text{cm}^{-1}$

A_2(CH$_2$ twisting)
$\bar{\nu} = 1{,}270 \, \text{cm}^{-1}$

B_1(CH stretching)
$\bar{\nu} = 2{,}950 \, \text{cm}^{-1}$

B_1(CH$_2$ rocking)
$\bar{\nu} \cong 800 \, \text{cm}^{-1}$

B_2(CH$_2$ wagging)
$\bar{\nu} = 1{,}330 \, \text{cm}^{-1}$

Exercise 8-15. Analyze the symmetries of the vibrations of a —CH_3 group, and draw diagrams to represent these vibrations. Classify the diagrams according to symmetry type and bending or stretching nature.

PRINCIPAL REFERENCES

1. Eyring, H., J. Walter, and G. E. Kimball: "Quantum Chemistry," John Wiley & Sons, Inc., New York, 1948.
2. Bellamy, L. J.: "The Infrared Spectra of Complex Molecules," John Wiley & Sons, Inc., New York, 1954.
3. Wigner, E. P.: "Group Theory," Academic Press, Inc., New York, 1959.

9   CALCULATION OF VIBRATIONAL FREQUENCIES AND NORMAL COORDINATES OF POLYATOMIC MOLECULES

It has been shown in Chap. 6 that certain natural, or normal, vibrations will occur in a many-particle system and that these normal vibrations are characterized by particle motions that are in phase and have the same frequency. In a molecular system each normal vibration leads to a vibrational energy-level pattern and, if the selection rules permit, an absorption band corresponding to the $v = 0$ to $v = 1$ transition in that energy-level pattern will be observed. Furthermore, weaker bands, due to overtones and combinations of fundamentals, may be observed.

For a diatomic molecule only one vibration occurs, only one vibrational energy-level pattern exists, and only one fundamental transition is observed spectroscopically. The frequency of this transition was, in Chap. 2, related to the force constant and the reduced mass of the molecule. It is now necessary to see how the frequencies of the $3n - 6$ fundamental transitions of a polyatomic molecule are related to the force constants and atomic masses of the molecule. We will also be interested in determining how the molecule vibrates, i.e., what the form of the normal coordinate is, in each one of the normal vibrations. When all this can be accomplished for a particular molecule, its infrared absorption spectrum, which may look like those of Figs. 2-1 and 7-1, is said to be analyzed or understood.

202

The treatment of diatomic molecules in Chap. 2 anticipated the use of Lagrange's equation rather than the $f = ma$ relation in calculations for polyatomic molecules. With this approach it is necessary to set up expressions for the kinetic energy T and the potential energy U of the molecule. After an initial discussion of how this can be done for a polyatomic molecule, the form of the equations that result from substitution of these functions in Lagrange's equation will be considered. Following consideration of these general features, some typical, simple examples will be worked through. Finally, the more systematic methods developed by Wilson for performing such calculations will be outlined.

9-1. The Kinetic-energy Expression for a Polyatomic Molecule

The kinetic energy that is here of interest is that due to the vibrations of the atoms of the molecule relative to each other. This contribution to the kinetic energy of the molecule can be treated in terms of coordinates that measure the positions of the atoms relative to a set of axes that move with the molecule as it undergoes translational and rotational motion. If the jth atom is located, in terms of these axes, by x_j, y_j, and z_j, the kinetic energy due to the vibrations of the molecule can be immediately written down as

$$T = \tfrac{1}{2} \sum_{j=1}^{n} m_j(\dot{x}_j^2 + \dot{y}_j^2 + \dot{z}_j^2) \tag{1}$$

This expression is the basis for the treatment of kinetic energy in vibrational problems. One should note that the orthogonality of the cartesian displacement coordinates results in an expression that contains squared terms and no cross products.

It is important to remember that a motion described as a vibration must not involve a net translation or rotation of the molecule. This requirement is imposed by requiring that no movement of the center of gravity of the molecule and that no angular momentum be imparted to the molecule by the velocity components $\dot{x}_j$, $\dot{y}_j$ and $\dot{z}_j$. In this way the kinetic-energy expression of Eq. (1) can be used along with the relations

$$\sum_{j=1}^{n} m_j\dot{x}_j = 0 \qquad \sum_{j=1}^{n} m_j\dot{y}_j = 0 \qquad \sum_{j=1}^{n} m_j\dot{z}_j = 0 \tag{2}$$

and

$$\sum_{i=1}^{n} m_j(y_j\dot{z}_j - z_j\dot{y}_j) = 0 \qquad \sum_{j=1}^{n} m_j(z_j\dot{x}_j - x_j\dot{z}_j) = 0$$

$$\sum_{j=1}^{n} m_j(x_j\dot{y}_j - y_j\dot{x}_j) = 0 \tag{3}$$

(The separation of vibration from translation and rotation suggested here is treated in a more rigorous manner in ref. 1.)

9-2. The Potential-energy Expression for a Polyatomic Molecule

The potential energy of a molecule is a function of the distortion of the molecule from its equilibrium configuration. It follows that displacement coordinates which show the change in the geometry of a molecule from its equilibrium configuration will form a suitable base for a potential-energy expression. This might be done in a number of ways. One approach would be to base the description of the geometry on the changes, δr_{ij}, from the equilibrium value of the distances between the nuclei i and j. With this coordinate system and the harmonic-oscillator approximation that assumes it is sufficient to keep only the quadratic terms in the potential-energy function, one might write

$$U = \tfrac{1}{2} \sum_{\substack{i,j=1 \\ i \neq j}}^{n} k_{ij}(\delta r_{ij})^2 \tag{4}$$

For H—O—H′, for example, this would lead to the potential function

$$
\begin{aligned}
U = \ & \tfrac{1}{2}k_{\mathrm{HO}}(\delta r_{\mathrm{HO}})^2 + \tfrac{1}{2}k_{\mathrm{HO}}(\delta r_{\mathrm{H'O}})^2 + \tfrac{1}{2}k_{\mathrm{HH'}}(\delta r_{\mathrm{HH'}})^2 \\
& + k_{\mathrm{HO,H'O}}(\delta r_{\mathrm{HO}})(\delta r_{\mathrm{H'O}}) + k_{\mathrm{HO,HH'}}(\delta r_{\mathrm{HO}})(\delta r_{\mathrm{HH'}}) \\
& + k_{\mathrm{HO,HH'}}(\delta r_{\mathrm{H'O}})(\delta r_{\mathrm{HH'}})
\end{aligned} \tag{5}
$$

where the fact that $k_{\mathrm{HO}} = k_{\mathrm{H'O}}$ has been recognized.

Such formulations, as Eq. (5), of the potential-energy function, while complete, are seldom satisfactory. Many more k_{ij} parameters are introduced than can be evaluated, except in favorable cases, from experimental data. Thus, for H_2O there would be four force constant terms in the potential-energy function, and these could not be determined from the $3n - 6 = 3$ fundamental transition frequencies that are observed spectroscopically. It is necessary, therefore, to attempt to find a way in which the change in the potential energy of the molecule as the molecule is distorted can be described without recourse to this most general quadratic potential function expression. Two different points of view as to the dimensions of the molecule that are most important in determining the potential energy have been used to approach this goal. These ideas led to the early use of the *central force field*, generally favored by physicists, and the *valence-bond force field*, more frequently used by chemists.

The central force field assumes that the change in potential energy that occurs when a molecule is distorted from its equilibrium position can best be described by terms in the potential-energy expression, each of which involves a force constant and a square of an internuclear distance.   Thus, for H — O — H' the simple central-force-field expression for the potential energy would be

$$U = \tfrac{1}{2}k_{\text{HO}}(\delta r_{\text{HO}})^2 + \tfrac{1}{2}k_{\text{HO}}(\delta r_{\text{H'O}})^2 + \tfrac{1}{2}k_{\text{HH}}(\delta r_{\text{HH'}})^2 \tag{6}$$

where δr_{HO}, $\delta r_{\text{H'O}}$, and $\delta r_{\text{HH'}}$ represent changes from the designated equilibrium internuclear distances.   The assumption of a central force field, therefore, reduces the number of terms in the description of the potential energy of the H_2O molecule to two, i.e., k_{HO} and $k_{\text{HH'}}$.

The valence-bond force field assumes that the potential energy of a distorted molecule can best be described in terms of the changes in length of chemical bonds and changes in angles between chemical bonds from their equilibrium values.   With this approach one would attempt to describe the potential-energy function of H_2O by the expression

$$U = \tfrac{1}{2}k_{\text{HO}}(\delta r_{\text{HO}})^2 + \tfrac{1}{2}k_{\text{HO}}(\delta r_{\text{H'O}})^2 + \tfrac{1}{2}k_{\alpha}(\delta \alpha)^2 \tag{7}$$

where $\delta \alpha$ is the change in the angle between the two bonds from its equilibrium value and, as before, δr_{HO} and $\delta r_{\text{H'O}}$ are changes of the HO and H'O bond lengths from their equilibrium values.   Again only two force constants appear in this simplified potential-energy expression. [Frequently one writes the final term of Eq. (7) as $\tfrac{1}{2}k_{\alpha}'(r_0\delta\alpha)^2$ so that k_{α}', like k_{HO}, will have the units of dynes per centimeter.   The two force constants k_{α} and k_{α}' are related by $k_{\alpha}' = k_{\alpha}/r_0^2$.]

As we will see later in the chapter, the absorption band frequencies corresponding to the fundamental transitions of H_2O can be used to deduce values of the constants in the potential-energy expression.   In fact, one can determine the two force constants in the previous potential-energy expressions so that the calculated frequencies are close to two of the observed absorption band frequencies.   The success of the potential function can then be judged by how well the calculated value of the third frequency agrees with that observed.   When such calculations are performed it is clear that neither simplified potential function is completely satisfactory.   The results suggest, however, that the valence-bond field is usually the preferable approach to a satisfactory potential function.

One can, if the available spectroscopic data warrant, add additional quadratic terms to improve on the simple force fields. Thus one might add a bond stretching–angle bending interaction constant to the simple valence-bond potential and write

$$U = \tfrac{1}{2}k_{HO}(\delta r_{HO})^2 + \tfrac{1}{2}k_{HO}(\delta r_{H'O})^2 + \tfrac{1}{2}k_\alpha(\delta\alpha)^2$$
$$+ \tfrac{1}{2}k_{HO,\alpha}(\delta\alpha\, \delta r_{HO} + \delta\alpha\, \delta r_{H'O}) \tag{8}$$

This function will certainly provide a better description for the way in which the potential energy varies with molecular distortion. Unless, however, one makes use of the spectra of isotopically substituted species, there is no way of verifying its success.

The significance of the various force constants can best be seen by determining the force that would act to restore a bond distance or angle to its equilibrium distance. Thus, one might investigate the force acting to restore the angle between the bonds of H_2O to its equilibrium value and obtain

$$\text{Restoring force on } \delta\alpha = -\frac{\partial U}{\partial(\delta\alpha)} = k_\alpha(\delta\alpha) + \tfrac{1}{2}k_{HO,\alpha}(\delta r_{HO} + \delta r_{H'O})$$

$$\tag{9}$$

One sees that the added terms allow for a restoring force to act on angular displacements, not only as the result of these displacements, but also as a result of changes in the bond lengths from their equilibrium distances. Furthermore, it seems reasonable, and turns out to be so, that interaction terms, such as $k_{HO,\alpha}$ should generally be small and need not always have positive signs.

Exercise 9-1. Write expressions for the potential-energy function for NH_3 on the basis of (a) the simple valence-bond force field and (b) the simple central force field.
Exercise 9-2. Draw a diagram showing a displacement of the atoms of the H_2O molecule from their equilibrium positions that would lead to a calculated increase in the potential energy that would be different for the simple valence-bond and central-force-field approximations.

Finally, it should be mentioned that a potential function, based on what is called a Urey-Bradley field, is now often used when fairly simple molecules are dealt with and several different isotopically substituted species can be studied. This field combines the features of both the central force field and the valence-bond field. It has, therefore, terms involving the distortion of chemical bond lengths and angles and also terms depending on the distances between nonbonded atoms.

9-3. Use of Lagrange's Equation in Molecular-vibration Problems

The motion of particles constrained by certain forces, i.e., subject to a particular potential-energy function, can, as pointed out in Chap. 2, be determined by application of Newton's $f = ma$ relation or, more conveniently, by Lagrange's equation. In the later method, Lagrange's equation is applied to each coordinate needed to describe the system. If a typical coordinate is q_i, one obtains the ith equation as

$$\frac{d}{dt}\left(\frac{\partial T}{\partial \dot{q}_i}\right) + \frac{\partial U}{\partial q_i} = 0 \tag{10}$$

For a vibrating molecule there will be, as we will see, $3n - 6$ such equations. The set of these equations can be solved for the $3n - 6$ vibrational frequencies and modes of vibration.

In order to apply Eq. (10) to a system, it is necessary that both T and U be expressions involving the same set of coordinates. This requirement creates considerable complexity in molecular-vibration problems since, as we have seen in the previous two sections, it is convenient to set up T in cartesian displacement coordinates and U in what are called *internal coordinates*, i.e., bond stretching and either angle bending or internuclear distance type coordinates. Thus, if $R_1, R_2, \ldots, R_{3n-6}$ represent the internal-displacement coordinates, i.e., the coordinates which describe the displacements of the atoms from their equilibrium internuclear distances and the bond angles from their equilibrium values, and the cartesian displacement coordinates are represented by $x_1, x_2, \ldots, x_{3n}$, one usually sets up the expressions

$$T = \frac{1}{2} \sum_{j=1}^{3n-6} m_j \dot{x}_j^2 \tag{11}$$

$$U = \frac{1}{2} \sum_{i,j=1}^{3n-6} k_{ij} R_i R_j \tag{12}$$

(The values of k_{ij} will, of course, generally be unknown at the beginning of the calculation. They generally are evaluated such that the observed frequencies are obtained.)

To proceed from Eqs. (11) and (12) one must be able to express either the R's in terms of the x's or the x's in terms of the R's. The first procedure, as we will see when an example is worked out in the following section, is generally easier to set up since equations of the type

$$R_i = f_i(x_1, \ldots, x_{3n})$$

can often be immediately written down. Transformation of Eqs. (11) and (12) to cartesian coordinates, of which there are $3n$, leads, however, to $3n$ equations when Lagrange's equation is applied. In molecules of any complexity it is usually better to obtain, by one means or another, transformations of the type $x_j = f_j(R_1, \ldots, R_{3n-6})$ and to proceed to solve the problem in terms of the $3n - 6$ internal coordinates. To illustrate how this can be done, a specific example will be worked out in the following section by this approach. It is true, however, that even $3n - 6$ equations become difficult to handle, even for fairly small molecules, and solution by these methods becomes rather troublesome. More systematic ways of handling the problem will be introduced later.

9-4. The Stretching Vibrations of a Linear Triatomic Molecule

A suitable example to illustrate the discussion of the previous sections is that which considers motion of a linear triatomic molecule of the type ①—②—③, i.e., HCN, OCS, and so forth, along the axis of the molecule. The 3 degrees of freedom along this axis will lead to two vibrations, which will involve stretching of the bonds, and one translation. The more general problem of a three-dimensional molecule will differ only in complexity.

The potential energy is best expressed in terms of changes from the equilibrium values of the distances between the atoms of the molecule. If the equilibrium bond lengths are denoted by r_{12}^0 and r_{23}^0 and changes from these values are denoted by δr_{12} and δr_{23}, the potential energy can be written, in the simple valence bond approach, as

$$U = \tfrac{1}{2}k_1(\delta r_{12})^2 + \tfrac{1}{2}k_2(\delta r_{23})^2 \tag{13}$$

More generally we will use R's to indicate internal displacement coordinates, and if we let R_1 represent δr_{12} and R_2 represent δr_{23}, the potential energy function is written as

$$U = \tfrac{1}{2}k_1R_1^2 + \tfrac{1}{2}k_2R_2^2 \tag{14}$$

The kinetic energy expression can be immediately written with respect to a set of axes fixed in space. If x_1, x_2, and x_3 represent the positions of the three atoms along the one-dimensional line of the molecule, as indicated in Fig. 9-1, the kinetic energy for the one-dimensional problem can be immediately written down as

$$T = \tfrac{1}{2}m_1\dot{x}_1^2 + \tfrac{1}{2}m_2\dot{x}_2^2 + \tfrac{1}{2}m_3\dot{x}_3^2 \tag{15}$$

We must now proceed to obtain expressions of the type

$$\dot{x}_1 = f_1(\dot{R}_1, \dot{R}_2)$$
$$\dot{x}_2 = f_2(\dot{R}_1, \dot{R}_2) \qquad (16)$$
$$\dot{x}_3 = f_3(\dot{R}_1, \dot{R}_2)$$

so that the kinetic energy expression of Eq. (15) can be written in terms of the internal coordinates R_1 and R_2. The two types of coordinates are related by the expressions.

$$\delta r_{12} = R_1 = (x_2 - x_1) - r_{12}^0 \qquad (17)$$

and

$$\delta r_{23} = R_2 = (x_3 - x_2) - r_{23}^0 \qquad (18)$$

Furthermore, since r_{12}^0 and r_{23}^0 are molecular properties that are not time dependent, the time derivatives of Eqs. (17) and (18) are

$$\dot{R}_1 = \dot{x}_2 - \dot{x}_1 \qquad (19)$$
$$\dot{R}_2 = \dot{x}_3 - \dot{x}_2 \qquad (20)$$

The ease with which these equations, of the type $\dot{R} = f(\dot{x}_1 \dot{x}_2, \ldots)$, are written is typical, while some further effort, as will be seen, is required to obtain the desired expressions which are of the type $\dot{x} = f(\dot{R}_1 \dot{R}_2 \ldots)$. In the convenient matrix notation, Eqs. (19) and (20) can be written as

$$\begin{pmatrix} \dot{R}_1 \\ \dot{R}_2 \end{pmatrix} = \begin{pmatrix} -1 & 1 & 0 \\ 0 & -1 & 1 \end{pmatrix} \begin{pmatrix} \dot{x}_1 \\ \dot{x}_2 \\ \dot{x}_3 \end{pmatrix} \qquad (21)$$

One cannot immediately solve Eqs. (19) and (20), or Eq. (21), for $\dot{x}_1$, $\dot{x}_2$, and $\dot{x}_3$ in terms of $\dot{R}_1$ and $\dot{R}_2$ because of the occurrence of three cartesian coordinates and two internal coordinates. In the matrix expression, one sees this in the impossibility of taking the inverse of the nonsquare matrix. The desired inverse relations can be obtained, however, if one imposes the condition that the motions to be studied be vibrations and, therefore, that no net linear momentum be involved. Thus one has the

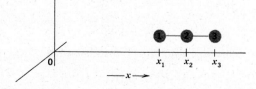

FIG. 9-1. The location of the atoms of a ①—②—③ type molecule moving in one-dimensional space by means of a set of axes fixed in space.

additional relation

$$m_1\dot{x}_1 + m_2\dot{x}_2 + m_3\dot{x}_3 = 0 \tag{22}$$

This expression allows, with Eqs. (19) and (20), or Eq. (21), the expression for $\dot{x}_1$, $\dot{x}_2$, and $\dot{x}_3$ in terms of $\dot{R}_1$ and $\dot{R}_2$ to be obtained. In matrix notation one can add this additional relation to give

$$\begin{pmatrix} \dot{R}_1 \\ \dot{R}_2 \\ 0 \end{pmatrix} = \begin{pmatrix} -1 & 1 & 0 \\ 0 & -1 & 1 \\ m_1 & m_2 & m_3 \end{pmatrix} \begin{pmatrix} \dot{x}_1 \\ \dot{x}_2 \\ \dot{x}_3 \end{pmatrix} \tag{23}$$

Now we can take the inverse of the square matrix to get, with the notation $M = m_1 + m_2 + m_3$, the desired result

$$\begin{pmatrix} \dot{x}_1 \\ \dot{x}_2 \\ \dot{x}_3 \end{pmatrix} = \begin{pmatrix} -\dfrac{(m_2 + m_3)}{M} & \dfrac{-m_3}{M} & \dfrac{1}{M} \\[2mm] \dfrac{m_1}{M} & \dfrac{-m_3}{M} & \dfrac{1}{M} \\[2mm] \dfrac{m_1}{M} & \dfrac{m_1 + m_2}{M} & \dfrac{1}{M} \end{pmatrix} \begin{pmatrix} \dot{R}_1 \\ \dot{R}_2 \\ 0 \end{pmatrix} \tag{24}$$

or one can obtain, by means of the necessary algebraic manipulations, the algebraic equations equivalent to this:

$$\dot{x}_1 = -\frac{(m_2 + m_3)}{M} \dot{R}_1 - \frac{m_3}{M} \dot{R}_2$$

$$\dot{x}_2 = \frac{m_1}{M} \dot{R}_1 - \frac{m_3}{M} \dot{R}_2 \tag{25}$$

$$\dot{x}_3 = \frac{m_1}{M} \dot{R}_1 + \frac{m_1 + m_2}{M} \dot{R}_2$$

Substitution of these expressions into Eq. (15) for T gives, after rearrangement,

$$T = \frac{m_1}{2M^2} (m_2^2 + 2m_2 m_3 + m_3^2 + m_1 m_3)\dot{R}_1^2$$

$$+ \frac{m_1}{2M^2} (2m_3^2 + 2m_1 m_3 + 2m_2 m_3)\dot{R}_1 \dot{R}_2$$

$$+ \frac{m_3}{2M^2} (m_2^2 + 2m_1 m_2 + m_1^2 + m_2 m_3 + m_1 m_3)\dot{R}_2^2 \tag{26}$$

This expression for T together with

$$U = \tfrac{1}{2}k_1 R_1^2 + \tfrac{1}{2}k_2 R_2^2 \tag{27}$$

leads, when Lagrange's equation is applied successively to R_1 and R_2, to

$$\frac{m_1}{M^2}(m_2^2 + 2m_2m_3 + m_3^2 + m_1m_2 + m_1m_3)\ddot{R}_1$$

$$+ \frac{m_1}{2M^2}(2m_3^2 + 2m_1m_3 + 2m_2m_3)\ddot{R}_2 + k_1R_1 = 0 \quad (28)$$

and

$$\frac{m_3}{M^2}(m_2^2 + 2m_1m_2 + m_1^2 + m_2m_3 + m_1m_3)\ddot{R}_2$$

$$+ \frac{m_1}{2M^2}(2m_3^2 + 2m_1m_3 + 2m_2m_3)\ddot{R}_1 + k_2R_2 = 0 \quad (29)$$

One can again see if solutions of the type

$$R_1 = A_1 \cos 2\pi\nu t$$

and

$$R_2 = A_2 \cos 2\pi\nu t \qquad\qquad (30)$$

exist for this pair of equations. Substitution of these trial functions and their second derivatives in Eqs. (28) and (29) leads to the expressions

$$\left[-4\pi^2\nu^2 \frac{m_1}{M^2}(m_2^2 + 2m_2m_3 + m_3^2 + m_1m_2 + m_1m_3) + k_1 \right] A_1$$

$$- \left[4\pi^2\nu^2 \frac{m_1}{2M^2}(2m_3^2 + 2m_1m_3 + 2m_2m_3) \right] A_2 = 0$$

and

$$\qquad\qquad\qquad\qquad\qquad\qquad\qquad\qquad (31)$$

$$- \left[4\pi^2\nu^2 \frac{m_1}{2M^2}(2m_3^2 + 2m_1m_3 + 2m_2m_3) \right] A_1$$

$$+ \left[-4\pi^2\nu^2 \frac{m_3}{M^2}(m_2^2 + 2m_1m_2 + m_1^2 + m_2m_3 + m_1m_3) + k_2 \right] A_2 = 0$$

Again, nontrivial solutions will exist for the A's only if the determinant of the coefficients is zero. This 2×2 determinantal equation leads, on expansion, to a quadratic in ν^2. The two roots of the equation (only positive values are appropriate for ν) give the desired frequencies.

It is now perhaps better to consider a particular case. If, for example, one were studying HCN, one would know from spectroscopic studies that the frequencies of the absorption bands corresponding to the two stretching modes are 2,089 and 3,312 cm^{-1}. One can now choose numerical values of k_1 and k_2 which, when inserted in the determinantal equation arising from Eq. (31) along with the values of the atomic masses, yield roots of the equation with frequencies corresponding to the observed values of 2,089 and 3,312 cm^{-1}. In this way one deduces that the force constants for the bonds in HCN are

$$k_{\text{HC}} = 5.8 \times 10^5 \text{ dynes/cm}$$
$$k_{\text{CN}} = 17.9 \times 10^5 \text{ dynes/cm} \tag{32}$$

Exercise 9-3. Verify that the force constants of Eq. (32) lead, when substituted in Eq. (31), to the observed stretching frequencies of the HCN molecule.

Exercise 9-4. Calculate the positions of the absorption bands due to the stretching vibrations to be expected for DCN.

Frequently one must make the calculation in this direction, i.e., deduce values of the k's to fit known frequencies. Sometimes, however, one can take force constants from some molecules and carry them over to other molecules and thereby reduce frequencies from a calculation of the type illustrated here.

It remains for us to see how a molecule, again the HCN example can be considered, vibrates in the vibrational modes that have the frequencies used in the calculation. One needs, therefore, the relative values of A_1 and A_2 that solve the set of equations, Eq. (31), when ν is $2,089(3 \times 10^{10})$ and ν is $3,312(3 \times 10^{10})$ cycles/sec. The relative values of A_1 and A_2, and thus the form of the vibrations, can be immediately obtained by rearranging Eq. (31). (More generally one takes the ratio of the cofactors of the determinant formed by the coefficients of the A's.) For the HCN example one has

$$\text{For } \bar{\nu} = 2,089 \text{ cm}^{-1} \qquad A_1 : A_2 = 0.405 : 1.00 \tag{33}$$

and

$$\text{For } \bar{\nu} = 3,312 \text{ cm}^{-1} \qquad A_1 : A_2 = 1.00 : -0.137 \tag{34}$$

One can recognize that the first vibration is predominantly one of C—N stretching while the second is predominantly one of C—H stretching.

Exercise 9-5. Draw diagrams illustrating the displacements of the atoms of HCN in the two stretching modes. Do this by attaching arrows to the atoms such that no net translation is given to the molecule and so that the relative amplitudes given by Eqs. (33) and (34) are obeyed.

Exercise 9-6. Deduce relative displacement amplitudes and draw suitable diagrams for the two stretching vibrations of DCN.

Exercise 9-7. Consider the basis for the fact that some calculation was necessary to draw the diagrams of the previous two exercises, whereas in Exercise 6-3 the corresponding vibrations of the CS_2 molecule could be drawn with less calculation.

Exercise 9-8. The fundamental transitions of the stretching modes of OCS lead to absorption bands at 2,050 and 863 cm^{-1}. If a simple potential function like that of Eq. (19) is assumed, what values of the stretching force constants for the C$=$O and C$=$S bonds are calculated?

Calculate the relative distortion amplitudes for the two bonds in each vibration, and draw diagrams to represent the nature of the vibrations.

Exercise 9-9. The fundamental stretching mode transitions of the CO$_2$ molecule correspond to frequencies of 1,388 and 2,349 cm^{-1} (the former is not infrared active). By the procedure outlined in Sec. 9-4, obtain a value for the C$=$O force constant from these data (a) on the basis of a potential function like that of Eq. (13) and (b) on the basis of a potential function that includes a cross term between the two bonds of the molecule.

The above examples, i.e., solution for the stretching modes of a inear X-Y-Z type molecule in internal coordinates, illustrate the procedures that can be used in the general case. It only needs to be mentioned that, when a more than one-dimensional problem is considered, the solution will require the imposition of zero angular momentum as well as zero linear momentum. Thus one imposes, in the general case, the conditions of Eqs. (2) and (3).

It should be apparent from the simple example treated here that the analysis of the vibrations of a molecule with many atoms will involve the solution of equations of high order. This is particularly troublesome when one knows the frequencies and must determine what force constants lead to these frequencies. Considerable simplification results, fortunately, when molecules have elements of symmetry. Some of these features will now be considered.

9-5. Use of Symmetry in Vibrational Problems

The determination of the relation between the force constants and the vibrational frequencies of all but the simplest molecules is frequently feasible only when the simplifications that result from the symmetry of the molecule are recognized. For example, the vibrational problem of benzene involves $3n - 6 = 30$ internal coordinates, and one would be led to a 30×30 determinant of the type that would arise from Eq. (31). On the other hand, if full use is made of the symmetry of the benzene molecule, the problem factors down to one 4×4, one 3×3, and several 2×2 and 1×1 determinants. The calculation is then perfectly feasible.

The basis for the simplifications that symmetry introduces is, as mentioned in Sec. 6-4, the necessary absence of cross terms in the kinetic- and potential-energy expressions if these expressions are set up in terms of symmetry coordinates. These coordinates consist of linear combinations of the cartesian or internal-displacement coordinates. The combinations are such that each symmetry coordinate is symmetric or antisymmetric with respect to each symmetry operation. One recalls that if S_i and S_p are symmetry coordinates that behave differently with respect to any symmetry operation, perhaps $S_i \rightarrow S_i$ and $S_p \rightarrow -S_p$ for a particular operation, then the cross term $\dot{S}_i\dot{S}_p$ must not occur in T and a term involving S_iS_p must not occur in U. If such cross terms did occur, the symmetry operation would convert $\dot{S}_i\dot{S}_p \rightarrow -\dot{S}_i\dot{S}_p$ and $S_iS_p \rightarrow -S_iS_p$ and would alter the kinetic and the potential energies of the molecule. This would be contrary to the conclusion reached in Sec. 6-4 that a symmetry operation cannot result in any change of the kinetic or potential energy of a molecule. The effect of the absence of cross terms between elements of different symmetry types means that the determinant resulting from application of Lagrange's equation to the symmetry coordinates will have blocks of zeros in the off-diagonal positions that correspond to the cross-term positions between the different symmetry coordinates. Thus the determinant has the form

$$
\begin{vmatrix}
\boxed{} & 0 & 0 & 0 \\
0 & \boxed{} & 0 & 0 \\
0 & 0 & \boxed{} & 0 \\
0 & 0 & 0 & \boxed{}
\end{vmatrix} = 0 \tag{35}
$$

where each shaded block will be a subdeterminant of order equal to the number of coordinates of that symmetry type. Since the total determinant will be zero if the determinant of any diagonal block is zero, each block can be set equal to zero and can be solved for the vibrational frequencies of that symmetry type. This reduction in the order of the determinants to be solved is very great in the case of molecules, such as benzene, of high symmetry.

The use of symmetry coordinates can be illustrated by the example of the H_2O molecule. The $3n - 6 = 3$ internal-coordinate problem can be expected to reduce, according to the discussion of Sec. 8-13, to one involving two totally symmetric coordinates, of type A_1, and one antisymmetric coordinate, of type B_2.

We consider the H_2O molecule of Fig. 9-2, and we set up coordinates which not only have the symmetry appropriate to the normal coordinates, i.e., two A_1 and one B_2, but also are such that they involve no translation or rotation of the molecule. Suitable coordinates are represented diagrammatically in Fig. 9-2 by the three figures. The proper relative lengths of the arrows in each figure can be designated by indicating that displacement according to S_1 consists of motion of H and H′ by S_1 units in the directions shown; displacement according to S_2 consists of motions of H and H′ by S_2 units; and O by $2m_H/m_O$ units as shown; and so forth. The relative atomic motions that constitute S_1, S_2, and S_3 are then compatible with the symmetry requirements and involve no translation or rotation. These coordinates are convenient for solving the vibrational problem of the H_2O type molecule.

Again one must write the expressions for T and U in the coordinates in which they can be immediately formulated. We can write, for motion of the molecule in the plane of the molecule,

$$T = \tfrac{1}{2}m_H(\dot{x}_H^2 + \dot{y}_H^2) + \tfrac{1}{2}m_O(\dot{x}_O^2 + \dot{y}_O^2) + \tfrac{1}{2}m_H(\dot{x}_{H'}^2 + \dot{y}_{H'}^2) \qquad (36)$$

and

$$U = \tfrac{1}{2}k_{OH}(\delta r_{OH})^2 + \tfrac{1}{2}k_{OH}(\delta r_{OH'})^2 + \tfrac{1}{2}k_\alpha(\delta\alpha)^2 \qquad (37)$$

FIG. 9-2 Three symmetry coordinates S_1, S_2, and S_3 that are convenient for the calculation of the vibrational frequencies and normal coordinates of the H_2O molecule.

Now it is necessary to have the coordinates $\dot{x}_H$, $\dot{y}_H$, . . . and δr_{OH}, . . . expressed in terms of S_1, S_2, and S_3 so that we can obtain

$$T = t(\dot{S}_1, \dot{S}_2, \dot{S}_3) \tag{38}$$

and

$$U = u(S_1, S_2, S_3) \tag{39}$$

It is first necessary to ask how displacements described by the symmetry coordinates S_1, S_2, and S_3 can lead to motions of the atoms equivalent to x_H, y_H, and so forth. Inspection of Fig. 9-2 allows one to write immediately the velocities that the atoms would have along the cartesian directions in terms of velocity contributions based on the symmetry coordinates as

$$\dot{x}_H = \dot{S}_1 - \dot{S}_3 \sin\alpha; \; \dot{x}_O = \frac{2m_H \dot{S}_3 \sin\alpha}{m_O}; \; \dot{x}_{H'} = -\dot{S}_1 - \dot{S}_3 \sin\alpha$$

$$\dot{y}_H = \dot{S}_2 - \dot{S}_3 \cos\alpha; \; \dot{y}_O = \frac{2m_H \dot{S}_2}{m_O}; \; \dot{y}_{H'} = \dot{S}_2 + \dot{S}_3 \cos\alpha \tag{40}$$

Substitution in Eq. (36) gives, after rearrangement,

$$T = m_H \dot{S}_1^2 + m_H\left(1 + \frac{2m_H}{m_O}\right)\dot{S}_2^2 + m_H\left(1 + \frac{2m_H}{m_O}\sin^2\alpha\right)\dot{S}_3^2 \tag{41}$$

The relation between the internal coordinates and the symmetry coordinates can best be found by first writing the cartesian displacements of the atoms that result in bond stretching and angle bending. Thus

$$\delta r_{OH} = (\delta x_O - \delta x_H)\sin\alpha + (\delta y_O - \delta y_H)\cos\alpha$$

$$\delta r_{OH'} = -(\delta x_O - \delta x_{H'})\sin\alpha + (\delta y_O - \delta y_{H'})\cos\alpha \tag{42}$$

$$\delta\alpha = \frac{1}{r_0}\left[(\delta x_{H'} - \delta x_H)\cos\alpha + (\delta y_{H'} + \delta y_H)\sin\alpha - 2\delta y_O \sin\alpha\right]$$

The expressions for the effect of changes in the symmetry coordinates on the cartesian displacements, written in Eq. (40) for the time element dt, can be used to convert Eqs. (42) to the desired relations

$$\delta r_{OH} = -\sin\alpha S_1 - \cos\alpha\left(1 + \frac{2m_H}{m_O}\right)S_2 + \left(1 + \frac{2m_H}{m_O}\sin^2\alpha\right)S_3$$

$$\delta r_{OH'} = -\sin\alpha S_1 - \cos\alpha\left(1 + \frac{2m_H}{m_O}\right)S_2 - \left(1 + \frac{2m_H}{m_O}\sin^2\alpha\right)S_3$$

$$\delta\alpha = \frac{2}{r_0}\cos\alpha S_1 + \frac{2}{r_0}\sin\alpha\left(1 + \frac{2m_H}{m_O}\sin\alpha\right)S_2 \tag{43}$$

These transformation equations between internal coordinates and symmetry coordinates can be substituted into the expression for U given in Eq. (37) to obtain, after rearrangement,

$$
\begin{aligned}
U = & \left[k_{\text{HO}} \sin^2 \alpha + \frac{2k_\alpha}{r_0^2} \cos^2 \alpha \right] S_1^2 \\
& + \left[k_{\text{HO}} \cos^2 \alpha \left(1 + \frac{2m_{\text{H}}}{m_{\text{O}}} \right)^2 + \frac{2k_\alpha}{r_0^2} \sin^2 \alpha \left(1 + \frac{2m_{\text{H}}}{m_{\text{O}}} \sin \alpha \right)^2 \right] S_2^2 \\
& + \left[2k_{\text{HO}} \sin \alpha \cos \alpha \left(1 + \frac{2m_{\text{H}}}{m_{\text{O}}} \right) \right. \\
& \left. + \frac{4k_\alpha}{r_0^2} \sin \alpha \cos \alpha \left(1 + \frac{2m_{\text{H}}}{m_{\text{O}}} \sin \alpha \right) \right] S_1 S_2 \\
& + k_{\text{HO}} \left[1 + \frac{2m_{\text{H}}}{m_{\text{O}}} \sin^2 \alpha \right]^2 S_3^2
\end{aligned}
\tag{44}
$$

Now that T and U are expressed, by Eqs. (41) and (44), in terms of the symmetry coordinates S_1, S_2, and S_3, Lagrange's equation can be applied to each of these coordinates. Again three equations are obtained, and solutions of the form

$$
\begin{aligned}
S_1 &= A_1 \cos 2\pi\nu t \\
S_2 &= A_2 \cos 2\pi\nu t \\
S_3 &= A_3 \cos 2\pi\nu t
\end{aligned}
\tag{45}
$$

can be sought. Nontrivial solutions of this form are then seen to exist if the determinant composed of the coefficients of the A's is zero.

The elements of the determinant are rather cumbersome, and it is convenient to introduce the notation

$$
T = a_{11}\dot{S}_1^2 + a_{22}\dot{S}_2^2 + a_{33}\dot{S}_3^2
\tag{46}
$$

and

$$
U = b_{11}S_1^2 + 2b_{12}S_1S_2 + b_{22}S_2^2 + b_{33}S_3^2
\tag{47}
$$

where the a's and b's refer to the coefficients of the terms of Eqs. (41) and (44). Furthermore, the customary procedure of designating the term $4\pi^2\nu^2$ by λ will be followed, and this leads to expressions comparable with those shown as Eq. (31) in the internal coordinate treatment of Sec. 9-4. The determinant of the coefficients of the amplitudes A_1, A_2, and A_3 is set equal to zero to give the equation

$$
\begin{vmatrix}
b_{11} - \lambda a_{11} & b_{12} & 0 \\
b_{21} & b_{22} - \lambda a_{22} & 0 \\
0 & 0 & b_{33} - \lambda a_{33}
\end{vmatrix} = 0
\tag{48}
$$

It is clear that the symmetry coordinates have led to the desired breakdown of the 3×3 determinant to a 2×2 and a 1×1 block. The two roots corresponding to the symmetric coordinates result from expansion of the 2×2 subdeterminant. On rearrangement one has

$$\lambda = \frac{1}{2}\left(\frac{b_{11}}{a_{11}} + \frac{b_{22}}{a_{22}}\right) \pm \frac{1}{2}\sqrt{\left(\frac{b_{11}}{a_{11}} - \frac{b_{22}}{a_{22}}\right)^2 + \frac{8b_{12}}{a_{11}a_{22}}} \qquad (49)$$

The third root of the determinantal equation, corresponding to the antisymmetric coordinate, is seen immediately to be $\lambda = b_{33}/a_{33}$.

The above equations can be solved, in a particular case, for the three frequencies of an H_2O type molecule if values of the atomic masses, interbond angle, and force constants are inserted. For the H_2O molecule, for example, the angle between the two H—O bonds has been determined to be 105 deg. One can then verify that the force constants

$$k_{HO} = 7.76 \times 10^5$$

and

$$\frac{k_{\alpha}}{r_0^2} = 0.69 \times 10^5 \qquad \text{dynes/cm}$$

lead to the calculation of frequencies in quite good agreement with the observed values of 3,652 and 1,595 cm^{-1} for the symmetric modes and 3,756 cm^{-1} for the antisymmetric mode.

The form of each of the three normal coordinates can now be determined. One of the roots of Eq. (48) is substituted into the determinant, and for this value of λ, or ν, the ratio $A_1 : A_2 : A_3$ is calculated. When this is done for each of the three roots, one sees that the two symmetric modes can be described by linear combinations of S_1 and S_2 while the antisymmetric normal coordinate is, apart from a constant factor, nothing other than the antisymmetric symmetry coordinate S_3.

Exercise 9-10. Repeat the calculations of Exercise 9-9, but use the method of symmetry coordinates illustrated here.

*9-6. Solution of Vibrational Problems in Internal Coordinates by the Method of Wilson

The treatment illustrated in the previous section can be systematized by an approach introduced by E. B. Wilson [*J. Chem. Phys.*, **9** : 76 (1941)]. This procedure is the basis for many of the calculations of molecular vibrations now being done. The original presentation of Wilson will therefore be elaborated. Additional material on this approach will be found in ref. 1. It should be pointed out that the procedure depends on a familiarity with matrix methods.

The Wilson method sets up both the kinetic and potential energies in terms of the internal coordinates R_k. As has been pointed out, the potential energy can be easily formulated in these coordinates, and one can immediately write the general expression as

$$2U = \sum_{kl} k_{kl}R_kR_l$$

The notation used by Wilson designates the force constants by f_{kl}. We will now follow this notation and write

$$2U = \sum_{kl} f_{kl}R_kR_l$$

or, in matrix notation,

$$2U = R'FR \qquad (50)$$

where R' is the transpose of R.

The general discussion of this section may be clarified if the particular equations appropriate to the ①—②—③ problem studied in Sec. 9-4 are set up to correspond to the general equations given here. Thus Eq. (14) of Sec. 9-4 can be written as

$$2U = (R_1R_2)\begin{pmatrix} k_1 & 0 \\ 0 & k_2 \end{pmatrix}\begin{pmatrix} R_1 \\ R_2 \end{pmatrix}$$

and the matrix F, for this example, is recognized to be

$$\begin{pmatrix} k_1 & 0 \\ 0 & k_2 \end{pmatrix}$$

To set up the kinetic-energy expression, one must start with the cartesian coordinate expression

$$2T = \sum_{i=1}^{3n} m_i\dot{x}_i^2 \qquad (51)$$

It is convenient to absorb the mass coefficients into the coordinates by defining new coordinates q_i that are proportional to the cartesian coordinates and are related to them by

$$q_i = (m_i)^{\frac{1}{2}}x_i \qquad (52)$$

With these coordinates Eq. (51) becomes

$$2T = \sum_{i=1}^{3n} \dot{q}_1^2 \qquad (53)$$

As we saw in the ①—②—③ molecule example of Sec. 9-4, the time derivatives of the cartesian coordinates, or the q_i's, are related by a set of linear equations to the time derivatives of the internal coordinates. With Wilson's notation one writes

$$\dot{R}_k = \sum_{i=1}^{3n} B_{ki}\dot{x}_i \tag{54}$$

or, in matrix form,

$$\dot{R} = B\dot{x} \tag{55}$$

where $\dot{R}$ is a column matrix with $3n - 6$ rows, $\dot{x}$ is a column matrix with $3n$ rows, and B is a transformation matrix consisting of $3n - 6$ and $3n$ columns. [Again it is suggested that the expressions here be compared with those which arose in Sec. 9-4 for the particular example of the ①—②—③ molecule. The general expression of Eq. (55) compares, for instance, with Eq. (21), which is appropriate to the ①—②—③ problem.]

The expressions corresponding to Eqs. (54) and (55), but involving the $\dot{q}_i$ coordinates, are

$$\dot{R}_k = \sum_{i=1}^{3n} D_{ki}\dot{q}_i \qquad \text{where } D_{ki} = B_{ki}\,(m_i)^{-\frac{1}{2}} \tag{56}$$

and

$$\dot{R} = D\dot{q}$$

The principal problem now is to proceed from

$$2T = \sum_{i=1}^{3n} m_i\dot{x}_i^2 = \sum_{i=1}^{3n} \dot{q}_i^2$$

and the transformation equation

$$\dot{R} = D\dot{q} \tag{57}$$

to an expression for T in terms of $\dot{R}$ that is comparable with the expression for U in terms of R given by Eq. (50). Considerable manipulation is necessary to impose the conditions of zero translation and zero angular momentum so that, in effect, the inverse transformation of Eq. (57) can be found and inserted into the kinetic energy expression.

The matrix D can be made square by writing, as six additional rows, the six conditions of zero translational and zero angular momentum. In this way the matrix $\mathfrak{D}$ where

$$\mathfrak{D} = \begin{pmatrix} D \\ D_0 \end{pmatrix} \tag{58}$$

could be formed, and one could calculate, in principle,

$$\mathfrak{D}^{-1} = (QQ_0) \tag{59}$$

where $\mathfrak{D}$ and $\mathfrak{D}^{-1}$ are square $3n \times 3n$ matrices. Furthermore, $\mathfrak{D}^{-1}$ has been arbitrarily divided into Q, a $3n \times 3n - 6$ matrix, and Q_0, a $3n \times 6$ matrix. (Note that Q depends on both D and D_0, as also does Q_0.)

In terms of the square matrix $\mathfrak{D}$, one has

$$\dot{\mathfrak{R}} = \mathfrak{D}\dot{q} \tag{60}$$

$$\dot{\mathfrak{R}} = \begin{pmatrix} \dot{R} \\ \dot{r} \end{pmatrix} = \begin{pmatrix} D \\ D_0 \end{pmatrix} \dot{q} \tag{61}$$

where $\dot{r} = D_0\dot{q}$ is a column matrix consisting of six zero elements.

Now the desired inverse of Eq. (60) can, formally, be written down as

$$\dot{q} = \mathfrak{D}^{-1}\dot{\mathfrak{R}} \tag{62}$$

With this relation one can express T in terms of the internal coordinates as

$$2T = \dot{q}'\dot{q} = \dot{R}'(\mathfrak{D}^{-1})'\mathfrak{D}^{-1}\dot{R} \tag{63}$$

Further manipulations allow the problem to be reduced to $3n - 6$, rather than $3n$, dimensions. Since

$$\mathfrak{R} = \begin{pmatrix} \dot{R} \\ \dot{r} \end{pmatrix} \quad \text{and} \quad \dot{\mathfrak{R}}' = (\dot{R}'\dot{r}') \tag{64}$$

$$\mathfrak{D} = \begin{pmatrix} D \\ D_0 \end{pmatrix} \quad \text{and} \quad \mathfrak{D}' = (D'D_0') \tag{65}$$

$$\mathfrak{D}^{-1} = (QQ_0) \quad \text{and} \quad (\mathfrak{D}^{-1})' = \begin{pmatrix} Q' \\ Q_0' \end{pmatrix} \tag{66}$$

the expression for $2T$ can be expanded as

$$2T = (\dot{R}'\dot{r}') \begin{pmatrix} Q' \\ Q_0' \end{pmatrix} (QQ_0) \begin{pmatrix} \dot{R} \\ \dot{r} \end{pmatrix} \tag{67}$$

$$\begin{aligned} 2T &= (\dot{R}'Q' + \dot{r}'Q_0')(Q\dot{R} + Q_0\dot{r}) \\ &= \dot{R}'Q'Q\dot{R} + \dot{R}'Q'Q_0\dot{r} + \dot{r}'Q_0'Q\dot{R} + \dot{r}'Q_0'Q_0\dot{r} \end{aligned} \tag{68}$$

Since $\dot{r}$ is a zero matrix, the last three terms are zero and one is left with

$$2T = \dot{R}'Q'Q\dot{R} \tag{69}$$

The desired reduction to $3n - 6$ matrices has now been formally accomplished. It remains to see how the matrix Q can be conveniently deduced.

The matrix Q arises in the inverse of the matrix $\mathfrak{D}$. A number of useful relationships become apparent if one writes

$$\mathfrak{D}^{-1}\mathfrak{D} = (QQ_0)\begin{pmatrix} D \\ D_0 \end{pmatrix} = (QD + Q_0D_0) = I_{3n\times3n} \tag{70}$$

and

$$\mathfrak{D}\mathfrak{D}^{-1} = \begin{pmatrix} D \\ D_0 \end{pmatrix}(QQ_0) = \begin{pmatrix} DQ & DQ_0 \\ D_0Q & D_0Q_0 \end{pmatrix} = I_{3n\times3n} \tag{71}$$

where I represents a diagonal unit matrix. The second result is convenient in that it allows us to recognize that DQ, which is composed of the $3n - 6 \times 3n$ matrix D, i.e., $3n - 6$ rows and $3n$ columns, and the $3n \times 3n - 6$ matrix Q, is a $3n - 6 \times 3n - 6$ identity matrix. The first relation can now be made to yield a valuable result. It is first transposed to give

$$D'Q' + D_0'Q_0' = I_{3n\times3n} \tag{72}$$

and then multiplied on the left by D and on the right by Q to give

$$DD'Q'Q + DD_0'Q_0'Q = DQ = I_{3n-6\times3n-6} \tag{73}$$

Now one must recognize that the internal coordinates will be the basis for descriptions of the pure vibrations of the molecule and that these coordinates will therefore be orthogonal to the over-all translational and rotational coordinates. It follows that D and D_0 are orthogonal matrices and that DD_0' is a zero matrix. This relationship eliminates the second term of Eq. (73) and leaves

$$DD'Q'Q = I \tag{74}$$

The product $Q'Q$ desired for T is then obtained as

$$Q'Q = (DD')^{-1} = G^{-1} \tag{75}$$

where the usually used symbol $G = DD'$ has been introduced for this important matrix. In view of the relation between the components of D and B given in Eq. (56), one can express the elements of $G = DD'$ as

$$G_{kl} = \sum_{i=1}^{3n} \frac{B_{ki}B_{li}}{m_i} \tag{76}$$

From this result we can calculate each element of the G matrix, i.e., G_{kl} for $k = 1, 2, \ldots, 3n - 6$ and $l = 1, 2, \ldots, 3n - 6$. (It will be recalled that the B matrix is the transformation matrix between the internal coordinates and the cartesian coordinates and that it can be written down from a consideration of a diagram of the molecule.)

One now has

$$2T = R'G^{-1}R \tag{77}$$

and

$$2U = R'FR \tag{78}$$

When Lagrange's equation is applied to each of the R_k coordinates and vibrational-type solutions

$$R_k = A_k \cos 2\pi\nu t$$

are sought, the secular determinant formed by the coefficients of the A_k's has the form

$$\begin{vmatrix} F_{11} - (G^{-1})_{11}\lambda & F_{12} - (G^{-1})_{12}\lambda & \cdots \\ F_{21} - (G^{-1})_{21}\lambda & F_{22} - (G^{-1})_{22}\lambda & \cdots \\ \cdots & \cdots & \cdots \end{vmatrix} = 0 \tag{79}$$

where $\lambda = 4\pi^2\nu^2$. If Λ is used to represent a diagonal matrix with λ's on the diagonals, this equation can be written as

$$|F - G^{-1}\Lambda| = 0 \tag{80}$$

Finally, it is sometimes more convenient to rearrange this determinant by multiplying through by $|G|$ to give

$$|G|\,|F - G^{-1}\Lambda| = |(G)(F - G^{-1}\Lambda)|$$
$$= |GF - \Lambda| = 0 \tag{81}$$

With either Eq. (80) or (81), and the procedure obtained for setting up the F and G matrices, we can solve for the $3n - 6$ values of λ that satisfy the equation. The ①—②—③ molecular type example can be used to illustrate Eq. (80) or (81). In more complicated cases the systematic nature of "Wilson's FG method" is of real value. Probably most of the molecular-vibration calculations that have been published have made use of this procedure.

*Exercise 9-11. Calculate the frequencies of the HCN molecule, from the given force constants, by the method of Sec. 9-6.

*9-7. Formation of the G Matrix by a Vectorial Method

In a second paper by Wilson a convenient method for setting up the G matrix introduced in the previous section is presented. The previous treatment required use of the relation

$$G_{kl} = \sum_{i=1}^{3n} \frac{1}{m_i} B_{ki} B_{li} \qquad k, l = 1, \ldots, 3n - 6 \qquad (82)$$

where the B_{ki} terms that arise are determined by the relations

$$\dot{R}_k = \sum_{i=1}^{3n} B_{ki} \dot{x}_i \qquad\qquad\qquad\qquad\qquad (83)$$

It is now suggestive to write out the atomic cartesian coordinates more specifically to show Eq. (83) in the form

$$\begin{aligned}
\dot{R}_k = \;& (B_{kx_1}\dot{x}_1 + B_{ky_1}\dot{y}_1 + B_{kz_1}\dot{z}_1) \\
& + (B_{kx_2}\dot{x}_2 + B_{ky_2}\dot{y}_2 + \cdots) \\
& + \cdots\cdots\cdots\cdots\cdots\cdots\cdots \\
& + (B_{kx_n}\dot{x}_n + B_{ky_n}\dot{y}_n + B_{kz_n}\dot{z}_n)
\end{aligned}$$

These many products of components can be more neatly expressed by introducing the vectors

ϱ_t with components $\dot{x}_t,\ \dot{y}_t,\ \dot{z}_t$

and

$\mathbf{s}_{kt}$ with components $B_{kx_t},\ B_{ky_t},\ B_{kz_t}$

where t numbers off the n atoms of the molecule. With this notation R_k is written as

$$R_k = \sum_{t=1}^{n} \mathbf{s}_{kt} \cdot \varrho_t \qquad\qquad\qquad\qquad\qquad (84)$$

and, as will be illustrated, the G matrix elements are simply

$$G_{kl} = \sum_{t=1}^{n} \frac{1}{m_t} \mathbf{s}_{kt} \cdot \mathbf{s}_{lt} \qquad\qquad\qquad\qquad (85)$$

This result for G_{kl} can be verified by considering atom t and recognizing that Eq. (84) gives its contribution to G_{kl} as

$$\frac{1}{m_t} \mathbf{s}_{kt} \cdot \mathbf{s}_{lt} = \frac{1}{m_t} (B_{kx_t}B_{lx_t} + B_{ky_t}B_{ly_t} + B_{kz_t}B_{lz_t}) \qquad (86)$$

This is the same contribution as is expected from Eq. (79), except for the notation based on $\dot{x}_t,\ \dot{y}_t,\ \dot{z}_t$ rather than on the running index i. The formulation of Eq. (85) is helpful only if there is a convenient way of expressing the $\mathbf{s}_{kt}$ vectors. This can be done by introducing unit vectors $\boldsymbol{\epsilon}_{\alpha\beta}$ along the bonds in the molecule. The subscripts α and β indicate the terminal atoms of the bond, and it is agreed that the unit vectors are directed from the atom labeled α to that labeled β.

With these ϵ vectors, it is possible to set up convenient recipes for determining and s_{kt} vectors, i.e., the s vector contributions of each atom t to a particular internal coordinate R_k. If R_k involves the stretching of a bond, say between atoms labeled α and β, the $s_{k\alpha}$ and $s_{k\beta}$ vectors must show how the terminal atoms must move to lead to a bond stretching. In this way one has simply

$$s_{k\alpha} = -\epsilon_{\alpha\beta}$$
and $\qquad\qquad\qquad\qquad\qquad\qquad\qquad\qquad\qquad\qquad\qquad$ (87)
$$s_{k\beta} = +\epsilon_{\alpha\beta}$$

Thus if one were dealing with the internal coordinate $R_1 = \delta r_{OH}$ for the molecule H—O—H′ and the ϵ vector had been indicated as

one would have

$$s_{1H} = +\epsilon_{OH}$$
and $\qquad\qquad\qquad\qquad\qquad\qquad\qquad\qquad\qquad\qquad\qquad$ (88)
$$s_{1O} = -\epsilon_{HO}$$

If R_k involves an angle bending, $\delta\alpha$ for H_2O, for example, one agrees to draw the ϵ vectors directed away from the apex angle thus

More generally, one might number the three atoms that fix the value of the interbond angle and draw the ϵ vectors as

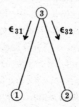

Furthermore one lets r_{31} and r_{32} denote the equilibrium bond lengths and φ the equilibrium value of the interbond angle. Some geometric manipulation is now necessary to arrive at the general expressions which show how, in terms of the vectors, the three atoms must move to result in an increase in the angle with no accompanying bond stretching. One finds that, if R_k is an angle bending coordinate,

$$s_{k1} = \frac{\cos \varphi \epsilon_{31} - \epsilon_{32}}{r_{31} \sin \varphi} \tag{89}$$

$$s_{k2} = \frac{\cos \varphi \epsilon_{32} - \epsilon_{31}}{r_{32} \sin \varphi} \tag{90}$$

$$s_{k3} = \frac{(r_{31} - r_{32} \cos \varphi)\epsilon_{31} + (r_{32} - r_{31} \cos \varphi)\epsilon_{32}}{r_{31}r_{32} \sin \varphi} \tag{91}$$

These relations between the s vectors and the ϵ vectors, the latter introducing the molecular geometry into the problem, allow, for very many molecules, the G matrix elements to be readily calculated according to the expression

$$G_{kl} = \sum_{t=1}^{n} \frac{1}{m_t} s_{kt} \cdot s_{lt} \tag{92}$$

The dot products between the various s vectors will lead to dot products between the ϵ vectors that are fixed along the directions of the bonds. In this way cosines of angles between bonds of the molecule will arise and will, in a very convenient way, introduce the molecular geometry into the G matrix.

*Exercise 9-12. Apply the Wilson FG method to the molecule HOD. Calculate the frequencies predicted on the basis of the force constants $k_{\text{HO}} = k_{\text{DO}} = 7.76 \times 10^5$ dynes/cm and $k_\alpha/r_{\text{OH}} = 0.69 \times 10^5$ dynes/cm. Compare with the observed absorption band frequencies of 1,402, 2,719, and 3,690 cm^{-1}.

*9-8. Use of Symmetry Coordinates in Wilson's Method

It has already been shown, in Sec. 9-5, that the use of symmetry coordinates, which can be expressed as linear combinations of internal coordinates, allow the secular determinant to be factored into a number of determinants of lower order. This reduction can be performed when the methods of the previous two sections are applied to symmetric molecules.

The symmetry coordinates S_l can be set up in terms of the internal coordinates R_k according to

$$S_l = \sum_{k=1}^{3n-6} U_{lk} R_k \tag{93}$$

or

$$S = UR \tag{94}$$

For H_2O, for example, one might write

$$
\begin{aligned}
S_1 &= \delta r_1 + \delta r_2 & \text{symmetric } (A_1) \\
S_2 &= \delta\alpha & \text{symmetric } (A_1) \\
S_3 &= \delta r_1 - \delta r_2 & \text{antisymmetric } (B_2)
\end{aligned}
\tag{95}
$$

or

$$
\begin{pmatrix} S_1 \\ S_2 \\ S_3 \end{pmatrix} =
\begin{pmatrix} 1 & 1 & 0 \\ 0 & 0 & 1 \\ 1 & -1 & 0 \end{pmatrix}
\begin{pmatrix} \delta r_1 \\ \delta r_2 \\ \delta\alpha \end{pmatrix}
\tag{96}
$$

Since, as this example illustrates, the symmetry coordinates can be set up to be orthogonal to one another, the U matrix is orthogonal, and the relation, which will be used below,

$$U^{-1} = U' \tag{97}$$

will hold.

In Wilson's procedure the kinetic energy is expressed as

$$2T = \dot{R}'G^{-1}\dot{R} \tag{98}$$

The corresponding expression involving symmetry coordinates can be obtained by inserting the identity matrices UU^{-1} and $U^{-1}U$ to give

$$2T = \dot{R}'U^{-1}UG^{-1}U^{-1}U\dot{R} \tag{99}$$

Now $U\dot{R}$ is recognized as $\dot{S}$, and $\dot{R}'U^{-1} = \dot{R}'U'$ is recognized as $\dot{S}'$. Thus, again with $U^{-1} = U'$, we can write

$$2T = \dot{S}'UG^{-1}U'\dot{S} = \dot{S}'\mathcal{G}^{-1}\dot{S} \tag{100}$$

where the notation

$$\mathcal{G}^{-1} = UG^{-1}U' \tag{101}$$

has been introduced. Since all three matrices are nonsingular, the $\mathcal{G}$ matrix can be expressed by

$$
\begin{aligned}
\mathcal{G} &= (U')^{-1}GU^{-1} \\
&= UGU'
\end{aligned}
\tag{102}
$$

This matrix equation allows, since U and U' are known from the way in which the symmetry coordinates were set up and the elements of G

can be calculated from Eq. (92), the calculation of $\mathcal{G}$. Expansion of Eq. (102) shows that the elements of $\mathcal{G}$ are given by

$$\mathcal{G}_{ll'} = \sum_{t=1}^{n} \left(\frac{1}{m_t} \sum_{k_1 k'=1}^{3n-6} U_{lk} U_{l'k'} s_{kt} \cdot s_{k't} \right) \tag{103}$$

This cumbersome expression can be used more conveniently if symmetry displacement vectors $\mathbf{S}_l^t$ that are comparable to the s_{kt} vectors are introduced. If $\mathbf{S}_l^t$ is defined as

$$\mathbf{S}_l^t = \sum_{k=1}^{3n-6} U_{lk} \mathbf{s}_{kt} \tag{104}$$

the elements of the kinetic-energy matrix can be calculated from

$$\mathcal{G}_{ll'} = \sum_{t=1}^{n} \frac{1}{m_t} \mathbf{S}_l^t \cdot \mathbf{S}_{l'}^t \tag{105}$$

With Eqs. (104) and (105) the kinetic-energy matrix $\mathcal{G}$ of Eqs. (100) and (101) can be set up.

Thus one calculates the various $\mathbf{S}_l^t$ vectors from Eq. (104) and substitutes these, along with the appropriate atomic-mass terms in Eq. (105), to obtain the desired kinetic-energy matrix based on the symmetry coordinates of the problem.

The potential-energy expression based on these coordinates presents no difficulty. One can write down, except for numerical values of the components of the F matrix, as shown in Sec. 9-7, the potential-energy expression

$$2U = R'FR \tag{106}$$

The internal coordinate matrices R and R' can be replaced by symmetry coordinate matrices by use of the relations, obtained from Eq. (94), and the relation of Eq. (97),

$$R = U^{-1}S = U'S \tag{107}$$

and

$$R'U' = R'U^{-1} = S' \qquad \text{or} \qquad R' = S'U \tag{108}$$

Substitution in Eq. (106) gives

$$2U = S'UFU'S \tag{109}$$

or

$$2U = S'\mathfrak{F}S \tag{110}$$

where the potential-energy matrix $\mathcal{F}$ based on symmetry coordinates has been introduced as

$$\mathcal{F} = UFU' \tag{111}$$

With Eqs. (100) and (110) and the methods for obtaining $\mathcal{G}$ and $\mathcal{F}$ given by Eqs. (105) and (111), the vibrations of a symmetric molecule can be analyzed in terms of symmetry coordinates and, as seen in Sec. 9-5, the convenient factoring of the secular determinant will occur.

*Exercise 9-13. Apply the Wilson FG method, making use of symmetry as indicated in Sec. 9-8, to the SO_2 molecule. The molecule is bent and has a bond angle of 120 deg. The force constants reported for a simple valence force field are $k_{so} = 9.97 \times 10^5$ dynes/cm and $k'_\alpha = 0.81 \times 10^5$ dynes/cm. (Compare with the observed frequencies of 519, 1,150, and 1,360 cm^{-1}.)

PRINCIPAL REFERENCES

1. Wilson, E. B., Jr., J. C. Decius, and P. C. Cross: "Molecular Vibrations," McGraw-Hill Book Company, Inc., New York, 1955.

10 ELECTRONIC SPECTRA OF DIATOMIC MOLECULES

Molecules can absorb, or emit, radiation not only as a result of changes in their rotational and vibrational energies but also as a result of changes in their electronic arrangement and, therefore, their electronic energy. The energy changes involved in a transition from one electronic state of a molecule to another are usually relatively large and correspond to radiation in the visible or ultraviolet regions. In the course of such high energy transitions, it must be expected that the vibrational energy and, since all materials considered in this chapter are gaseous, the rotational energy of the molecule will also change in the transition. We will see, in fact, that electronic transitions result in broad absorption or emission bands and that these bands contain a large amount of fine structure. Analysis of this structure often leads to a wealth of information on the moments of inertia and the potential-energy function for the electronic states involved in the transition. Furthermore, diatomic molecules exhibit many different excited electronic states, and the energies of these states can also be deduced from studies of electronic transitions. The lack of a simple, generally adopted pattern for the energies of these excited states makes, as we will see, the assignment of transitions to particular states a problem of considerable difficulty. For only a few diatomic molecules can a reasonably complete diagram of the energies of the excited electronic states be drawn.

The analysis of electronic bands of diatomic molecules is perhaps best introduced by considering the vibrational and rotational structure that is found in typical electronic absorption or emission bands. Following this analysis of the fine structure of typical bands, a consideration of the kinds of electronic states that can occur for a particular molecule will be given, and mention will be made of how an observed band can be assigned to a transition between two of these states.

It should, perhaps, be mentioned here that the analysis of the electronic spectra of diatomic molecules is a rather specialized study and that most chemists are likely to encounter only electronic spectra of polyatomic molecules, or ions. Furthermore, the visible and ultraviolet spectra of these species are likely to be obtained on solution samples. Much of the detailed analysis of the rotational structure observed in the gas-phase spectra of diatomic molecules does not carry over to the analysis of these polyatomic solution spectra. We will, therefore, treat only the principal features of the electronic spectra of diatomic molecules and will make reference to the very complete treatment given in ref. 2 for those who wish to pursue further the detailed study of the electronic spectra of diatomic molecules.

10-1. The Vibrational Structure of Electronic Bands

The way in which the potential energy of a diatomic molecule might vary, as a function of the internuclear distance for two different arrangements of the electrons of the molecule, i.e., two different electronic states, is shown in Fig. 10-1. We will see later that on such diagrams potential-energy curves occur variously placed and with various shapes for the different electronic states of a particular molecule. The curves shown in Fig. 10-1 are, however, typical of a ground and an excited electronic state. The potential-energy curves of Fig. 10-1 imply that for each of the two electronic arrangements the molecule will vibrate, and, as in Chap. 2, horizontal lines are drawn to represent the energies of the allowed vibrational states. Furthermore, the probabilities of the molecule being found at various internuclear distances, i.e., the square of the harmonic oscillator wave functions, are shown on the energy levels to which they refer.

We will now consider an absorption or emission of radiation that changes the molecule from one electronic state to the other. The question immediately arises as to which transitions are to be expected between the various vibrational levels, labeled $v'' = 0, 1, 2, \ldots$, of the lower electronic state and the various vibrational levels, labeled $v' = 0, 1, 2, \ldots$, of the upper electronic state. Three factors must be kept in mind to answer this question.

1. As observation of the vibrational structure of electronic bands

FIG. 10-1   Potential-energy functions, vibrational energy levels, and vibrational probability functions ψ^2 for two typical electronic states of a diatomic molecule.

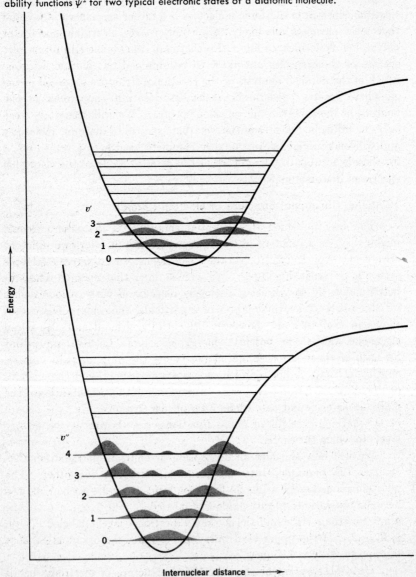

will confirm, there are no general restrictions on the changes in v for a transition going from one electronic state to another. This result is in contrast to the rule of $\Delta v = \pm 1$ that is operative in vibrational transitions within a given electronic state.

2. It must be kept in mind that electrons can move and rearrange themselves much faster than can the nuclei move to alter the internuclear distance. (The relative times for electronic and nuclear motion can be recognized, for instance, from the fact that an electron in a Bohr orbit of an atom completes a revolution around the nucleus in about 10^{-15} sec whereas a typical molecule vibrates with a period of about 10^{-13} sec.) This characteristic of electronic and nuclear motions leads to the Franck-Condon principle that *an electronic transition in a molecule takes place so rapidly compared to the vibrational motion of the nuclei that the internuclear distance can be regarded as fixed during the transition.* It follows that on a diagram, such as that of Fig. 10-1, electronic transitions must be represented by essentially vertical lines connecting the initial and final states at some fixed internuclear distance.

3. The fact that the probability of the molecule being at a particular internuclear distance is a function of the distance, as shown by the probability curves of Fig. 10-1, must be taken into account. An electronic transition must be expected, in view of the transition moment integral defined in Eq. (4-25), to be most favored if it occurs while the molecule has an internuclear distance such that the transition connects probable states of the molecule. This rule is usually simplified, in view of the shapes of the probability functions shown in Fig. 10-1, by considering transitions to be relatively more probable if they begin or end at the middle of the $v = 0$ level or either end of any of the higher vibrational levels.

With these three statements one can draw, as is done in Fig. 10-2, the expected transitions for the potential curves of Fig. 10-1.

In an absorption experiment the temperature is often near room temperature, and the $v'' = 0$ level is most populated. One expects, therefore, to see a *progression* of absorption lines in the electronic absorption band due to transitions, with $v'' = 0$ and v' varying perhaps from $v' = 0$ to large values. Figure 10-3 shows absorption bands of CO and I_2 which illustrate this behavior.

Exercise 10-1. Draw potential-energy curves for ground and excited electronic states such that, as observed in the absorption spectrum of Fig. 10-3a, only the transition to high vibrational levels of the upper electronic state is observed.

234

INTRODUCTION TO MOLECULAR SPECTROSCOPY

In emission spectra the temperature is usually high enough so that many of the v' levels are appreciably populated. In emission spectra, therefore, many lines arising from transitions from various upper state levels, i.e., various v' values, to various lower levels, i.e., various v'' values, are to be expected. The many probable transitions that occur generally lead to a band of such complexity, as that of the molecule N_2 shown in Fig. 10-4, that without considerable experience one cannot recognize how the band structure is related to transitions such as those exhibited in Fig. 10-2b. The components of such a vibrational-electronic band are usually analyzed by arranging the frequencies of the components in a table, called a Deslandres table, in such a way that the difference in the frequencies in adjacent columns is approximately constant and varies uniformly, and the difference in the frequencies in adjacent rows is likewise approximately constant and varies uniformly. The

FIG. 10-2 (a) Some of the most probable transitions, for an absorption experiment at a relatively low temperature, for the potential-energy curves of Fig. 10-1. (b) Examples of the most probable emission transitions between vibrational levels of two electronic states. (Note, as Table 10-1 shows, that for a given value of v' transitions to states with two different values of v'' are preferred.)

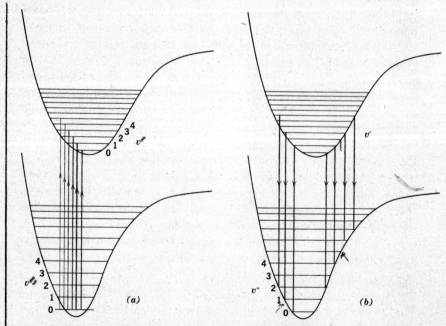

components of an electronic emission band of the molecule PN, arranged to conform to these requirements, as shown by the frequency differences also exhibited, are given in Table 10-1. This pattern is understandable in terms of the emission transitions of Fig. 10-2b if the columns are labeled with the vibrational quantum number v'' of the lower electronic state and the rows with the quantum numbers v' of the upper state. Each frequency in the table can then be identified as a transition between the v' value of the row it occupies and the v'' value of its column. The most intense lines, moreover, tend to follow a parabolic-like curve as would be expected from the potential curves of Fig. 10-1 and the three statements given earlier in this section. For $v' = 6$, for example, preferred transitions are apparently those going to $v'' = 3$ and $v'' = 9$ or 10. Thus for a given value of v' one expects transitions to two different v'' levels to be preferred. The differences between the rows of the Deslandres table can now be recognized as giving the spacing of the vibrational levels in the upper electronic state, while the differences between the values in the columns give the vibrational spacing in the lower electronic state.

It should now be clear that data from electronic absorption or emission bands provide much more information on the vibrational energy-level pattern of a diatomic molecule than can be obtained from direct studies of vibrational transitions. One obtains information on the energies of levels with high vibrational quantum numbers, and one can learn, therefore, much about the potential-energy function. For example, there is an electronic transition of I_2 that leads to an absorption band at about 2,000 A connecting the ground electronic state with an excited state. The vibrational structure of this band has been measured in considerable detail, and transitions involving ground-state vibrational quantum numbers up to $v'' = 114$ have been reported. From the data on these vibrational spacings, some of which are summarized in Table 10-2, a well-defined potential-energy function can be deduced. This is shown in Fig. 10-5 along with, for comparison, the Morse curve that was introduced in Sec. 2-3. (The Morse curve is generally accepted as a good approximation to the potential function of a diatomic molecule.)

In favorable cases, such as the I_2 transition mentioned in the previous paragraph, the pattern of vibrational levels almost up to the limit of dissociation can be obtained, and the dissociation energy for the molecule in that electronic state can be deduced by a suitable extrapolation. It is particularly important to recognize that this information on the shape of the potential function, and often on the dissociation energy, can be

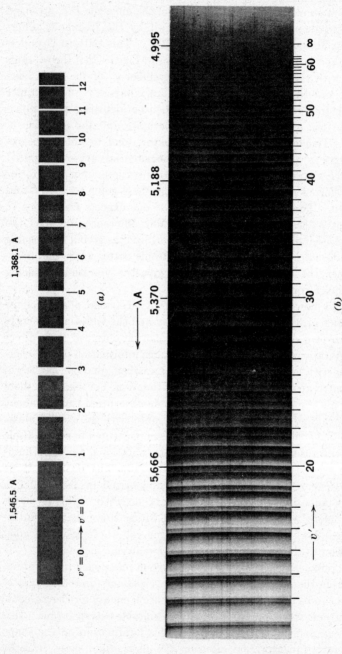

FIG. 10-3 Absorption bands due to electronic transition showing vibrational structure. (a) The absorption band of CO at about 1,400 A. (Adapted from G. Herzberg, "Spectra of Diatomic Molecules," D. Van Nostrand Company, Inc., Princeton, N.J., 1950.) (b) The absorption band of I_2 in the visible spectral region. The indicated values of v' are for the series of transitions that start from $v'' = 0$. (Courtesy of J. A. Marquisee, Case Institute of Technology, Cleveland, Ohio.)

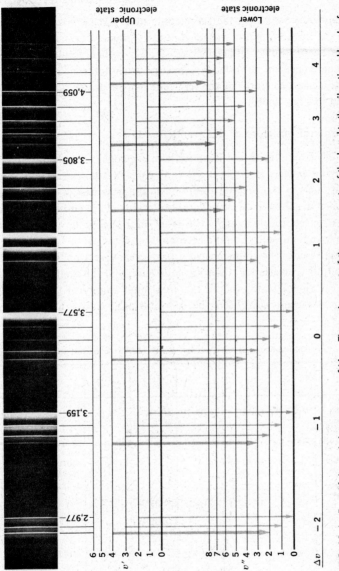

FIG. 10-4 Part of the emission spectrum of N_2. The assignment of the components of the band to the vibrational levels of the two electronic states shown below the spectrum has been worked out with the aid of a treatment like that illustrated in Table 10-1. The heavy arrows are drawn to call attention to the series of transitions that occur from a given v' level to various v'' levels. (Courtesy of J. A. Marquisee, Case Institute of Technology, Cleveland, Ohio.)

obtained not only for the ground electronic state but also, in contrast to studies in the infrared region, for excited electronic states. (Some molecules have been studied sufficiently so that a rather detailed diagram showing the variation of potential energy with internuclear distance for various electronic states of the molecule can be drawn. An example is provided in Fig. 10-20.)

10-2. Rotational Structure of Electronic Bands

If an electronic band is studied with a spectrograph with sufficiently high resolving power, it is observed that each of the vibrational components, studied in the previous section, does not consist of a single line but is rather a subband of considerable detail. This additional detail can be attributed to changes in the rotational energy of the molecule that accompany the vibrational-electronic transition.

If $\bar{\nu}_0$ represents the frequency of a particular vibrational component of an electronic transition, $\bar{\epsilon}'_J$ the rotational energy of the excited molecule in the J' rotational state, and $\bar{\epsilon}''_J$ the rotational energy of the molecule in a lower electronic state and the J'' rotational state, the rotational

TABLE 10-1 The Components of an Emission Band of PN Arranged in a Deslandres

v'' / v'	0		1		2		3	
0	39,698.8	(1322.3)	38,476.5	(1307.5)	37,068.7			
	(1087.4)		(1090.7)		(1086.8)			
1	40,786.2	(1319.0)	39,467.2	(1311.7)	38,155.5	(1294.2)	36,861.3	
	(1072.9)		(1069.0)				(1071.6)	
2	41,859.1	(1322.9)	40,536.2				37,932.9	(1280.4)
			(1061.2)					
3			41,597.4	(1309.1)	40,288.3			
					(1042.9)			
4					41,331.2			
5							41,066.1	
							(1015.9)	
6							42,082.0	
7								
8								
9								

* From G. Herzberg, "Molecular Spectra and Molecular Structure," D. Van Nostrand Company,

details of the subband can be discussed in terms of the expression

$$\bar{\nu} = \bar{\nu}_0 + (\bar{\epsilon}'_J - \bar{\epsilon}''_J) \tag{1}$$

(It should be mentioned that, particularly in studies of the rotational and vibrational structure of electronic bands, use is generally made of a different notation than has been used here to designate the various types of energy that a molecule can have. T is used to denote the total energy of a given state of the molecule; T_e is used to denote the electronic energy, i.e., the energy that the molecule would have if it were not rotating and remained at the minimum of the potental-energy curve for that state. The symbol G is used to represent the vibrational energy of the molecule, while F represents its rotational energy. Finally, a double prime represents a lower energy state; a single prime, a higher energy state. Since detailed analyses of electronic bands will not be given here, it will not be necessary to change over to this standard notation.)

Although many excited electronic states have electronic angular momentum contributions that couple with the rotational angular momentum of the molecule, which lead to considerable complexity, it is here

Table* (The wave numbers, in cm^{-1}, of the spectral lines are given.)

4		5		6		7	
36,652.5	(1265.3)	35,387.2					
(1060.0)		(1059.2)					
37,712.5	(1266.1)	36,446.4	(1252.4)	35,194.0			
(1043.9)				(1042.6)			
38,756.4				36,236.6	(1238.3)	34,998.3	
						(1029.4)	
		38,519.4				36,027.7	(1225.5)
41,798.3							
		41,522.6					
				41,239.4			

Inc., Princeton, N.J., 1950.

sufficient to consider the simpler cases in which the rotational energies for the two electronic states can be expressed by the simple, rigid rotor expressions. In such cases the subband structure can be expressed as

$$\bar{\nu} = \bar{\nu}_0 + \bar{B}'_v J'(J' + 1) - \bar{B}''_v J''(J'' + 1) \tag{2}$$

where $\bar{B}'_v$ and $\bar{B}''_v$ are the rotational constants for the vibrational and electronic states involved in the transition. In general, further complications arise in that the selection rules on J depend on the types of electronic states involved in the transition. However, one frequently has situations in which $\Delta J = 0, \pm 1$ are allowed. For these rotational branches one has, if the value of J'' is simply labeled as J,

P branch: $J'' = J, J' = J - 1$

$$\bar{\nu} = \bar{\nu}_0 \qquad - (\bar{B}'_v + \bar{B}''_v)J + (\bar{B}'_v - \bar{B}''_v)J^2$$

Q branch: $J'' = J, J' = J$

$$\bar{\nu} = \bar{\nu}_0 \qquad + (\bar{B}'_v - \bar{B}''_v)J + (\bar{B}'_v - \bar{B}''_v)J^2 \tag{3}$$

TABLE 10-2 Some of the Vibrational Energy-level Spacings for the Ground Electronic State of I_2 Obtained from Studies of the Electronic Band at 2,000 A*

v''	$\Delta\bar{\epsilon}$ (cm^{-1})
0	213.31
1	
10	200.68
11	
40	154.62
41	
60	110.09
61	
80	52.33
81	
100	9.0
101	
114	0.5
115	

* From R. D. Verma, *J. Chem. Phys.*, **32:** 92 (1960).

R branch: $J'' = J$, $J' = J + 1$

$$\bar{\nu} = \bar{\nu}_0 + 2\bar{B}'_v + (3\bar{B}'_v - \bar{B}''_v)J + (\bar{B}'_v - \bar{B}''_v)J^2$$

These expressions are similar to those encountered in Chap. 7 where vibration-rotation bands were treated. There, it will be recalled, it was a good approximation to set the B values for the different vibrational states equal and to neglect the terms equivalent to $(\bar{B}'_v - \bar{B}''_v)$.

The principal difference that is apparent when the rotational structure of vibrational-electronic transitions are analyzed is that $\bar{B}'_v$ and $\bar{B}''_v$, and therefore the moments of inertia and the bond lengths, can be very different for different electronic states of the molecule. (As can be seen in Fig. 10-20, the minima of the potential-energy curves for different

FIG. 10-5 The potential-energy curve for the ground electronic state of I_2. The solid line is computed from the vibrational energy levels deduced from an electronic emission band that is observed at about 2,000 A. The dashed line is a Morse curve for I_2. [From R. D. Verma, J. Chem. Phys., 32: 738 (1960).]

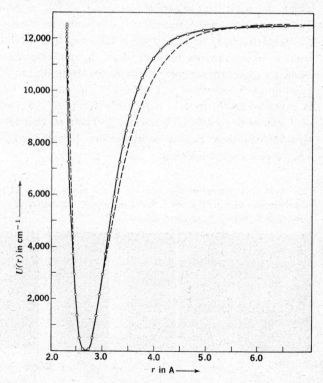

electronic states can occur at quite different bond lengths.)   It follows that the coefficient of the J^2 term of Eqs. (3) can be quite large, and the components of the P and R branches will not, therefore, move out linearly from the band origin.   In fact, if, for example, $\bar{B}'_v$ is greater than $\bar{B}''_v$, the J^2 terms of the P branch can, at high J values, dominate the terms linear in J and the branch components will "turn around" and move to higher, instead of lower, frequencies as J increases.   Similarly, if $\bar{B}''_v$ is greater than $\bar{B}'_v$, the J^2 terms of the Q branch can dominate the linear terms and the high J components of the band can turn around and move to lower, instead of higher, frequencies as J increases.   This behavior leads to the often striking feature of a *band head*, an example of which is shown in Fig. 10-6, in the rotational structure of each vibrational component of an electronic band.   A large difference in B'_v and B''_v has the further effect, as shown by the second of Eqs. (3), of spreading out the Q branch components and thereby preventing the sharp Q branch that is often a dominant feature of vibration-rotation spectra.

A vibrational component of an electronic transition of CuH, for which the rotational selection rule is $\Delta J = \pm 1$, is shown in Fig. 10-7. The components of the branches of such bands are usually sorted out, and this is particularly necessary when the branch is overlapped or forms a band head and moves back on itself, by plotting the line frequencies against a quantum number, as shown for the 0—0, i.e., $v'' = 0 \to v' = 0$, band of a CN transition in Fig. 10-8.   The parabolic behavior that is to be expected on the basis of Eqs. (3) is then observed, and the assignment of J values to individual lines can be made so that all points fall on a smooth parabola.   Such a parabola, first recognized by Fortrat, is now known as a *Fortrat parabola*.

FIG. 10-6   Enlargement of a component of the emission band of N_2 showing that the apparent lines of Fig. 10-4 are in fact band heads.   (*Courtesy of J. A. Marquisee, Case Institute of Technology, Cleveland, Ohio.*)

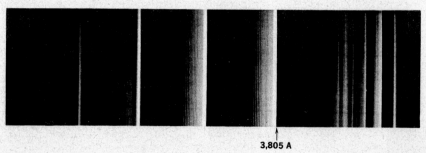

3,805 A

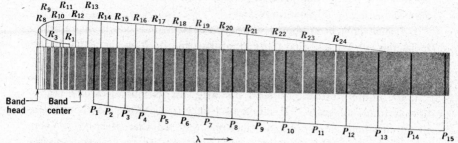

FIG. 10-7   The rotational fine structure of a component of the electronic band of CuH at 4,280A.   [From H. Schuler, H. Hahn, and H. Gallnow; Z. Physik, 111: 484 (1939).]

Analysis of the structure of the rotational branches leads, with Eqs. (3), to values of the rotational constants $\bar{B}'_v$ and $\bar{B}''_v$ for the two states involved in the transition.   In this way one obtains information on the equilibrium bond lengths not only for the ground but also for various excited electronic states.   These data, moreover, are often obtained with

FIG. 10-8   A Fortrat parabola formed by plotting the frequencies of the rotational lines of the 0–0 component of a CN band against the rotational quantum number in the lower energy electronic state.   (From G. Herzberg, "Spectra of Diatomic Molecules," D. Van Nostrand Company, Inc., Princeton, N.J., 1950.)

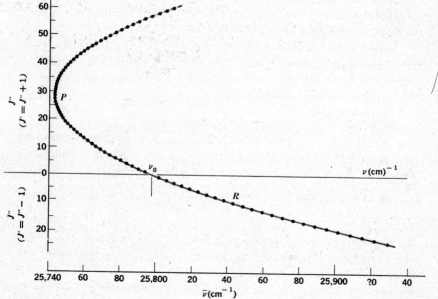

an accuracy comparable to that provided by direct studies of rotational transitions in the microwave region.

It has now been shown how typical electronic bands of diatomic molecules can be analyzed to yield information both on the shape of the potential-energy curve, as a function of the internuclear distance, and on the internuclear distance at the minimum of this potential-energy curve, i.e., the equilibrium internuclear distance, for various electronic states of a diatomic molecule. It is now necessary to see if the states involved in an electronic transition can, in some way, be characterized. When this can be done, the potential-energy functions can be assigned to particular electronic arrangements and a vast amount of information on molecular bonding is made available. It is essential for the chemist, if he is to have access to this information, to learn something of the notation, and the implications of the notation, used to describe electronic states. The remainder of the chapter will be devoted primarily to this end. The material of Sec. 10-4 is, however, of additional interest in that the molecular orbitals discussed there will be used again in connection with studies of the electronic states of polyatomic molecules in the following chapter.

10-3. Electronic States of Atoms

A review of some features of the way in which the electronic states of atoms are described is necessary before the corresponding descriptions of states of molecules are attempted.

Application of the Schrödinger equation to a hydrogenlike atom, i.e., a one-electron atom or ion, shows that various orbitals, each identified by the values of three quantum numbers, are available to the electron. These three quantum numbers are

$n = 1, 2, 3, \ldots$ principal quantum number
$l = 0, 1, 2, \ldots, n - 1$ (or $s, p, d, \ldots$)   angular momentum quantum number

and

$m = -l, -l + 1, \ldots, 0, \ldots, +l$ magnetic quantum number

An electronic state of a one-electron atom is defined, that is, the energy and probability function for the electron are given, by values for the three quantum numbers. Furthermore, as application of the appropriate operator would show, the value of the quantum number l implies an orbital angular momentum of $\sqrt{l(l+1)}(h/2\pi)$ and the value of the quantum number m implies a component of this angular momentum of $m(h/2\pi)$ along a specified direction.

This procedure for describing the electronic state of a one-electron system in terms of quantum numbers can be extended to atoms, or ions, consisting of one electron outside one or more filled inner shells by using an effective nuclear charge in place of the actual charge. By such an extension, however, our ability to predict a precise energy and spatial distribution for the outer electron is lost. The energy of the outer electron becomes dependent on l as well as on n. This is shown schematically in Fig. 10-9. It can be shown, however (see, for example, H. Eyring, J. Walter, and G. E. Kimball, "Quantum Chemistry," pp. 124–143, John Wiley & Sons, Inc., New York, 1944), that, since closed inner shells provide spherically symmetric screening effects and no angular momentum contribution, the important angular momentum implications of l and m for an outer electron are not destroyed. The shapes, possible orientations, and magnetic quantum numbers m for the s, p, and d orbits, which are important in spectroscopic studies, are shown in Fig. 10-10.

With the theoretically and experimentally established result that inner shells do not upset the angular momenta associated with the quantum numbers l and m and, for the lighter elements, do not greatly

FIG. 10-9 Schematic representation of the effect of filled inner shells on the allowed energies of an outer electron.

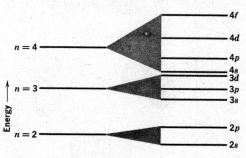

upset the approximate energy and spatial implications of the three quantum numbers, one can proceed to describe atoms in terms of their outer electrons. If there are several outer electrons, and if for the moment they are assumed to behave relatively independently, one can begin to describe an electronic state by assigning each outer electron to an available electron orbit; i.e., one can assign values of n, l, and m

FIG. 10-10 The shapes and orientations of the s, p, and d orbitals. Note that, rather like the classical rotation situation, the angular momentum along the field direction is greater the more the orbital projects out from the axis in this direction.

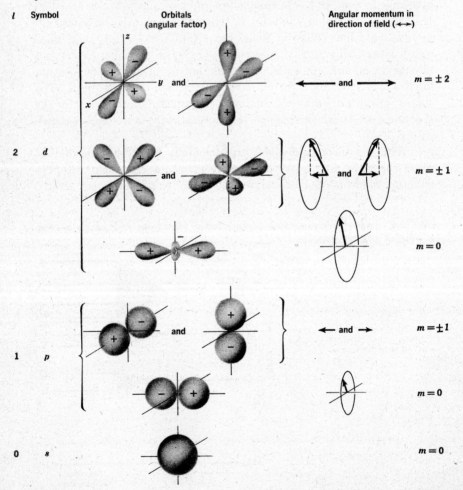

to each electron. Furthermore, since each electron can be assigned a spin quantum number of $+\frac{1}{2}$ or $-\frac{1}{2}$, the Pauli exclusion principle allows two electrons to be assigned identical values of n, l, and m. One would indicate the ground state of the oxygen atom, for example, by

$$[(1s)^2](2s)^2(2p_x)^2(2p_y)^1(2p_z)^1$$

The number of electrons in each orbit is indicated by the superscript, and as is customary, the inner closed shells are set off with brackets. Such an abbreviation, giving a description of an electronic state in terms of the orbitals occupied by the individual electrons, is said to specify the *electronic configuration* of the atom. (In the next section we will see that the writing of an electronic configuration can also be the first step in describing an electronic state of a molecule.)

Exercise 10-2. Write the ground-state electron configurations for the fluorine atom and for the phosphorus atom. Suggest electron configurations of these two atoms that would correspond to excited electronic states.

For an actual atom, or molecule, however, the supposition that the electrons are noninteracting cannot be made. It is not even clear what is meant by the contribution of the individual electrons of the atom when they interact with each other to give some net effect. It turns out, however, as can be seen from a rather lengthy quantum-mechanical argument (see, for example, Eyring, Walter, and Kimball, "Quantum Chemistry," chap. 9), which need not be given here, that the electronic state of an atom is determined, in part, by the quantum number L which is the counterpart of the individual electron quantum number l. (The effect of a magnetic field on a many-electron atom will be treated later, and then the counterpart of the individual electron quantum number m will be introduced.) The quantum-mechanical treatment further shows that there is a simple relation between the values of l_i of the individual, presumed noninteracting outer electrons and the values of L for the atom as a whole. The possible electronic states, for example, of an atom with two outer electrons in orbits with quantum numbers l_1 and l_2, are described by values of L calculated according to

$$L = l_1 + l_2, \, l_1 + l_2 - 1, \, l_1 + l_2 - 2, \, \ldots \, , \, (l_1 - l_2)$$

If the electronic configuration under consideration has, for example, two p electrons outside the inner closed shells, the possible values of L are

$$L = 2, 1, \text{ or } 0$$

In the same way that one uses $s, p, d, \ldots$ to indicate l values of 0, 1, 2, $\ldots$ for individual electrons, one uses $S, P, D, \ldots$ to indicate $L = 0$, 1, 2, $\ldots$. For the present example with two p electrons one would designate the electronic states corresponding to $L = 0$, 1, or 2 by the letters $S, P,$ or D. Although the fact that the two electrons are p electrons, rather than, say, one p and one d, is of primary importance in determining the energy of the electronic state, the way in which the two electrons are arranged in the p orbitals, i.e., the value of L, has some bearing on the energy. Thus, in this example, the possible $S, P,$ and D states of the p^2 configuration would have somewhat different energies. The relative energies of these states cannot readily be calculated but can be deduced from spectroscopic studies.

The net electron spin of the atomic state is described by a quantum number S and, again, this atomic quantity can be deduced from the spins of the individual outer electrons. For two outer electrons, the values that S can have are calculated according to

$$S = s_1 + s_2 \quad \text{or} \quad S = s_1 - s_2$$

and, since the spin quantum number has the fixed value of $\frac{1}{2}$, one can have

$$S = 1 \quad \text{or} \quad S = 0$$

for a two outer electron system.

The energy of the electronic state of an atom, with a given electron configuration, is also dependent on the net electron spin. Exact calculations of the relative energies of states with different net spins cannot be made. There is, however, a general rule formulated by Hund, which applies both to atomic and molecular systems, that *states with greater spin lie at lower energies than those with smaller spin*. Thus, for the two outer electron example, it would be expected that states with $S = 1$ would have lower energies than those with $S = 0$. This rule can be easily remembered in terms of the obvious electron repulsion and, therefore, increased energy that would set in if, for example, two electrons were paired up in a single p orbital. If they occupy different p orbitals, the repulsion will be much less. For the former case the spins must be paired, i.e., $S = 0$, and for the latter they may be parallel, i.e., $S = 1$.

In spectroscopy it is often helpful to focus one's attention on the angular momentum implications of the quantum numbers L and S. Just as the value of l implies an orbit in which an electron has an angular momentum of $\sqrt{l(l+1)}\,(h/2\pi)$, so also does L imply an angular momentum of $\sqrt{L(L+1)}\,(h/2\pi)$ for the electronic state of the atom. Furthermore, $s = \frac{1}{2}$ implies an electronic spin angular momentum of $\frac{1}{2}(h/2\pi)$ on the part of the individual electrons, and S implies a net spin angular momentum of $S(h/2\pi)$.

Instead of using the previous equations to deduce the possible values of the quantum numbers L and S from the quantum numbers of the individual electrons, one can ask how the angular momentum contributions of the individual electrons could lead to net angular momenta for the electronic state of the molecule. To combine the angular momentum contributions, it is convenient to introduce vectors and to deal with what is known as the *vector model of the atom*. The vector model assigns an orbital angular momentum vector **l** to represent the magnitude $\sqrt{l(l+1)}\,(h/2\pi)$ and the direction of the orbital angular momentum contribution that each of the electrons of the atom would make if the electrons were noninteracting. Similarly, a vector **L** represents the magnitude $\sqrt{L(L+1)}\,(h/2\pi)$ and the direction of the orbital angular momentum of the atom when it is in the electronic state specified by L. The possible values of the vector **L** are correctly given by the vector combinations

$$\mathbf{L} = \sum_i \mathbf{l}_i$$

which lead to vectors **L** that correspond to integral values of L.

It turns out to be much easier to draw the vector diagrams, such as those which give **L** from the values of $\mathbf{l}_i$, if one returns to the early, and not really correct, idea that the quantum number L implies an angular momentum of $L(h/2\pi)$ rather than $\sqrt{L(L+1)}\,(h/2\pi)$ and l an angular momentum of $l(h/2\pi)$ rather than $\sqrt{l(l+1)}\,(h/2\pi)$. In this way one would draw vector diagrams such as those of Fig. 10-11 to represent the various possible combinations of **l** to form the net vector **L**.

Similarly, one describes the total angular momentum due to the spin of the electrons of the atom by a vector **S**, and in terms of the angular momentum contributions of the individual spinning electrons one has

$$\mathbf{S} = \sum_i \mathbf{s}_i$$

The previous discussion has assumed that the orbital and spin quantum numbers, and the corresponding angular momentum contributions, can be separately treated. In fact this is not so; although in some systems it turns out to be a satisfactory approximation. Since it is the

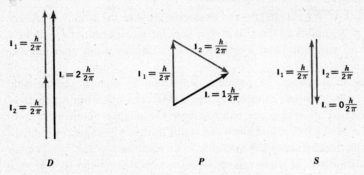

FIG. 10-11   The vector additions of the angular momentum vectors of two p-orbit electrons to give the total an angular momentum vector for the atom.

total angular momentum of the atom that is really quantized, the meaningful quantum number of the atom is that which determines this total amount.   The quantum number J is used, and the value of the total angular momentum of the atom is given by $\sqrt{J(J+1)}\,(h/2\pi)$.   Again the vector model of the atom introduces a vector $\mathbf{J}$ to represent this magnitude and the direction of the total angular momentum.   It turns out again, and this is another illustration of the reason for using the vector model, that the correct vectors $\mathbf{J}$ are obtained by vectorially combining $\mathbf{L}$ and $\mathbf{S}$.   This is illustrated in Fig. 10-12.   In terms of

FIG. 10-12   The vector diagrams that represent the ways in which the L and S vectors can be combined to give resulting vectors.

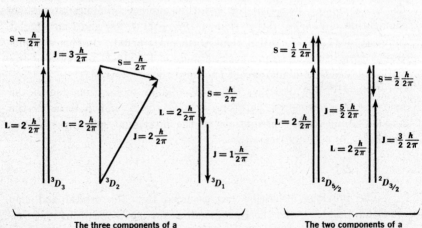

The three components of a
^3D term resulting from
$S = 1, L = 2$

The two components of a
^2D term resulting from
$S = \frac{1}{2}, L = 2$

quantum numbers, the value of J is given correctly by

$$J = L + S, L + S - 1, L + S - 2, \ldots, |L - S|$$

The electronic state of a free atom can now be described, in a manner suitable for spectroscopic studies, by the values of the quantum numbers L, S, and J.

It is customary to indicate the values of these three angular momentum quantum numbers by a term symbol. To indicate that L has the value 0, 1, 2, . . . one writes, as mentioned earlier, S, P, D, ... Since the number of ways that the spin quantum number can be combined with the orbital angular momentum quantum number is often an important feature (energy levels with a given value of L are sometimes split into sublevels, depending on the coupling between L and S), we indicate this number of ways $(2S + 1)$ as a left superscript on the symbol for L. Finally, the value of J is written as a right subscript on the symbol for L. Thus one encounters descriptions such as $^2S_{\frac{1}{2}}$, $^2P_{\frac{3}{2}}$, $^2P_{\frac{1}{2}}$, and so forth, for the electronic state of an atom.

We will see that the electronic states of diatomic molecules are similar, in many respects, to those of atoms under the influence of an electric field. Experimental, as well as theoretical, results for such atoms indicate that the atomic orbitals must orient themselves so that the component of the angular momentum of the atom must be quantized along the direction of the electric field. Just as for the case of a rotating molecule, treated in Chap. 5, a quantum-mechanical treatment shows that, if the total angular momentum of the atom is $\sqrt{J(J + 1)}\,(h/2\pi)$, the component along the direction of the applied field will be $M(h/2\pi)$, where

$$M = J, J - 1, \ldots, 0, \ldots, -J$$

Again the vector model is convenient in that it suggests that the angular momentum vector $\mathbf{J}$ can take up various orientations relative to the applied field and that these orientations are such that the component angular momentum along the field is an integral, or half integral if J is half integral, multiple of $(h/2\pi)$. This is illustrated in Fig. 10-13.

We are now in a position to proceed to a similar description of possible electronic states of molecules and then to assign these states to the observed electronic transitions.

10-4. Electron Orbitals in Diatomic Molecules

As for polyelectronic atoms it is generally impossible to calculate the energies and detailed electronic arrangements for the possible electronic states of molecules.   Again it is necessary to describe the allowed states by means of values of the quantum numbers of the properties, principally angular momenta, whose quantization can be immediately recognized.   Just as for the case of atoms, this can best be done by first considering the allowed individual electron orbits and then investigating the molecular states that result when certain of these orbits are occupied by electrons.

The electron orbits of diatomic molecules are best described in terms of the orbits to which they would go in the limits of the *united atom*, i.e., the internuclear distance diminished to zero, and the *separated atoms*, i.e., the internuclear distance increased to infinity.

Let us first consider the united atom of some diatomic molecule and investigate how the electron orbits are to be described as the nucleus of the united atom is imagined to be subdivided and the separate nuclei that correspond to those of the diatomic molecule are formed.   The initial effect on the atomic orbits can be understood on the basis of the fact that the divided nucleus presents a field of axial rather than spherical symmetry.   The effect on the orbits is comparable to that of an external electric field applied along the direction in which the bond is being formed. It becomes necessary, therefore, if the orbits of such a deformed atom are to be described, to specify, not only the orbital angular momentum, but also the component of this along the internuclear axis.   Thus, although an orbit of the united atom is characterized by its total angular momentum, as indicated by the quantum number $l = 0, 1, 2, \ldots, n-1$

FIG. 10-13   Vector diagrams illustrating that three orientations can be taken up relative to an applied field by the angular momentum vector corresponding to a $J = 1$ state. On the left the simpler diagram based on vectors of length $J(h/2\pi)$ is shown.   On the right the correct diagram, with $\sqrt{J(J+1)}(h/2\pi)$ vectors, is given.   Either diagram shows that the $J = 1$ state splits into three components.

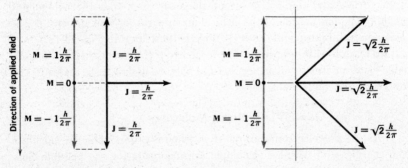

or by the letters s, p, d, . . . , as the atom is deformed toward a diatomic molecule, these orbits will be characterized also (and for large distortions better) by the component of the angular momentum along the molecular axis.

For a given value of l of the initial atomic orbit, the quantized angular momentum components along the bond direction can have the quantum numbers 0, 1, 2, . . . , l. The symbol λ is usually used to designate the quantum number for the component along the internuclear axis, and values of $\lambda = 0$, 1, 2, . . . are usually indicated by saying that the orbit is a σ, π, δ, . . . orbit. (The nomenclature principle that is followed consists of using Greek letters for molecular quantities and Roman letters for atomic properties. Thus, in the spherical field of an atom, the orbital angular momentum quantum number is of major importance and is designated for each electron by l. For the cyclindrical field of a diatomic molecule, the principal orbital angular momentum feature is the component along the axis of the molecule, and the quantum number for this is, therefore, designated by λ.) With this notation the initial step in the formation of a diatomic molecule from the united atom can be illustrated as in Fig. 10-14. It is well to note the geometric arrangement of the electron orbit associated with each energy level as well as their angular momentum contributions.

In a similar way, when the two separated atoms that correspond to the diatomic molecule are allowed to approach one another, the electron orbits are affected by the imposition of an axial direction. The perturbation that this causes when the separated atoms are different, i.e., when the diatomic molecule is heteronuclear, is illustrated in Fig. 10-15a. (It is customary to represent the united-atom limit at the left of the page and the separated-atom limit at the right of the page. This order is maintained in the diagrams for initial effects in Figs. 10-14 and 10-15.) A second atom affects the orbitals of a given atom by imposing a direction in space. This distinguishes between orbitals of the given atom that have the same value of l but different orientations relative to the internuclear axis that is being formed. The three p orbitals, for example, which might be labeled p_x, p_y, and p_z, are identical in the spherical symmetry of an isolated atom. When an axial direction is imposed, the orbit projecting along this direction, which has zero angular momentum in this direction and is therefore labeled as σp, is differently affected than the two orbitals that project perpendicularly from the axis, have one unit of angular momentum along this axis, and are designated as πp orbitals.

FIG. 10-14 The splittings of the atomic-energy levels that result from the initial step in breaking apart a united atom. The notation based on angular momenta and the orientations of the orbitals are shown.

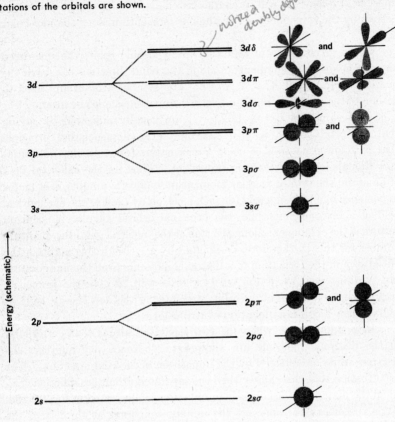

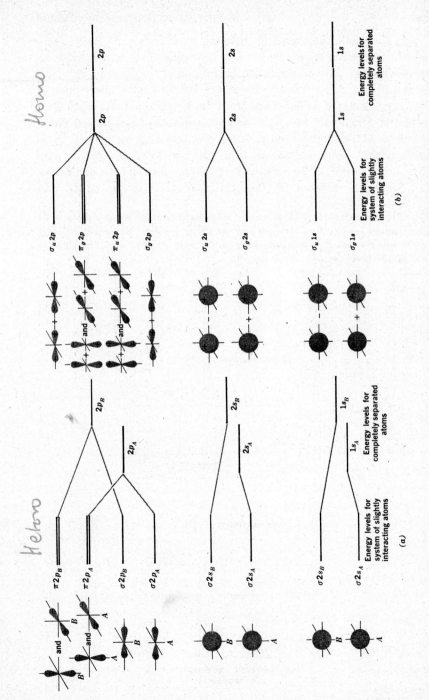

FIG. 10-15 Effect of initial interactions on some of the lower energy levels as the separated atoms begin to approach one another. (a) Bonded atoms A and B are different. (b) Bonded atoms are identical.

In the case of homonuclear diatomic atoms, one additional feature must be recognized in order to see how the orbits of the separated atoms interact as they go over into molecular orbitals of the diatomic molecule. As should be familiar from studies of the Heitler-London description of the H_2 molecule, or as is evident from the simple one-dimensional illustration of Fig. 10-16, two like wave functions can be combined either symmetrically, designated by g, or antisymmetrically, designated by u. These symbols must be attached to the description of the orbitals, as is done in Fig. 10-15b, when molecular orbitals are formed from like atoms.

The states deduced for the perturbed limits of the united and

FIG. 10-16   A square-well analogy to show the importance of the g and u character of wave functions resulting from the uniting of two similar systems.   Notice that the wave function with the node goes to higher energy as the bond is formed while that without a node goes to lower energy.

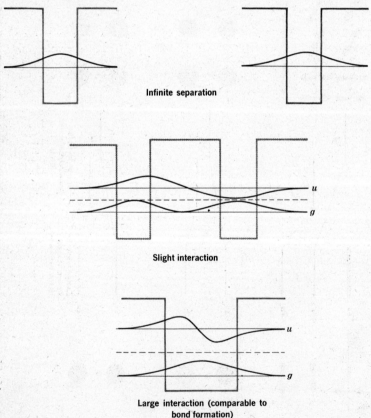

Infinite separation

Slight interaction

Large interaction (comparable to
bond formation)

separated atoms must now be connected to give the desired molecular orbitals appropriate to intermediate nuclear distances. The two limits can be correlated with each other, to give a *correlation diagram*, when it is realized that the quantum number λ is a good one even when the axial field is very important as it is at intermediate internuclear distances. Thus, one joins up, as in Figs. 10-17 and 10-18, states with the same values of λ, i.e., a σ with a σ state, a π with a π state, and so forth. Furthermore, for homonuclear molecules it is necessary to preserve the g and u character of the orbital. This can be done by joining orbitals designated by u for separated atoms with, for example, σp states which, as shown by the wave-function sketches in Fig. 10-14, have the correct antisymmetry character.

The correlation diagrams of Figs. 10-17 and 10-18 allow the electron orbits of a diatomic molecule to be described and the order of their

FIG. 10-17 A correlation diagram describing the energies of the electron orbitals of heteronuclear diatomic molecules. (From G. Herzberg, "Spectra of Diatomic Molecules," D. Van Nostrand Company, Inc., Princeton, N.J., 1950.) The vertical broken lines indicate the approximate positions which give the correct ordering of the energies of the molecular orbitals for the indicated molecules.

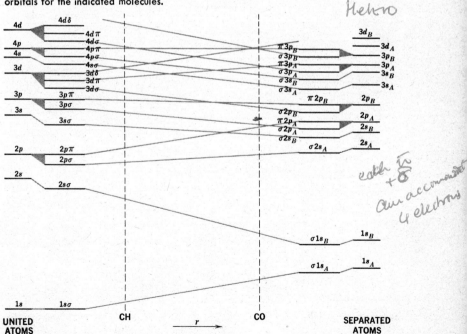

energies to be roughly estimated. They are, therefore, equivalent to
Fig. 10-9 and provide essentially the same basis for describing the electronic state of a molecule as does the use of the hydrogenlike wave functions for a many-electron atom.

Correlation diagrams are resorted to because of the relative ease
with which the general shapes and energies of electron orbits of atoms
can be described and the great difficulty of doing the same for molecules.
The correlation diagram gives immediately some information on the
relative energies of molecular orbitals. Something of the shape of the
corresponding orbitals can also be deduced by looking at the shapes
of the limiting atomic orbitals. This is illustrated for the case of σp
and πp orbitals in Fig. 10-19. One should notice that two arrangements
of the two orbitals that overlap, when the molecule is formed, are always
possible. The one that overlaps to form a high electron density between
the nuclei is of lower energy (recall the ordering of particle-in-a-box

FIG. 10-18 A correlation diagram describing the energies of the electron orbitals of
homonuclear diatomic molecules. (*From G. Herzberg, "Spectra of Diatomic Molecules,"
D. Van Nostrand Company, Inc., Princeton, N.J., 1950.*)

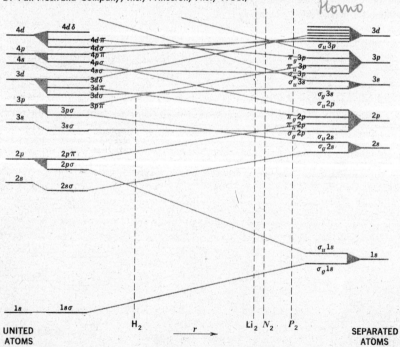

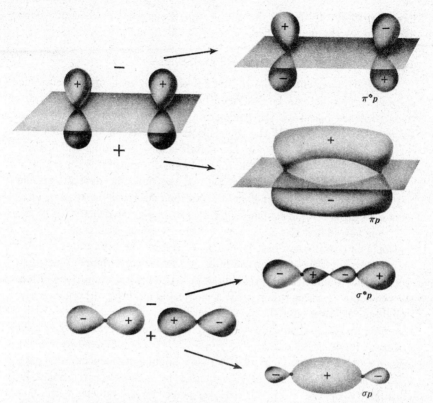

FIG. 10-19 Diagrams indicating something of the shape of some molecular orbitals. These shapes indicated for σp, $\sigma^* p$, πp, and $\pi^* p$ apply, for example, to the energy levels labeled $2\sigma p_A$, $2\sigma p_B$, $2\pi p_A$, and $2\pi p_B$ in Fig. 10-17 and $\sigma_g 2p$, $\sigma_u 2p$, $\pi_u 2p$, and $\pi_g 2p$ in Fig. 10-18.

wave functions according to the number of nodes) and is said to be a bonding orbital. The second arrangement, in which the function must change sign and have a node between the nuclei, is of higher energy and is known as an antibonding orbital. In a similar way, one can draw the bonding and antibonding orbitals that are formed from the coming together of other atomic orbitals. These qualitative pictures of electron orbitals are often used, particularly when polyatomic molecules are studied, as a basis for describing electron changes that occur.

Exercise 10-3. With the aid of Fig. 10-17, suggest an electronic configuration for the ground state of the molecule NO. (Note that each π and δ energy level can accommodate a total of four electrons.)

Exercise 10-4. With the aid of Fig. 10-18 suggest an electronic configuration for the molecule O_2.

10-5. Electronic States of Diatomic Molecules

The arrangement of the individual electrons in a given electronic state of a molecule can be described by the individual electron descriptions that are based on the correlation diagram. Some examples are shown in Table 10-3. If the molecule is composed of like atoms, the separated atom designation for the orbitals is more revealing and is used. For heteronuclear molecules, the united atom designation is used.

As for atoms, the electronic state of the molecule depends on the net or total electronic arrangement. Various electronic states can arise from a given electronic configuration, i.e., from a given description of the electrons considered one at a time. The electronic arrangement of the molecule as a whole can best be characterized by the net orbital angular momentum component along the internuclear axis and the net electronic spin angular momentum along this axis. The orbital component along the molecular axis, designated by Λ since this quantity depends on the individual electron contributions designated by λ, is easily obtained by summing up the contributions of the separate atoms, 0 for σ, 1 for π, 2 for δ, and so forth. The value of $\Lambda = 0, 1, 2, \ldots$ is indicated by writing a term symbol $\Sigma, \Pi, \Delta, \ldots$. The spin angular momentum along the axis is, as for the atomic case, indicated by a superscript giving the multiplicity of the state. If the molecule is homonuclear, the net symmetry, i.e., the g or u property, is significant for the molecule as well as for the individual orbitals. (The electronic state is even and labeled with a g if the number of u electrons is even, and the state is odd and labeled with a u if the number of u electrons is odd.) Finally,

TABLE 10-3   Some Examples of the Descriptions Used for Electronic States
(K is used to denote 2 electrons in $1s$ orbits, L to denote 8 electrons in the $2s$ and $2p$ orbits)

Molecule	Ground configuration		First excited configuration	
H_2	$(\sigma_g 1s)^2$	$^1\Sigma_g^+$	$(\sigma_g 1s)\sigma_u 1s$	$^1\Sigma_u^+, \, ^3\Sigma_u^+$
Li_2	$KK(\sigma_g 2s)^2$	$^1\Sigma_g^+$	$KK(\sigma_g 2s)\sigma_u 2s$	$^1\Sigma_u^+, \, ^3\Sigma_u^+$
N_2	$KK(\sigma_g 2s)^2(\sigma_u 2s)^2(\pi_u 2p)^4$ $(\sigma_g 2p)^2$	$^1\Sigma_g^+$	$KK(\sigma_g 2s)^2(\sigma_u 2s)^2(\pi_u 2p)^4$ $(\sigma_g 2p)^1\pi_g 2p$	$^1\Pi_g, \, ^1\Pi_u$
LiH	$K(2s\sigma)^2$	$^1\Sigma^+$	$K(2s\sigma)2p\sigma$	$^1\Sigma^+, \, ^3\Sigma^+$
CH	$K(2s\sigma)^2(2s\sigma)^2 2p\pi$	$^2\Pi$	$K(2s\sigma)^2 2p\sigma(2p\pi)^2$	$^4\Sigma^-, \, ^2\Delta, \, ^2\Sigma^+, \, ^2\Sigma^-$

if a molecule is in a Σ state as a result of the opposition of two π or δ angular momentum vectors, these vectors can have either the orientation $\rightarrow \leftarrow$ or $\leftarrow \rightarrow$. It turns out, by an argument not easily given, that these alternatives correspond to molecular orbitals that are either symmetric or antisymmetric with respect to a plane through the molecular axis. In view of this, and the discussion of Sec. 5-4, we label Σ states, which arise from two π or two δ orbitals, as Σ^+ and Σ^-. (It should be clear, in view of Fig. 10-14, that antisymmetry with respect to any plane through the internuclear axis cannot be achieved from σ orbitals.) The notation used for molecular electronic states is illustrated, along with the indicated orbital occupancy, in Table 10-3.

We are now at a stage where we can describe, in terms of angular momenta, the different electronic states that can be expected for a given molecule, and with the aid of the correlation diagrams, we can tell, although only approximately, the order of these states on an energy scale.

10-6. Potential-energy Curves for Electronic States of Diatomic Molecules

Although the energies of states arising from different electronic arrangements for diatomic molecules cannot yet be calculated, the electronic states of diatomic molecules can, as indicated by the lengthy discussions of the previous sections, be described and labeled. It can now be pointed out that a given electronic transition can, in some cases, be associated with a particular pair of states. When this can be done, the detailed information obtained from analysis of the rotational and vibrational structure of the spectral band can be used along with the electronic configurations of the states involved so that diagrams, such as that of Fig. 10-20, can be constructed.

The way in which electronic states are assigned to the transition resulting in an electronic absorption or emission band cannot be treated here. The subject is covered in considerable detail in the references given at the end of this chapter. It need only be mentioned here that the principal basis for the assignment stems from a comparison of the observed rotational structure with that expected for transitions between various types of electronic states. The nature of the rotational transitions is strongly affected by the coupling between the electronic angular momenta of the states involved and the rotational angular momentum of the molecule. As a result one observes such features as P and R branches with or without a Q branch, P and R branches with each line

FIG. 10-20   The potential-energy curves for various electronic states of the molecule C_2. (From G. Herzberg, "Spectra of Diatomic Molecules," D. Van Nostrand Company, Inc., Princeton, N.J., 1950.)   (More recent data indicate that some revision is necessary.)   The symbol X is inserted to identify the ground state.   The notation a, b, c, . . . and A, B, C, . . . is added to identify the different states of the same multiplicity.

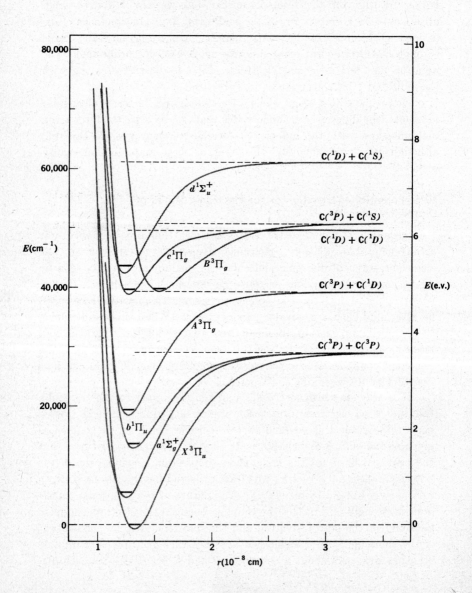

split into two or three lines, missing early members of the P, Q, and R branches, and so forth.

For some diatomic molecules, a fairly complete analysis of the ground and lower excited states can be made. For many more molecules, only a few of the observed bands can be definitely attributed to specific electronic states. Much of the wealth of chemical bonding information that has arisen from studies of electronic transitions is summarized in the Appendix of ref. 2. A summary of some more recent results has been given by P. G. Wilkinson [$J.$ $Molecular$ $Spectroscopy$, $6:1$ (1961)].

PRINCIPAL REFERENCES

1. Herzberg, G.: "Atomic Spectra and Atomic Structure," Dover Publications, New York, 1944.
2. Herzberg, G.: "Spectra of Diatomic Molecules," D. Van Nostrand Company, Inc., Princeton, N.J., 1950.
3. Gaydon, A. G.: "Dissociation Energies and Spectra of Diatomic Molecules," Dover Publications, New York, 1950.
4. Mulliken, R. S.: $Rev.$ $Mod.$ $Phys.$, $2(60):506$ (1930); $3:90$ (1931); $4:3$ (1932).

11

ELECTRONIC SPECTRA
OF POLYATOMIC MOLECULES

The wealth of experimental data and detailed analyses that characterize the spectroscopy of electronic states of diatomic molecules is in sharp contrast to the situation encountered with most polyatomic molecules. Since the energy of an electronically excited polyatomic molecule can usually be distributed so as to break a weak chemical bond of the molecule, bound high-energy electronic states are not so abundant as in diatomic molecules. A further consequence of this is that a sample usually cannot be heated to a temperature at which emission spectra can be obtained without risk of decomposition. The only transitions that are normally observed are, therefore, those from the ground to an excited electronic state that show up in absorption spectra. Only a few bands arising from such transitions are usually obtained, and since the samples under study are often solutions or solids, the absorption bands are often broad and relatively structureless. (Spectra of compounds that will be studied later in this chapter are shown in Figs. 11-2, 11-10, and 11-18.) The revealing rotational structure of diatomic absorption bands is, therefore, absent, and a band does not immediately reveal the nature of the electronic states involved in the transition.

In spite of the relatively greater difficulty involved in the analysis of the electronic spectra of polyatomic molecules, much work has been and is being done in this area. Spectral data on the nature and energies of electronic configurations of states other than the ground state of the molecule provide important testing data for theories of chemical bonding. The geometry of molecules in excited states is not necessarily the

264

same as that of the ground state; formaldehyde and ethylene are, for example, nonplanar in one or more of their excited states. In studies of reaction mechanisms, particularly those resulting from photochemical excitation, such information on excited electronic states is basic to a detailed understanding of the mechanism.

It should also be mentioned that the absorption bands due to electronic transitions, which usually occur in the ultraviolet or visible spectral regions, have long played an important role in the analysis and characterization of both organic and inorganic compounds. A number of important empirical generalizations have been developed which predict the effect of structural changes on the frequency and intensity of the absorption bands of a parent molecule. The relation between the electronic structure of the absorbing molecule and its absorption spectrum that will be introduced in this chapter provides some basis for the understanding of such empirical relations and for the use of ultraviolet and visible spectra as a tool for the study of electronic structures.

The material falling within the scope of the title of this chapter can be conveniently divided into four topics.

The first topic concerns itself with molecules that absorb radiation because of an electronic transition that is essentially localized in a bond, or group, of the molecule. Most studied of such systems, and suitable to illustrate the procedures used, are molecules containing a carbonyl group $\diagdown\!\!\!\diagup$ C=O The analysis of the spectra of such systems is similar to that for diatomic molecules, but important differences arise because of the experimental limitations mentioned previously and the loss of the axis along which angular momentum would be quantized.

The second molecular type to be studied consists of molecules containing conjugated π-electron systems. Aromatic molecules constitute the largest and most studied group in this category, and after a brief discussion of linear conjugated systems, the way in which one attempts to describe the various electronic states resulting from excitation, of the π electrons in these molecules will be introduced.

The next topic deals with the absorption spectra produced by systems that contain a transition metal ion in a coordination compound. Many such systems are colored; i.e., they have electronic transitions that result in absorption in the visible region. The spectrum of such a compound is, therefore, an often referred to characteristic of the material. Analyses of such absorption bands in terms of the electronic states involved lead to further understanding of the bonding in these coordination compounds.

Finally, the process by which a molecule or an ion in an excited electronic state can get rid of its excess energy and return to its ground state will be investigated, and some features of the processes of fluorescence and phosphorescence will be introduced.

TRANSITIONS LOCALIZED IN BONDS OR GROUPS

11-1. Electronic States of Localized Groups

Chemists have devised a number of ways for describing the ground electronic state of a molecule. One of these, due to G. N. Lewis, uses dot diagrams to indicate the number of bonding and nonbonding electrons in a molecule. Thus, for formaldehyde, H_2CO, this approach would give a diagrammatic description of the ground electronic state as

$$H$$
$$H:\ddot{C}::\ddot{O}:$$

where the placement of the dots represents the role of the outer electrons in the molecule. With the advent of quantum-mechanical descriptions based on the Schrödinger equation solutions for the hydrogen-atom problem, these diagrams could be refined to show in somewhat more detail the spatial arrangement of the electrons. Thus, the diagrams of the type used in the previous chapter, i.e.,

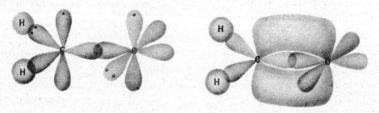

could be drawn.

These atomic orbital type diagrams suggest a method for describing the available electron orbits in molecules of this type. In view of the notation used for diatomic molecules, bonding p, or s and p hybrid, orbitals projecting in the direction of the bond are said to be σ orbitals, and the bonding orbital resulting from the overlap of such orbitals is known as a σ bond. There will also be, as can be seen by inspection of the correlation diagrams of Figs. 10-17, 10-18, and 10-19, a corresponding higher energy antibonding σ orbital, not occupied in the ground state, produced by the overlap of the two σ atomic orbitals. This antibonding orbital is usually denoted by σ^*. The principal distinguishing feature of σ and σ^* orbitals is, as shown in Fig. 10-19, the node in the σ^* orbital. The atomic p orbitals that project perpendicularly from the bond direction and form a bond are said to be π orbitals. The overlap of such atomic orbitals leads to a bonding π orbital, which will be occupied in the ground state of H_2CO, and a higher energy antibonding orbital designated by π^*. The remaining electrons that are of interest in the study of electronic transitions of such groups are "lone-pair" or "nonbonding" electrons on the oxygen atom. They can, if hybridization of the atomic orbitals on oxygen is not considered, be located in the available oxygen-atom orbitals, which are a low-lying $2s$ orbital and the remaining $2p$ orbital. If only the higher-energy $2p$ orbital is considered to be involved in the observed transitions, it can be designated simply as a nonbonding orbital and the symbol n can be used for it.

It should be recognized that, as for diatomic molecules, the exact spatial distribution corresponding to these orbitals cannot be calculated. Furthermore, no exact angular momentum values can be used to characterize the orbitals. We will see, however, that the shapes of the orbitals can be drawn well enough so that the symmetry of the orbitals can be deduced, and the behavior under the symmetry operations of the molecule will be seen to provide the best characterization of orbitals in polyatomic molecules. In anticipation of this, the diagrams given in Fig. 11-1 for the orbitals of the carbonyl bond that are important in electronic transitions of that group should be noted.

Once the available individual electron orbits for a given molecule are recognized, electrons can be assigned to these orbitals to specify an electronic configuration of the molecule. Thus, the ground state of H_2CO can be expected to correspond to the designation, which later will be abbreviated,

$$[(1s_C)^2(1s_O)^2(2s_O)^2(\sigma_{CH})^2(\sigma_{CH'})^2(\sigma_{CO})^2](\pi_{CO})^2(n_O)^2$$

The three σ bonds to the carbon atom are thought of as being formed from sp^2 trigonal hybrid orbitals on the carbon atom. The π bond between the carbon and oxygen atoms then is formed from the remaining carbon atom p orbital and one of the oxygen p orbitals. The brackets enclose the low-lying inner and bonding electron orbitals that are not normally expected to be involved in the transitions studied. It is enough, therefore, to write, for the ground-state electron arrangement,

[Inner electrons]$(\pi_{CO})^2(n_O)^2$

or simply

[Inner electrons]$(\pi)^2(n)^2$

Similarly, some of the excited states that might be expected to be important can be indicated by

[Inner electrons]$(\pi)^2(n)(\pi^*)$
[Inner electrons]$(\pi)(n)^2(\pi^*)$
[Inner electrons]$(\pi)^2(n)(\sigma^*)$

FIG. 11-1 Some spectroscopically important orbitals of H_2CO and their symmetry properties.

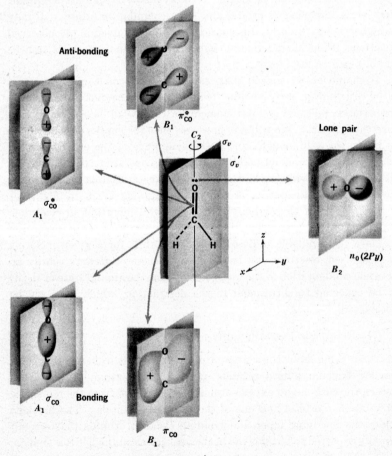

and so forth. In the above, as is customary, a superscript 1 is understood and is not written when an orbital is singly occupied.

Expressions such as those given above constitute *electronic configurations* for the various electronic states of the H_2CO molecule considered here.

Exercise 11-1. Write the electronic configurations for the ground and several excited states of the acetonitrile CH_3CN molecule.

For some purposes the electronic state of a molecule is adequately described by such electronic configurations, i.e., by such individual electron descriptions. A more thorough understanding of the electronic transitions of polyatomic molecules requires, as for diatomic molecules, a description, for a given assignment of electrons to the individual orbitals, of the electronic state of the molecule as a whole. As previously mentioned, this cannot be done for nonlinear molecules on the basis of a net orbital angular momentum along an axis. One can, however, recognize that the total electronic wave function must have a symmetry that is compatible with the symmetry of the molecular skeleton. It is this symmetry behavior that best characterizes electronic states of polyatomic molecules.

First one must consider the symmetry types of the individual orbitals. The molecule being used as an illustration here, H_2CO, or effectively any symmetric ketone, belongs to the point group C_{2v}. The character table for this group is shown in Table 11-1. Assignment of the orbitals of Fig. 11-1 to symmetry species can readily be made by investigating whether the orbital is left unchanged or changes sign as a result of the four symmetry operations of the group. In this way the symmetry classification of the individual orbitals, shown in Fig. 11-1, is obtained.

It is now necessary to assign the total electronic wave function of the molecule to a symmetry type. First one recognizes that, to an approxi-

TABLE 11-1   The C_{2v} Character Table

C_{2v}	E	C_2	σ_v	σ_v'	
A_1	1	1	1	1	T_z
A_2	1	1	-1	-1	
B_1	1	-1	1	-1	T_x
B_2	1	-1	-1	1	T_y

TABLE 11-2 The Effect of Symmetry Operations on $\varphi(1)$, Presumed to Be of the Type A_2, and $\varphi(2)$, of the Type B_1, and on the Product $\varphi(1)\varphi(2)$

	E	C_2	σ_v	σ_v'
$R\varphi(1) =$	$+1\varphi(1)$	$+1\varphi(1)$	$-1\varphi(1)$	$-1\varphi(1)$
$R\varphi(2) =$	$+1\varphi(2)$	$-1\varphi(2)$	$+1\varphi(2)$	$-1\varphi(2)$
$R\varphi(1)\varphi(2) =$	$(+1)(+1)\varphi(1)\varphi(2)$	$(+1)(-1)\varphi(1)\varphi(2)$	$(-1)(+1)\varphi(1)\varphi(2)$	$(-1)(-1)\varphi(1)\varphi(2)$
	$= +1\varphi(1)\varphi(2)$	$= -1\varphi(1)\varphi(2)$	$= -1\varphi(1)\varphi(2)$	$= +1\varphi(1)\varphi(2)$

mation sufficient for symmetry considerations, the total wave function for the molecule can be written as the product of the wave functions describing the individual behavior of the electrons. Thus one writes

$$\psi = \varphi(1)\varphi(2)\varphi(3) \cdots \tag{1}$$

where $\varphi(1)$ is the wave function for the orbital occupied by electron 1, $\varphi(2)$ the wave function for that occupied by electron 2, and so forth.

The results of the various symmetry operations on the φ's are known. Thus, for example, if electron 1 is in an orbital of type A_2 and electron 2 is in an orbital of type B_1, the result of symmetry operations on $\varphi(1)$ and $\varphi(2)$ could be tabulated as shown in Table 11-2.

The effect of the symmetry operations on the product $\varphi(1)\varphi(2)$ is given in the third row of the table. We have used again, as we did in investigations of the symmetry behavior of the transition-moment integral, the fact that *the character for such a product of functions is equal to the product of the characters of the individual functions.* (In group theory one uses the term *direct product* for such a product of two functions.) The product $\varphi(1)\varphi(2)$ is found, according to the results of Table 11-2, to transform according to the symmetry type B_2.

With this result and the symmetries of the individual orbitals, one can calculate the symmetry type of the total electronic wave function of the molecule with given electronic assignments. The task is greatly simplified when it is recognized (1) that many (in the ground state, usually all) of the orbitals are occupied by two electrons and (2) that the product of one nondegenerate representation and itself necessarily leads to the totally symmetric representation. In view of this, the net character for all the doubly occupied orbitals is the set of $+1$'s that constitute the totally symmetric representation. The symmetry types of the electronic states of H_2CO, corresponding to the configurations previously displayed, can then be easily deduced from the symmetries of the singly occupied orbitals. The results are shown in Table 11-3.

TABLE 11-3   Some Electronic Configurations and Electronic States of Formaldehyde

Configuration	Symmetry of electronic state	Transition moments from ground state
[Inner electrons] $(\pi)^2(n)^2$	A_1	
[Inner electrons] $(\pi)^2(n)(\pi^*)$	A_2	$|\mu_x| = |\mu_y| = |\mu_z| = 0$
[Inner electrons] $(\pi)(n)^2(\pi^*)$	A_1	$|\mu_x| = |\mu_y| = 0; |\mu_z| \neq 0$
[Inner electrons] $(\pi)^2(n)(\sigma^*)$	B_2	$|\mu_x| = |\mu_z| = 0; |\mu_y| \neq 0$

Exercise 11-2. Verify the symmetry assignments shown in Table 11-3 for the various electron configurations.

One further feature of the electronic states of molecules must be mentioned. The description has, so far, ignored the relative directions of spin of the electrons. The Pauli principle requires that the spins of two electrons occupying the same orbital be opposed but allows, when orbitals are occupied by single electrons, either spin orientation. It follows that the ground state of H_2CO must be a singlet state, i.e., the net spin must equal zero, since all the electrons are paired and each pair must have opposite spins. For the excited states considered above, however, the net spin can be either zero, i.e., the molecule can be in a singlet state, or unity, i.e., the molecule can be in a triplet state. The designation singlet or triplet must, therefore, be added to the description of a molecular state. It can be mentioned in this connection that the rule based on atomic spectral results, and known as Hund's rule, is also applicable to molecular systems. This rule states that, if both singlet and triplet configurations are possible with the same set of orbitals, the triplet state will have a lower energy than the corresponding singlet state. Thus, lower energy electronic states are to be expected when the above excited configurations are occupied by electrons with parallel spins than when they are occupied with paired spins. This qualitative discussion is as far as we need go in attempting to describe the electronic states that are involved in the electronic transitions with which we will be concerned. Now we must see if the observed absorption bands can be correlated with transitions between the various electronic states.

11-2. Electronic Transitions and Absorption Bands

A schematic absorption spectra of a carbonyl compound such as formaldehyde or methyl ethyl ketone, is shown in Fig. 11-12. The object of this section is to see if such absorption spectra can be understood on the basis of the electronic states of molecules as described, for example, in the previous section. If assignments of the absorption bands to transitions between given states can be made, the relative energies of the various electronic arrangements of the molecule can be deduced.

The excited states of a carbonyl compound that are usually suspected of being involved in electronic spectral transitions are those described in the previous section. It is first necessary, therefore, to see if transitions between the ground state and each of these excited states can be expected to be induced by electromagnetic radiation. According to the discussion of Sec. 4-9 it is necessary for one of the integrals

$$|\mu_x| = \int \psi_{\text{excited}} \mu_x \psi_{\text{ground}} \, d\tau$$
$$|\mu_y| = \int \psi_{\text{excited}} \mu_y \psi_{\text{ground}} \, d\tau$$

or

$$|\mu_z| = \int \psi_{\text{excited}} \mu_z \psi_{\text{ground}} \, d\tau$$

to be nonzero for the transition to be induced. Knowledge of the

FIG. 11-2 A schematic diagram for the ultraviolet absorption spectrum of a carbonyl compound.

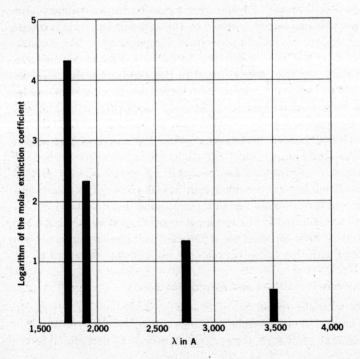

symmetry of the wave functions is sufficient to decide whether or not the integrals may be nonzero. (One can, in fact, use approximate wave functions for the orbitals shown diagrammatically in the previous section and perform the integrations in order to get some idea, not only of whether a transition is allowed or not, but also of how intense the absorption will be.) The integrals, like all observable properties, must not be changed by the symmetry operations which take the molecule from one orientation to an indistinguishable one. Thus, unless the symmetry species to which $\psi_{excited}\mu_x\psi_{ground}$ belongs is A_1, the value of the integral must be zero. Similar statements can be made for the transition-moment integral in the y and z directions. The ground state for the molecules considered here, and for all molecules with no unpaired electrons, has the symmetry type A_1. It follows that the entire integrand has the symmetry A_1 if $\psi_{excited}$ and μ_x, $\psi_{excited}$ and μ_y, or $\psi_{excited}$ and μ_z belong to the same symmetry type. Thus, just as in vibrational transitions, an electronic transition from a totally symmetric ground state is allowed if the excited state belongs to a symmetry type that contains μ_x, μ_y, or μ_z, i.e., T_x, T_y, or T_z. The results of such an analysis applied to CH_2O are shown in Table 11-3.

The selection rule prohibiting changes in spin that is operative in small atoms and diatomic molecules appears to be fairly well obeyed in simple polyatomic molecules. Again, however, the presence of a nucleus with a large nuclear charge results in a strong coupling of the spinning electron with the orbital motion of the electron and allows the relative spins of electrons to be altered. Even in simple molecules, such as formaldehyde, transitions to an excited triplet state cannot be entirely ruled out. While triplet states are relatively unimportant in absorption studies, i.e., they lead to very weak absorption bands, we will see that they play an interesting and important role in fluorescence and phosphorescence.

A comparison of the observed band intensities with those expected on the basis of the transition-moment integrals provides the most frequently used approach to the assignment of electronic states to absorption bands. As mentioned in Sec. 4-9, a completely allowed transition, such as that from the ground state to the A_1 excited state of formaldehyde, is expected to have an intensity $\int \alpha(\bar{\nu})\,d\bar{\nu}$ which corresponds to an oscillator strength, or f value, near unity. On the other hand, transitions that are predicted to be forbidden on the basis of the symmetry treatment illustrated above can occur to such an extent that weak absorption bands are observed. The f values for such bands will be much less than unity. One mechanism that allows forbidden transitions to occur involves vibrations of the molecule that lead to nuclear configurations that do not have the same symmetry as does the molecule in its equilibrium configuration. As a result, the skeletal symmetry to which the electronic wave functions must conform is, for the H_2CO example, not strictly C_{2v}, and the prohibitions based on that symmetry group are not strictly adhered to. The generally accepted assignment for the observed carbonyl bands is shown in Table 11-4.

Two other general methods for aiding in the assignment of absorption bands are used. The first of these is concerned with the direction of the transition moment, i.e., the polarization of the absorption. The analyses given in Table 11-3 indicate that a determination of the direction of polarization would identify the upper state involved in the transition. Considerable experimental difficulty is, however, encountered in aligning the absorbing molecules so that studies with polarized radiation can be used to determine the direction of the transition moment. In some cases, a suitable crystalline form can be found that permits such studies.

Another assignment aid comes from the shift in the wavelength of the absorption band that accompanies solvation of the molecule. It is found, for example, principally on the basis of empirical correlations, that absorptions due to $n \rightarrow \pi^*$ transitions are shifted to shorter wavelengths while those due to $\pi \rightarrow \pi^*$ transitions are shifted to longer wavelengths as the solvation, or dielectric environment, of the absorbing molecule is increased. This correlation is frequently useful and has some theoretical basis. [Cf. H. McConnell, *J. Chem. Phys.*, **20**: 700 (1952).] One expects, for example, a hydrogen bond to the carbonyl group to tie up, to some extent, the nonbonding electrons on the oxygen. This

TABLE 11-4   The Ultraviolet Absorption Bands of Carbonyl Compounds and Suggested Assignments
(Values of λ and f are Typical Values for a Number of Compounds)

$\lambda_{\text{band max}}$ (A)	f (osc. strength)	Assignment		
		Configuration change	Upper state symmetry	Selection rule
1,700	0.5	$\pi \rightarrow \pi^*$	$^1A_1$	Allowed
1,800	0.02	$n \rightarrow \sigma^*$	$^1B_1$	Symmetry forbidden
2,800	0.0004	$n \rightarrow \pi^*$	$^1A_2$	Symmetry forbidden
3,500	10^{-5}	$n \rightarrow \pi^*$	$^3A_2(?)$	Symmetry and spin forbidden

would lower their energy and lead to a greater energy change, or a shorter wavelength band, for a transition that promotes one of these electrons.

An interesting and important aspect of electronic transitions that has not been considered but which is pertinent to a discussion of localized absorbing groups, and to the conjugated and aromatic systems that will be dealt with in the final section of this chapter, is the process by which molecules in excited electronic states lose their excess energy and revert to ground-state molecules. This process, as we will see, can involve fluorescence and phosphorescence emission of radiation.

(It should be mentioned that, since the symbols for electronic states do not immediately reveal the relative energies of the states, it is becoming standard, when transitions between two electronic states are considered, always to write the higher-energy state first. Thus, for example, the band in the H_2CO absorption spectrum at about 1,800 A would be referred to as due to a $^1B_1 \leftarrow {}^1A_1$ transition. If the same transition were studied in emission, one would write $^1B_1 \rightarrow {}^1A_1$. When, as is often the case, both absorption and emission spectra are dealt with, designations according to this system avoid much of the confusion that can arise. However, when the transition is discussed in terms of the configuration change of an electron of the molecule, the relative energies of the two configurations are usually evident, and one writes the initial electron orbit first and then an arrow pointing to the new orbit reached by the electron.)

Exercise 11-3. Draw the π and π^* orbitals of ethylene, and assign them to symmetry types in the point group to which ethylene belongs. To what symmetry types do the ground and first excited $(\pi)(\pi^*)$ states belong? Would a transition between these states be allowed, and, if so, in what direction would it be polarized?

ELECTRONIC TRANSITIONS OF CONJUGATED AND AROMATIC SYSTEMS

In molecules containing conjugated double bonds and in aromatic systems it is now clear that the π electrons, i.e., those in the $2p$ orbitals that project perpendicularly from the plane of the trigonal sp^2 orbitals forming σ bonds, are responsible for the absorption found in the near-ultraviolet or even the visible region. In studying such systems we can, therefore, concern ourselves with the possible orbitals that can arise from the atomic $2p\pi$ orbitals. A very simple but surprisingly successful approach, known as the free-electron model, will be introduced for linear conjugated systems. This treatment puts obvious emphasis on the delocalization of the electrons; i.e., the molecular orbitals that it leads to are spread out over the entire molecular skeleton. In the following section, aromatic systems will be considered, and molecular orbitals will be set up for benzene by means of the classical molecular orbital approach which combines the $2p\pi$ atomic orbitals into appropriate molecular orbitals.

11-3. Conjugated Systems by the Free-electron Model

It is well known that conjugated systems have absorption bands at longer and longer wavelengths as the number of conjugated double bonds gets greater and greater. In fact, long conjugated systems are often colored, i.e., the absorption band is in the visible region. These general features, as well as the wavelength and intensity of the absorption band for a given molecule, can be understood on the basis of a very simple model for the π electrons of the molecule.

Let us consider the specific case of the molecule octatetraene, C_8H_{10}. The structure, as indicated in Fig. 11-3, consists of a planar nuclear array. The carbon atoms can be considered to form σ bonds with sp^2 trigonal orbitals and π bonds with the remaining p orbitals. A total of eight electrons will occupy the π orbital system.

A treatment of the π electrons can be based on the idea, long held by chemists, that these electrons are delocalized and are not confined to a given atom or even to a given bond position. This suggests that one might treat the molecular skeleton as a region of roughly uniform potential throughout which, subject to the wave functions that can be calculated from the Schrödinger equation, the electrons are free to move. Outside the molecule the potential energy, on the simplest model, is

FIG. 11-3 The bonding and structure of octatetraene. Each carbon atom forms three σ bonds, indicated by —, with sp^2 hybrid orbitals. Each remaining $2p$ orbital, shown as an atomic orbital here, enters into the delocalized π bonding.

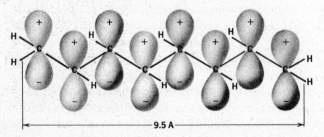

|← ———————— 9.5 A ———————— →|

assumed to be infinitely high. This free-electron or particle-in-a-box model, although clearly rather crude, leads to quite satisfactory results.

The potential-energy function for octatetraene is shown in Fig. 11-4. The exact width of this potential well is not unambiguously set. One usually assumes that the π electrons are free to move about half a bond length beyond each end carbon atom. Likewise, one usually assumes that an end-to-end measurement of the molecule is appropriate rather than one that follows the zigzag of the chain. With these assumptions, and ignoring repulsion between the π electrons, one can deduce the allowed orbitals and their energies.

The quantum-mechanical problem has already been solved in Sec. 1-5. There it was found that the wave functions for the particle-in-a-box problem are

$$\psi = A \sin \frac{n\pi x}{a} \qquad n = 1, 2, 3, \ldots \tag{2}$$

and that the energies of these solutions are

$$\epsilon_n = \frac{n^2 h^2}{8ma^2} \tag{3}$$

The Pauli exclusion stipulation that no two electrons can have the same quantum numbers requires that no more than two electrons, one with spin $+\frac{1}{2}$ and one with spin $-\frac{1}{2}$, be assigned to a wave function with a

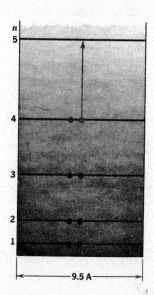

FIG. 11-4 Occupancy of molecular orbitals by the electrons of octatetraene in the ground state. The arrow indicates the transition that leads to the observed absorption band.

given value of n. The occupation of the available π molecular orbitals for octatetraene can then be illustrated as in Fig. 11-4.

The longest wavelength transition that is expected is that which takes one of the $n = 4$ electrons to the $n = 5$ orbital as indicated by the arrow in Fig. 11-4. The energy involved in this transition is given by

$$\epsilon_5 - \epsilon_4 = (5^2 - 4^2) \frac{h^2}{8ma^2} \tag{4}$$

The frequency of radiation that would cause this transition is calculated, with $a = 9.5$ A, to be

$$\bar{\nu} = 27,000 \text{ cm}^{-1} \tag{5}$$

This calculated result is to be compared with the absorption band maximum found at $33,100$ cm^{-1}. The agreement is surprisingly good.

A further advantage of this simple model is that, as discussed in Sec. 4-6, the intensity with which a sample absorbs radiation can be calculated. The prediction, for octatetraene, that the integrated absorption coefficient be, according to Eq. (58) in Chap. 4,

$$A = \frac{32Ne^2a^2\nu}{3\pi hc1,000}$$
$$= 1.9 \times 10^{19} \text{ sec}^{-1} \text{ cm}^{-1} \text{ mole}^{-1} \text{ liter} \tag{6}$$

can be compared with the experimental value of approximately

$$\int \alpha(\bar{\nu}) \, d\bar{\nu} = 1.1 \times 10^{19} \text{ sec}^{-1} \text{ cm}^{-1} \text{ mole}^{-1} \text{ liter} \tag{7}$$

Again the agreement is satisfactory.

A number of elaborations of this simple method for calculating the electronic states of conjugated systems have been introduced. The chief merit of this approach, which clearly oversimplifies the potential experienced by the π electrons, is, however, its simplicity.

Exercise 11-4. Note the similarity between the orbitals of Exercise 11-1 and the $n = 1$ and $n = 2$ particle-in-a-box wave functions that would be drawn for the ground and first excited orbitals for ethylene using the particle-in-a-box model.

Exercise 11-5. What are the calculated and observed f values for the longest wavelength π-electron transition of octatetraene?

Exercise 11-6. Lycopene is a linearly conjugated hydrocarbon consisting of all double bonds alternating with single bonds. It is responsible for the red color of tomatoes. Calculate the wavelength expected for the $\pi \rightarrow \pi^*$ transition and compare with the observed band maximum which occurs at $\lambda = 4,700$ A.

11-4. Electronic States and Transitions in Aromatic Systems

An adequate description of the ground electronic state of aromatic systems was a goal that occupied the attention of many early organic and physical-organic chemists. Following the advent of quantum mechanics, attention could be extended to the excited electronic states and the spectral transitions that occur between these states. A number of approaches to the description of the excited π-electron states of aromatic systems have been used. An introduction to the electronic spectra of aromatic systems can, perhaps, best be given in terms of a simple molecular orbital treatment, based on $2p\pi$ atomic orbitals, applied to the example benzene. The importance of the symmetry classification of the molecular orbitals and the electronic states will be brought out, and it will be shown that some assignments of observed absorption bands to the states involved in the transitions can be made. The treatment can be extended to other aromatic systems, but this will not be done here.

As in the previous section, attention will be centered on the $2p\pi$ orbitals, shown for benzene in Fig. 11-5. It is first necessary to see how these atomic orbitals can be combined to provide suitable molecular orbitals. The guiding principle here is that an electronic wave function, or molecular orbital, of the benzene molecule must conform to the symmetry of the molecule. That is, by an argument analogous to that used in discussing the symmetry of normal coordinates in Sec. 6-4 and illustrated for localized orbitals in Sec. 11-1, each molecular orbital must transform, under the various symmetry operations, according to one of the irreducible representations of the group. Let us now see if such molecular orbitals can be obtained by suitable combinations of the six $2p\pi$ atomic orbitals.

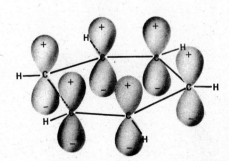

FIG. 11-5 The 2p atomic orbitals of the carbon atoms of benzene.

TABLE 11-5   The D_6 Character Table

D_6	E	$2C_6$	$2C_6^2$	C_6^3	$3C_2$	$3C_2'$	
A_1	1	1	1	1	1	1	
A_2	1	1	1	1	-1	-1	T_z
B_1	1	-1	1	-1	1	-1	
B_2	1	-1	1	-1	-1	1	
E_1	2	1	-1	-2	0	0	T_x, T_y
E_2	2	-1	-1	2	0	0	

The point group to which the nuclear skeleton of the benzene molecule belongs is D_{6h}. The treatment can be somewhat simplified if the symmetry about the plane of the molecule is, for the time being, ignored. It is enough to treat the wave function above the horizontal plane of the molecule or below that plane. Later the fact that all $p\pi$ orbitals are antisymmetric with respect to this plane can be added in. With this simplification, the problem can be analyzed in terms of the simpler point group D_6, for which the character table is given in Table 11-5 and the symmetry elements are illustrated in Fig. 11-6.

The six $2p\pi$ atomic orbitals form a basis for a reducible representation of the group, i.e., the transformation matrices that are obtained when the various symmetry operations are applied to these atomic orbitals will lead to representation matrices that can later be reduced. Thus to obtain the reducible representation, one investigates the operations on the individual π orbitals and writes the transformation equations

FIG. 11-6   The symmetry elements of the D_6 point group. Note that, unlike the case for the D_{6h} point group, symmetry with regard to the plane of the molecule is not considered.

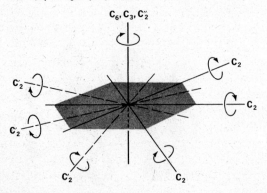

as

$$E \begin{pmatrix} p^A \\ p^B \\ p^C \\ \cdot \\ \cdot \\ \cdot \end{pmatrix} = \begin{pmatrix} 1 & 0 & 0 & 0 & 0 & 0 \\ 0 & 1 & 0 & 0 & 0 & 0 \\ \cdot & \cdot & \cdot & \cdot & \cdot & \cdot \end{pmatrix} \begin{pmatrix} p^A \\ p^B \\ p^C \\ \cdot \\ \cdot \\ \cdot \end{pmatrix} \qquad \text{character for } E = 6$$

$$C_2 \begin{pmatrix} p^A \\ p^B \\ p^C \\ \cdot \\ \cdot \\ \cdot \end{pmatrix} = \begin{pmatrix} 0 & 0 & 0 & 1 & 0 & 0 \\ 0 & 0 & 0 & 0 & 1 & 0 \\ \cdot & \cdot & \cdot & \cdot & \cdot & \cdot \end{pmatrix} \begin{pmatrix} p^A \\ p^B \\ p^C \\ \cdot \\ \cdot \\ \cdot \end{pmatrix} \qquad \text{character for } C_2 = 0$$

and so forth. In this way one finds that the character of the reducible representation corresponding to the six $2p\pi$ orbitals is

	E	$2C_6$	$2C_6^2$	C_6^3	$3C_2$	$3C_2$
$\chi_{\text{red.}}$	6	0	0	0	2	0

As in the normal vibration problem, this representation can be analyzed in terms of the irreducible representations that correspond to it. Thus, application of Eq. (51) in Chap. 8 shows, as can readily be checked, that the reducible representation contains representations of the types A_1, B_1, E_1, and E_2, i.e.,

$$\Gamma_{\text{red.}} = A_1 + B_1 + E_1 + E_2 \tag{8}$$

We see from this that the atomic orbitals should be combined to give molecular orbitals, one of which transforms according to the symmetry type A_1, one according to B_1, one pair according to the degenerate class E_1, and another pair according to E_2. We must now see what combinations of the atomic orbitals have these transformation properties.

A systematic group theoretical procedure is available for obtaining the suitable combinations. Rather than develop this, we will present the results and merely check that they have the correct transformation properties. (The two nondegenerate orbitals can, in fact, be constructed by inspection.) The molecular orbitals that have the correct symmetry properties are given in Table 11-6. (The degenerate pairs can be written

TABLE 11-6   Molecular Orbitals for the π Electrons of Benzene

Symmetry type	Molecular orbital*
A_1	$\psi_{a_1} = \varphi_A + \varphi_B + \varphi_C + \varphi_D + \varphi_E + \varphi_F$
B_1	$\psi_{b_1} = \varphi_A - \varphi_B + \varphi_C - \varphi_D + \varphi_E - \varphi_F$
E_1	$\psi_{e_1} = 2\varphi_A + \varphi_B - \varphi_C - 2\varphi_D - \varphi_E + \varphi_F$
	$\psi_{e_1} = \varphi_A + 2\varphi_B + \varphi_C - \varphi_D - 2\varphi_E - \varphi_F$
E_2	$\psi_{e_2} = 2\varphi_A - \varphi_B - \varphi_C + 2\varphi_D - \varphi_E - \varphi_F$
	$\psi_{e_2} = \varphi_A - 2\varphi_B + \varphi_C + \varphi_D - 2\varphi_E + \varphi_F$

* Lower-case letters are used as subscripts to identify the molecular orbitals, just as lower-case letters were used for individual electron orbitals in atoms and diatomic molecules. Capital letters are reserved for the symmetry type and the net electronic state of an atom or molecule.

in various ways, and it may be more revealing to consider the sum and the difference of the two functions given in Table 11-6.)

The form of the molecular orbitals can be seen by drawing the wave functions as in Fig. 11-7. One should recognize that a corresponding function, but with opposite signs, will project out on the other side of the benzene ring. Also one should keep in mind that each molecular orbital can accommodate two electrons.

The order of the energies of these individual molecular orbitals can be recognized by recalling that, as can readily be seen from the particle-in-a-box problem, the more nodes there are in a wave function, the higher is its energy. The wave functions of Fig. 11-7 have been ordered so that the a_1 function at the bottom of the diagram has the lowest energy and the b_1 function at the top has the highest energy.

Calculations of the energies of these orbitals can be made, and the simplest calculation leads to the spacing shown in Fig. 11-8. These energy spacings are usually expressed in terms of a quantity β which represents an integral that is difficult to evaluate.

The symmetry designations for the orbitals on the basis of the D_{6h} point group, for which the character table is given in Table 11-7, are also shown in Figs. 11-7 and 11-8. The fact that the $p\pi$ wave functions, or any linear combination of them, have opposite signs on opposite sides of the plane of the molecule allows, after inspection of the wave-function diagrams of Fig. 11-7, these designations to be given to the orbitals previously labeled a_1, e_1, e_2, and b_1 in accordance with the D_6 group.

Exercise 11-7. By inspection of the molecular orbital diagrams of Fig. 11-7, verify the D_{6h} classifications of a_{1g}, e_{1g}, e_{2u}, and b_{1g} for the orbitals classified on the basis of D_6 symmetry as a_1, e_1, e_2, and b_1, respectively.

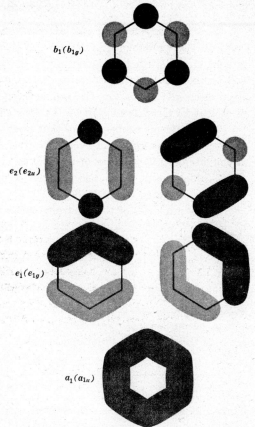

$b_1(b_{1g})$

$e_2(e_{2u})$

$e_1(e_{1g})$

$a_1(a_{1u})$

FIG. 11-7 Schematic representation of the molecular orbitals for benzene. Dark gray outlines positive parts of ψ; light gray outlines negative parts. (The symmetry type is given in terms of D_6 and, in parentheses, D_{6h}.)

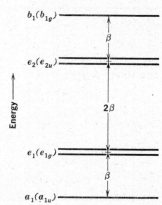

FIG. 11-8 The relative energies of the individual molecular orbitals of benzene. Symmetry designations are given on the basis of the D_6 point group and, in parentheses, on the basis of the D_{6h} group.

Now it is necessary to consider the assignment of the six $2p\pi$ electrons to the available orbitals in ways that correspond to the states, ground and excited, that are involved in spectroscopic transitions. It will be important, furthermore, to determine the symmetry of each of these electronic states, i.e., the symmetry resulting from the occupancy of orbitals of given symmetry by the six π electrons.

The electronic configurations that need to be considered (remembering that two electrons can occupy a given orbital and four a double-degenerate orbital) are that of the ground state and that of the excited states which result when one electron is promoted to an e_{2u} orbital. These are indicated in Fig. 11-9.

The symmetries of the electronic states of these configurations can be derived from the products of the characters for the symmetry species of the orbitals occupied by each electron as described for localized groups in Sec. 11-1. Thus, since the ground state involves pairs of electrons occupying the same orbitals, the total symmetry of this electronic state must be A_{1g}. The symmetries of the excited states can be obtained by analyzing the direct product of the representations of the orbitals e_{1g} and e_{2u} occupied by the lone electrons. The direct product of the characters of the E_{1g} and E_{2u} representations is

	E	$2C_6$	$2C_6^2$	C_6^3	$3C_2$	$3C_2'$	σ_h	$3\sigma_v$	$3\sigma_d$	$2S_6$	$2S_3$	i
$\chi_{E_{1g}} \cdot \chi_{E_{2u}}$	4	-1	1	-4	0	0	4	0	0	-1	1	-4

Now, unlike the situation encountered with nondegenerate representations, a reducible representation is obtained. It is necessary to analyze

TABLE 11-7   The D_{6h} Character Table

D_{6h}	E	$2C_6$	$2C_6^2$	C_6^3	$3C_2$	$3C_2'$	σ_h	$3\sigma_v$	$3\sigma_d$	$2S_6$	$2S_3$	i	
A_{1g}	1	1	1	1	1	1	1	1	1	1	1	1	
A_{1u}	1	1	1	1	1	1	-1	-1	-1	-1	-1	-1	
A_{2g}	1	1	1	1	-1	-1	1	-1	-1	1	1	1	
A_{2u}	1	1	1	1	-1	-1	-1	1	1	-1	-1	-1	T_z
B_{1g}	1	-1	1	-1	1	-1	-1	-1	1	1	-1	1	
B_{1u}	1	-1	1	-1	1	-1	1	1	-1	-1	1	-1	
B_{2g}	1	-1	1	-1	-1	1	-1	1	-1	1	-1	1	
B_{2u}	1	-1	1	-1	-1	1	1	-1	1	-1	1	-1	
E_{1g}	2	1	-1	-2	0	0	-2	0	0	-1	1	2	
E_{1u}	2	1	-1	-2	0	0	2	0	0	1	-1	-2	T_x, T_y
E_{2g}	2	-1	-1	2	0	0	2	0	0	-1	-1	2	
E_{2u}	2	-1	-1	2	0	0	-2	0	0	1	1	-2	

this in terms of its component irreducible representations in order to determine the symmetries of the states arising from single-electron occupancy of the e_{1g} and e_{2u} orbitals. This can be done by application of Eq. (52) in Chap. 8, and the result is obtained, as can be readily checked, that

$$\chi_{E_{1g}} \cdot \chi_{E_{2u}} = \chi_{B_{1u}} + \chi_{B_{2u}} + \chi_{E_{1u}} \tag{9}$$

The electronic states of benzene corresponding to the lowest excited electronic configuration are, therefore, expected to consist of two states with symmetries B_{1u} and B_{2u} and a degenerate pair of states with symmetry E_{1u}.

To a first approximation these four states, since they involve occupancy of the same set of individual orbitals, correspond to the same total electronic energy. It is a matter of considerable difficulty to deduce, in a purely theoretical way, the relative energies of these states and the ground state. Furthermore, two electrons in each of these excited states need not have their spins paired. It is possible, therefore, to have both singlet and triplet states, and as suggested by Hund's rule cited previously, calculations indicated that the triplet states lie lower than the corresponding singlet states. Many attempts have been made to calculate the energy pattern for the excited states of the benzene

FIG. 11-9 Distribution of the π electrons of benzene in the ground and first excited electron configurations.

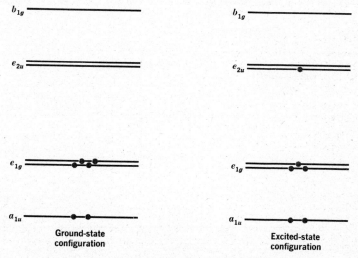

molecule, but so far it has not been possible to make, on a theoretical basis, a certain assignment of energies to the various electronic states.

One must, therefore, make what deductions one can from the observed spectrum, shown in Fig. 11-10, about the states involved in the various absorption bands.

It is first necessary to consider which transitions will be allowed, and just as for localized groups, one needs to ask which upper states belong to a symmetry type that contains T_x, T_y, or T_z. One sees from Table 11-7 that, for a D_{6h} molecule, transitions to the states with symmetries A_{2u} and E_{1u} would be allowed. Furthermore, changes in multiplicity are expected to be forbidden, and one expects only singlet-singlet transitions to lead to strong absorption bands. Thus the most intense band in the absorption spectrum of benzene should be assigned to the completely allowed transition to the $^1E_{1u}$ state.

The absorption spectrum of benzene shows, however, more absorption bands than the single most intense band that is assigned to the $^1E_{1u} \leftarrow {}^1A_{1g}$ transition.

Some assignments of the remaining absorption bands can be made. The very short wavelength band, around 1,500 A, is attributed to a

FIG. 11-10 The absorption spectrum of benzene in the ultraviolet spectral region. (*From K. S. Pitzer, "Quantum Chemistry," Prentice-Hall, Inc., Englewood Cliffs, N.J., 1953.*)

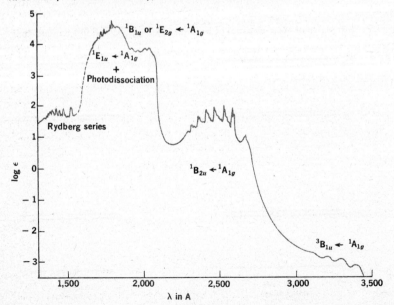

"Rydberg" type transition in which the principal quantum number of one of the $2p\pi$ electrons is increased, as in the Rydberg series usually discussed in connection with the hydrogen atom. Such high-energy transitions have not been included in the treatment given here. It has been suggested that the band near 2,100 A is due to either the transition $^1B_{1u} \leftarrow {}^1A_{1g}$ or $^1E_{2g} \leftarrow {}^1A_{1g}$. These forbidden transitions could occur as a result of "borrowing" intensity from the nearby intense band at 1,800 A or by coupling with a vibration of appropriate symmetry. The band near 2,500 A is attributed to the transition $^1B_{2u} \leftarrow {}^1A_{1g}$. This transition, prohibited on the basis of the selection rule derived from the electronic states, can again be allowed as a result of coupling with a vibration of suitable symmetry. The very weak absorption at about 3,300 A is attributed to the highly forbidden transition $^3B_{1u} \leftarrow {}^1A_{1g}$. It should be apparent from these comments that, although the electronic states of benzene can be classified as to symmetry, it remains a task of considerable difficulty definitely to identify each absorption band with a transition to a particular state. The assignments suggested here are included in the spectrum of Fig. 11-10.

Similar attempts can be made to assign the ultraviolet absorption bands of other aromatic systems to transitions between electronic states of certain symmetries. As in studies of molecules with localized absorbing groups, aids to the assignment are provided by oriented-molecule spectra studied with polarized radiation, the effect of solvents, and the effect of substituents. Some of the ways in which more complicated aromatic systems can be approached have been discussed by R. N. Jones [*J. Am. Chem. Soc.*, **67**: 2127 (1945)].

Exercise 11-8. On the basis of the assignments of the absorption bands of Fig. 11-10 to electronic states of the benzene molecule, draw an energy-level diagram showing, by means of horizontal lines, the energies of the various electronic states of the molecule. Attach electron volt and kcal per mole energy scales to the diagram.

Exercise 11-9. Treat the molecule cyclobutadiene

in a similar manner to that in which benzene was treated above.

(a) Deduce the number of molecular orbitals of the various symmetry types.

(b) Draw, by inspecting the way in which the orbitals must transform, these molecular orbitals.

(c) Arrange these orbitals in order of their energy.

(d) Assign the π electrons to these orbitals in accordance with the lowest and the first excited electronic configurations. What are the symmetry species and multiplicities of the electronic states that arise from these configurations?

(e) What transitions between the ground and these excited states would be allowed?

ELECTRONIC TRANSITIONS OF COORDINATION COMPOUNDS

The absorption spectra of compounds or ions containing transition metals have long been used to characterize these species empirically. Coordination compounds, in which a number of electron-rich groups, called ligands (such as $: NH_3, H_2O :, : Cl : ^-$), coordinate to the metal ion, comprise the most extensively studied type of transition metal species. In this class one has, for example, the familiar, colorful ions $[Cu(NH_3)_4]^{++}$, which gives an intense blue color, and Ni (dimethylglyoxime)$_2$, which forms a red crystal. Almost all coordination compounds of the transition metals have absorption bands in the visible, as these familiar examples do, or in the near-infrared or near-ultraviolet spectral regions.

In recent years an earlier theory developed by Bethe and by Van Vleck has been applied, and extended, to these systems, and it has become clear that the principal absorption of these compounds can be interpreted, for the most part, in terms of transitions involving the electrons in the incomplete outer d shell of the metal ion. (Other absorptions, usually more intense and farther out in the ultraviolet, that occur are attributed to what are called charge-transfer transitions. In these transitions electrons are, to some extent, transferred from the ligands to the metal or from the metal to the ligands. These charge-transfer transitions will not be dealt with here.)

The treatment of the d orbitals that has been used and that allows the absorption spectrum of a coordination compound to be related to the properties of the metal ion and the ligands is known, in its simplest form, as the *crystal-field theory* and, when a more detailed treatment of the participation of the ligands is made, as the *ligand-field theory*. In its simplest form, which is all that will be introduced here, the theory supposes that the ligands impose on the central metal ion an electric field whose symmetry depends on the number and arrangement of the ligands and whose strength depends on the electrical nature of the ligands and, more particularly, on the repulsion which those electron-rich groups exert on the d electrons of the metal ion. (The coordination compound is pictured as being held together primarily by the attractive interaction of the charge of the metal ion with the charges or dipoles of the ligands.)

11-5. Electron Orbitals of Coordination Compounds

It is first necessary to investigate the effect of the ligand field on the d orbitals of the metal ion. It will be recalled that in a spherical potential such as exists in the free ion the five d orbitals have identical energies, i.e., they constitute a degenerate set. The effect of the ligand field is to break this degeneracy, i.e., to change the energies of some of the d orbitals relative to other d orbitals. To analyze these changes we must proceed, as in the benzene analysis of the previous section, to find orbitals that have symmetries compatible with that of the system, i.e., with the arrangement of the ligands. When this is done, the relative energies of these orbitals can be investigated and the available electrons can be assigned to these orbitals.

The procedure is adequately illustrated by treating only the important example of octahedral complexes. An illustration of the geometry of such complexes is shown in Fig. 11-11. Since all six ligands are equivalent, such ions have the symmetry of the point group O_h. The character table for this group is given as Table 11-8, and some of the

TABLE 11-8   The O_h Character Table

O_h	E	$8C_3$	$6C_2$	$6C_4$	$3C_4^2$	i	$6S_4$	$8S_6$	$3\sigma_h$	$6\sigma_d$	
A_{1g}	1	1	1	1	1	1	1	1	1	1	
A_{1u}	1	1	1	1	1	-1	-1	-1	-1	-1	
A_{2g}	1	1	-1	-1	1	1	-1	1	1	-1	
A_{2u}	1	1	-1	-1	1	-1	1	-1	-1	1	
E_g	2	-1	0	0	2	2	0	-1	2	0	
E_u	2	-1	0	0	2	-2	0	1	-2	0	
T_{1g}	3	0	-1	1	-1	3	1	0	-1	-1	
T_{1u}	3	0	-1	1	-1	-3	-1	0	1	1	T_x, T_y, T_z
T_{2g}	3	0	1	-1	-1	3	-1	0	-1	1	
T_{2u}	3	0	1	-1	-1	-3	1	0	1	-1	

symmetry elements are shown in Fig. 11-11. Treatments similar to that given here for octahedral complexes can, of course, also be given for complexes with other symmetries.

The d orbitals of an atom or ion are those corresponding to the solution functions with $l = 2$ for an electron of a hydrogenlike atom. Five functions occur since, for $l = 2$, the magnetic quantum number m can have the values 0, ± 1, ± 2. The five d orbital wave functions that arise in this way were shown in terms of $J = 2$ in Table 5-1. (These, of course, define only the angular factors of the orbitals. A radial factor that depends on the principal quantum number must also be introduced to determine the wave function completely. For considerations of symmetry, it is enough to concern ourselves with angular factors.)

The d-orbital functions of Table 5-1 are appropriate to a system with spherical symmetry. They provide, furthermore, basic functions from which orbitals can be constructed that have symmetries compatible with the octahedral arrangement of the ligands that are now imagined to be located about the central ion. The procedure is similar to that in which the separate $2p\pi$ atomic orbitals in benzene were combined to give molecular orbitals consistent with the skeletal symmetry of the benzene molecule. Again the details of the way in which this is done will be passed over, and only the results will be given.

It is found that the reducible representation that the five d orbital wave functions lead to under the operations of the octahedral point

FIG. 11-11 (a) The geometry of an octahedral complex. All six ligands are equivalent, and the complex belongs to the symmetry point group O_h. (b) Some representative symmetry elements of the O_h point group.

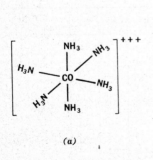

(a)

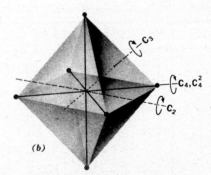

(b)

σ planes are perpendicular to C_2 and C_4

group O_h can be recognized as containing the doubly degenerate irreducible representation E_g and the triply degenerate one T_{2g}. A set of three orbitals that transform according to the latter representation can be directly constructed from the original wave functions. These are indicated diagrammatically, along with the d_{xy}, d_{xz}, d_{yz} notation usually used, in Fig. 11-12. Diagrams can be drawn to represent the two orbitals that transform according to the E_g representation by drawing three pictures and imagining linear combinations of these to be made so that two orbitals result. It is customary, however, to illustrate the E_g orbitals by combining two of these diagrams to yield the two orbitals, shown in Fig. 11-12, corresponding to the notation $d_{x^2-y^2}$ and d_{z^2}. One must, however, keep in mind that no axis is unique and that the orbitals with E_g symmetry consist of a pair of orbitals that project along the cartesian axis. (To be consistent with the use of lower-case symbols, such as s, p, d, . . . and σ, π, δ, . . . , to describe individual electron orbits, the symbols t_{2g} and e_g will be used to describe orbits that transform

FIG. 11-12   Diagrammatic representations of the angular factors of the d orbitals.

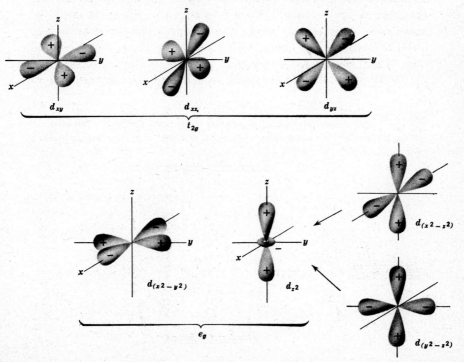

according to the symmetry types T_{2g} and E_g.)   We now consider the relative energies of the t_{2g} and e_g orbitals that must be occupied by the outer d electrons of a transition metal ion when the metal ion forms a octahedral complex.

The energy difference between the two sets of d orbitals can, in a qualitative way, be immediately recognized.   (This step corresponds, it might be mentioned, to the deduction that the energies of the molecular orbitals of benzene are arranged as in Fig. 11-8.)   One supposed that the six ligands occupy sites along the cartesian axes of Fig. 11-12.   These ligands present electron-filled lone-pair orbitals in the direction of the metal ion and, therefore, produce an electron-repulsing effect along these axes.   It follows that a metal-ion electron in an e_g orbital will experience, since such orbitals point in the direction of the ligand electrons, more repulsion than one in a t_{2g} orbital.   Thus the e_g orbitals can be expected, as indicated in Fig. 11-13, to lie at a higher energy than do the t_{2g} orbitals.   The exact amount of splitting of the two sets of orbitals cannot be satisfactorily calculated.   It depends on the details of the interaction between the electron of the metal ion and those of the ligands.   The amount of splitting must be deduced empirically, and as we will see, spectroscopic studies often allow this to be done.   Finally it should be mentioned that it has become customary to use either the quantity Δ or $10Dq$ to designate the energy splitting between the e_g and t_{2g} orbital sets.   For bivalent ions one generally finds $\Delta = 10Dq$ to be of the order of 10,000 cm^{-1}, while for trivalent ions this splitting is increased to

FIG. 11-13   The removal of d orbital degeneracy by an octahedral field.   The extent of splitting is customarily discussed either in terms of Δ or $10Dq$.   Both notations are included here.

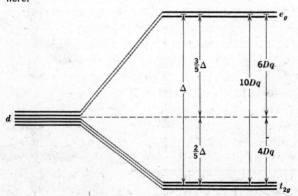

around 20,000 cm^{-1}. The quantity Δ, or $10Dq$, must, however, be expected to be characteristic of both the metal ion and the ligands. A number of interesting correlations can be made between this quantity and chemical properties of both the transition metal ions and the ligands that have been studied.

We have now obtained the symmetry-correct orbitals for a metal ion in an octahedral complex and have recognized that the ligand field splits the original fivefold degeneracy. Now we must consider the electronic states that arise when the d electrons of the transition metal ion occupy the available orbitals.

11-6. Electronic States of Coordination Compounds

The electronic states of an ion with only one outer d electron, such as Ti^{3+}, are most easily treated. The effect of the crystal field on the states of such an ion will, therefore, be discussed first.

In view of the survey of atomic, or ionic, electron states indicated in Sec. 10-3, one d electron species must be expected to give a ^2D state; i.e., the net orbital angular momentum quantum number L must be 2 and the net spin S must be $\frac{1}{2}$, and thus $2S + 1 = 2$. For no crystal field, therefore, the electronic state of the Ti^{3+} ion is a ^2D state. When ligands are now placed in octahedral positions about such an ion, the degenerate d orbitals, in which the single d electron is accommodated, split to give a set of lower-energy t_{2g} orbitals and a set of higher-energy e_g orbitals. Now, depending on which set of orbitals the electron is assigned to, there are two different electronic states. The electronic configurations corresponding to these two states are indicated as $(t_{2g})^1$ and $(e_g)^1$. Since there is only one electron, the electronic states are similarly described and are labeled with the capital letter designations T_{2g} and E_g. Furthermore, as for the original ^2D atomic state, one indicates the spin and writes the two states as $^2T_{2g}$ and ^2E_g.

One sometimes indicates the effect of the crystal field for this one d electron example by a diagram like that of Fig. 11-14. In a sense, which will be more evident later, this is a correlation diagram between the situation for the spherical field of the ion at the left and the strong crystal field at the right. Various ligands will have crystal fields of various strengths and will correspond to positions along the abscissa. For example, the aquated Ti^{3+} ion [Ti(H$_2$O)$_6$]$^{3+}$ has an absorption band at 4,900 A, or 20,400 cm^{-1}, which can be identified with the transition $^2E_g \leftarrow {}^2T_{2g}$. This observation allows the vertical dashed line to be drawn in Fig. 11-14 at a position where the splitting is 20,400 cm^{-1}. Alternatively we can say that for $[Ti(H_2O)_6]^{3+}$ the value of the crystal-field splitting factor Δ, or $10Dq$, is 20,400 cm^{-1}.

Now let us consider the situation when there are two d electrons. The ion V^{3+} serves as an example since it has two outer d electrons and forms octahedral complexes. We wish to draw a diagram, like that of Fig. 11-14, so that the energy-level pattern for any strength of crystal field can be picked off. For the zero crystal-field limit, the two $l = 2$ electronic contributions can, as discussed in Sec. 10-3, be combined to give L values of 4, 3, 2, 1, or 0, i.e., G, F, D, P, or S states. Now, and these features were not mentioned in the earlier discussion, the assignment of the two electrons to the available d orbitals must be made in accordance with the Pauli exclusion principle. An illustration of how

FIG. 11-14   The energy-level diagram for a metal ion with one d electron, i.e., d^1 configuration, showing the effect of increasing crystal field effect. The energy scale is arbitrarily assigned the value zero for the ground state of the undisturbed ion. The position of $[Ti(OH_2)_6]^{3+}$ is located and the value Δ determined by the frequency of 20,400 cm^{-1} of the observed absorption band.

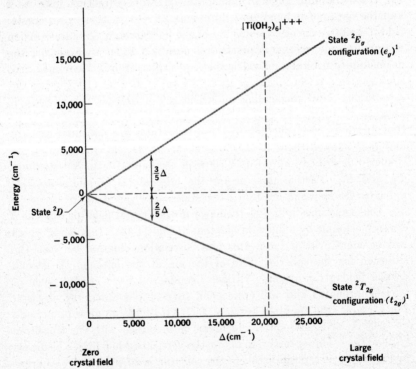

these restrictions operate to allow only certain spin arrangements of the two electrons for certain values of L can be followed through according to the detailed discussion given by G. Herzberg, "Atomic Spectra and Atomic Structure" (pp. 130–135, Dover Publications, New York, 1944) and will not be repeated here. One finds by this means that the d^2 configuration can only lead to states ^3P, ^3F, ^1S, ^1D, or ^1G. The energy pattern of these states is not easily predicted but can be determined from analyses of atomic spectra. In this way the pattern at the origin of Fig. 11-15 can be drawn for the V^{3+} ion.

Let us now move over to the far right-hand side of the diagram and consider the states that would be expected for a d^2 ion subjected to a strong crystal field. The three possible electronic configurations that must be considered are, in order of increasing energy, $(t_{2g})^2$, $(t_{2g})^1(e_g)^1$, and $(e_g)^2$. Now, to find what electronic states these configurations correspond to we must, as in the previous treatments of localized groups and conjugated systems, form the direct product of the representations of each electron in a given configuration. Analysis of the $(t_{2g})^2$ configuration is illustrated in Table 11-9. In a similar way the states for the other two configurations can be found, and the results of these analyses are shown in Table 11-10. Similarly, the electronic states that arise from other electronic configurations can be found from the appropriate direct products of irreducible representations, and these results for all nine configurations of an incomplete d shell subject to octahedral symmetry

TABLE 11-9 Illustration of the Determination of the Electronic States Arising from the Configuration $(t_{2g})^2$

O_h	E	C_3	C_2	C_4	C_4^2	i	S_4	S_6	σ_h	σ_d
Formation of direct product										
$\chi_{T_{2g}}$	3	0	1	-1	-1	3	-1	0	-1	1
$\chi_{T_{2g}} \times \chi_{T_{2g}}$	9	0	1	1	1	9	1	0	1	1
Analysis in terms of characters of irreducible representations										
$\chi_{A_{1g}}$	1	1	1	1	1	1	1	1	1	1
χ_{E_g}	2	-1	0	0	2	2	0	-1	2	0
$\chi_{T_{1g}}$	3	0	-1	1	-1	3	1	0	-1	-1
$\chi_{T_{2g}}$	3	0	1	-1	-1	3	-1	0	-1	1
$\chi_{A_{1g}} + \chi_{E_g} + \chi_{T_{1g}}$ $+ \chi_{T_{2g}} =$	9	0	1	1	1	9	1	0	1	1

TABLE 11-10   Electronic States Arising from an Electron System Subject to Octahedral Symmetry

Electronic configuration		Electronic states
Free ion	Ion subject to octahedral symmetry	
d^1, d^9	$(e_g)^1$	^2E_g
	$(t_{2g})^1$	$^2T_{2g}$
d^2, d^8	$(e_g)^2$	$^3A_{2g}, \, ^1A_{1g}, \, ^1E_g$
	$(t_{2g})^1(e_g)^1$	$^3T_{1g}, \, ^3T_{2g}, \, ^1T_{1g}, \, ^1T_{2g}$
	$(t_{2g})^2$	$^3T_{1g}, \, ^1A_{1g}, \, ^1E_g, \, ^1T_{2g}$
d^3, d^7	$(e_g)^3$	^2E_g
	$(t_{2g})^1(e_g)^2$	$^4T_{2g}, \, 2{}^2T_{1g}, \, 2{}^2T_{2g}$
	$(t_{2g})^2(e_g)^1$	$^4T_{1g}, \, ^4T_{2g}, \, ^2A_{1g}, \, ^2A_{2g}, \, 2{}^2T_{1g}, \, 2{}^2T_{2g}$
	$(t_{2g})^3$	$^4A_{2g}, \, ^2E_g, \, ^2T_{1g}, \, ^2T_{2g}$
d^4, d^6	$(e_g)^4$	$^1A_{1g}$
	$(t_{2g})^1(e_g)^3$	$^3T_{1g}, \, ^3T_{2g}, \, ^1T_{1g}, \, ^1T_{2g}$
	$(t_{2g})^2(e_g)^2$	$^5T_{2g}, \, ^3E_g, \, 3{}^3T_{1g}, \, 2{}^3T_{2g}, \, 2{}^1A_{1g}, \, ^1A_{2g}, \, 3{}^1E_g, \, ^1T_{1g}, \, 3{}^1T_{2g}$
	$(t_{2g})^3(e_g)^1$	$^5E_g, \, ^3A_{1g}, \, ^3A_{2g}, \, 2{}^3E_g, \, 2{}^3T_{1g}, \, 2{}^3T_{2g}, \, ^1A_{1g}, \, ^1A_{2g}, \, ^1E_g,$
		$\quad 2{}^1T_{1g}, \, 2{}^1T_{2g}$
	$(t_{2g})^4$	$^3T_{1g}, \, ^1A_{1g}, \, ^1E_g, \, ^1T_{2g}$
d^5	$(t_{2g})^1(e_g)^4$	$^2T_{2g}$
	$(t_{2g})^2(e_g)^3$	$^4T_{1g}, \, ^4T_{2g}, \, ^2A_{1g}, \, ^2A_{2g}, \, 2{}^2E_g, \, 2{}^2T_{1g}, \, 2{}^2T_{2g}$
	$(t_{2g})^3(e_g)^2$	$^6T_{1g}, \, ^4T_{1g}, \, ^4A_{2g}, \, 2{}^4E_g, \, ^4T_{1g}, \, ^4T_{2g}, \, 2{}^2A_{1g}, \, ^2A_{2g}, \, 3{}^2E_g,$
		$\quad 4{}^2T_{1g}, \, 4{}^2T_{2g}$
	$(t_{2g})^4(e_g)^1$	$^4T_{1g}, \, ^4T_{2g}, \, ^2A_{.g}, \, ^2A_{2g}, \, 2{}^2E_g, \, 2{}^2T_{1g}, \, 2T_{2g}$
	$(t_{2g})^5$	$^2T_{2g}$

are given in Table 11-10. (We will see later that the configurations and states for d^n systems are similar to those for d^{10-n} systems.) Again, it is necessary to obey Pauli's exclusion principle in assigning electron spins when, as in the $(t_{2g})^2$ and $(e_g)^2$ configurations, two electrons have the same orbital description. By a procedure similar to that which allows spins to be assigned to the atomic states, one would arrive at the spin assignments included in the electronic states listed in Table 11-10.

Exercise 11-10. Verify that the $(e_g)^2$ configuration leads to the states A_{2g}, A_{1g}, and E_g and that the $(t_{2g})^1(e_g)^1$ configuration leads to two states each of the type T_{1g} and T_{2g} as listed in Table 11-11.

For large crystal fields, the energy of an electronic state is determined by the number of electrons in the low-energy t_{2g} orbitals and the number in the high-energy e_g orbitals. The right-hand limit of Fig. 11-15 can be drawn, with the states of the d^2 configuration, on this basis.

For intermediate field strengths the tendency for the electrons to occupy the low-energy t_{2g} orbitals as well as their tendency to avoid one another, which produces the different states of the free atom, are important. The energy-level pattern for such situations can be drawn

FIG. 11-15 A schematic correlation diagram for the states of a d^2 ion. On the left is the energy-level pattern for the free ion; on the right is the pattern for very strong crystal fields. The correlation lines are drawn with regard to the multiplicities of the levels and the correlations of Table 11-11.

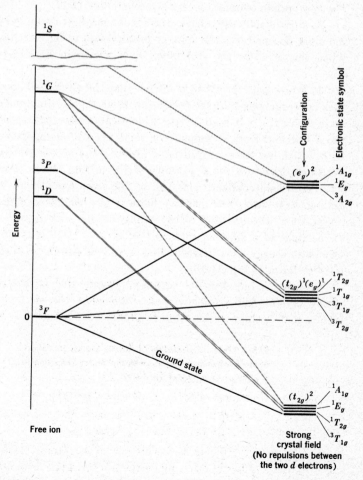

by joining up the appropriate states of the right and left sides of Fig. 11-14.

The way in which such correlations must be made was first shown by H. Bethe [*Ann. Phys.*, 57 : **3,** 133 (1929)] by means of a group-theoretical derivation of the relation between the atomic states of the spherically symmetric problem and those states described by the crystal-field notation appropriate to the potential field of octahedral symmetry. The derivation shows that it is the net angular momentum of the atomic state that determines the correlation. It follows that, for any atom, the correlation of atomic states and the octahedral crystal-field descriptions are determined by the atomic-state symbol, i.e., S, P, D, and so forth. The appropriate correlations are given in Table 11-11.

In a particular case, such as the d^2 configuration shown in Fig. 11-15, one must also preserve the spin, or multiplicity, of the electronic states. When this is done, the correlation lines shown in Fig. 11-14 can be drawn.

It is now appropriate to point out that the often used spectroscopic trick of recognizing that the treatment for an atom with two d electrons, i.e., a d^2 system, is in many respects identical to that for an atom lacking two d electrons from a completed d shell, i.e. a d^8 configuration. Thus Ni^{++}, which has the configuration d^8, has a set of atomic states arranged like those drawn for the d^2 example of V^{3+} in Fig. 11-15. Furthermore the crystal-field configurations will be the same except that we will be dealing, as it were, with positive holes in the completed d shell. As a consequence, the ordering of the configurations with regard to energy at the right of a diagram such as that of Fig. 11-15 is reversed. The schematic energy-level diagram that would be drawn on this basis for Ni^{++} is shown in Fig. 11-16.

In practice one does not encounter ligands that have a sufficiently strong crystal field completely to overshadow the electron-repulsion factors that operate in the atom to produce the different atomic states

TABLE 11-11   Correlation of Atomic States, for Which Spherical Symmetry Exists, with the States Occurring in a Field of Octahedral Symmetry

Atomic state symbol	Octahedral symmetry states
S	A_{1g}
P	T_{1g}
D	$E_g + T_{2g}$
F	$A_{2g} + T_{1g} + T_{2g}$
G	$A_{1g} + E_g + T_{1g} + T_{2g}$

for a given number of d electrons. One usually, therefore, focusses one's attention on the left-hand part of the diagrams that have just been discussed. The left-hand part for the Ni^{++} ion, which is often studied in coordination chemistry, is shown in Fig. 11-17. Here account is also taken of the fact that like quantum-mechanical states tend to "mix" and to form somewhat modified states whose energies remain different from one another. The energy levels of like states are said to repel

FIG. 11-16 The schematic correlation diagram between the free ion and the strong octahedral field complex for d^8 ions.

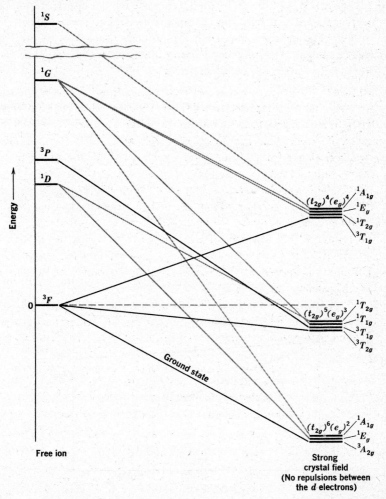

one another. In Fig. 11-17, this effect is noticed in the curvatures of the two $^3T_{1g}$, the two $^1T_{2g}$, and the two ^1E_g energy-level lines.

Exercise 11-11. What are the differences in the limit of strong crystal fields of the energies of the configurations $(t_{2g})^3$, $(t_{2g})^2(e_g)^1$, $(t_{2g})^1(e_g)^2$, and $(e_g)^3$. Illustrate the answer by an energy diagram and show the energy scale in terms of both the parameter Δ and the parameter $10D_q$.

Exercise 11-12. Arrange according to energy, as in Exercise 11-11, the possible configurations of a d^7 ion in an octahedral complex.

Before the predicted energy-level pattern of a Ni^{++} complex, such as that of Fig. 11-16, can be used as a basis for the interpretation of the observed spectral transitions, it remains for us to consider the selection rules governing transitions from the ground, $^3A_{2g}$ state, to the higher-energy states. One can immediately carry over the rule that forbids

FIG. 11-17 The energy-level diagram for a d^8 ion, such as Ni^{++}, in a field of octahedral symmetry. The energies of the important states with the same multiplicity as the ground state are shown as heavy lines. The position of $[Ni(H_2O)_6]^{++}$ is located along the abscissa to fit the observed spectrum. (*From L. E. Orgel, "An Introduction to Transition-Metal Chemistry,* "*Methuen & Co., Ltd., London, 1960.*)

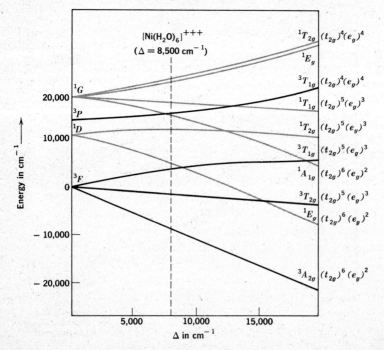

changes in the net spin of the system and can therefore, in this case, expect the important spectral bands to be interpretable on the basis of the other triplet states, the $^3T_{2g}$ state and the two $^3T_{1g}$ states. Furthermore, consideration of the transition-moment integral leads to the conclusion, well known in atomic spectra and referred to as the *Laporte rule*, that no transitions between states arising from a given configuration such as d^2 are allowed. This is based on the symmetry result that, as Fig. 11-12 shows, all d orbitals are symmetric with respect to their origin, and since the dipole-moment term itself is antisymmetric, the product of the terms in the transition-moment integral would be antisymmetric and, therefore, according to the discussion of Sec. 4-5, the integral would necessarily be zero. For a coordination compound this rule is broken down, to some extent, because some of the vibrations of the ligands with respect to the metal ion destroy the symmetry of the system. One finds, however, that d-d transitions, i.e., transitions between energy levels such as those of Fig. 11-17, lead to relatively weak absorption bands. Typical values of $\alpha(\bar{\nu})$ at the maximum of the absorption band for such absorptions is

$$\alpha(\bar{\nu})_{max} = \frac{1}{cl} \log \left(\frac{I_0}{I} \right)_{max} \cong 5 \text{ cm}^{-1} \text{ mole}^{-1} \text{ liter} \tag{10}$$

The corresponding typical oscillator strength is about 10^{-4}. (It should be mentioned that the $\Delta S = 0$ selection rule can also be violated. Transitions involving spin changes lead, however, to very weak bands, with f values of perhaps 10^{-7}, and these are not generally observed when the much more intense $\Delta S = 0$ bands occur.)

Now the energy-level pattern for a given octahedrally coordinated metal ion can be used as a base for the interpretation of the observed spectrum. The example of Ni^{++} is still suitable. The spectrum of the aquated ion $[Ni(H_2O)_6]^{++}$ is shown in Fig. 11-18. The three absorption bands can be attributed to the states indicated above each absorption band, and the positions of these bands match up rather well with the spacing between the energy levels of Fig. 11-17 if one assumes a value of $\Delta = 8,500$ cm^{-1} for the $[Ni(H_2O)_6]^{++}$ ion.

One final illustration of the crystal field interpretation of the d-electron energy levels and the spectrum resulting from transitions between these levels can be given. The d^5 configuration, found in Mn^{++} and Fe^{++}, is different from the previous examples in two regards. First, for not too strong a crystal field, the ground-state configuration is $(t_{2g})^3(e_g)^2$, and this configuration has an energy that is independent of the value of Δ. This leads to the horizontal ground-state energy level for the ${}^6S$ state shown in Fig. 11-19. Secondly, this ground state configuration has a spin of 5/2, and this is greater than can be achieved by any of the other possible electron configurations.

Although, to interpret the electronic spectrum, one would now normally focus one's attention primarily on the higher energy states with the same spin as the ground state, such states do not exist. The highest spin found in the excited configurations corresponds to two electrons being paired with opposite spins, and this situation produces a net spin of 3/2 and quartet states. The energy levels for these states, which now must serve as the excited states when radiation is absorbed in a d-d transition, are shown in the region of relatively low crystal field energy in Fig. 11-19.

The spectrum of $[\mathrm{Mn(H_2O)_6}]^{++}$, shown in Fig. 11-20, is in line with the predictions that would be made on the basis of Fig. 11-19. First, the low extinction coefficients, as compared for example with the corresponding spectrum of the aquated Ni^{++} ion, should be noticed. The oscillator strengths are less for Mn^{++} by a factor of about one hundred and this can be attributed to the violation of the $\Delta S = 0$ rule that must accompany the d-d transitions of the $[\mathrm{Mn(H_2O)_6}]^{++}$ ion. (The reader may, in fact, have noticed the generally pale colors displayed by manganese solutions, and this again can be attributed to the spin change involved in the visible region transitions.) The number and positions of the absorption bands of various Mn^{++} coordination complexes have led to the suggestion that a value of Δ of about 7,800 cm^{-1} for $[\mathrm{Mn(H_2O)_6}]^{++}$,

FIG. 11-18 The absorption spectrum due to the octahedral ion $[\mathrm{Ni(H_2O)_6}]^{++}$. [*From Holmes and McClure, J. Chem. Phys., 26: 1686 (1957).*]

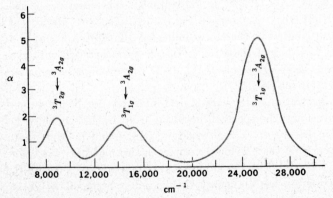

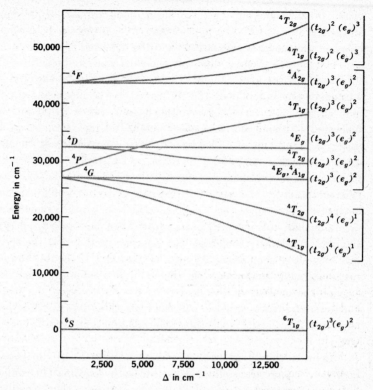

FIG. 11-19 The energy-level diagram for a d^5 ion such as Mn^{++}. Only the ground state, designated as ^6S and $^6T_{1g}$, and quartet states are shown. (*From L. E. Orgel, "An Introduction to Transition-Metal Chemistry," Methuen & Co., Ltd., London, 1960.*)

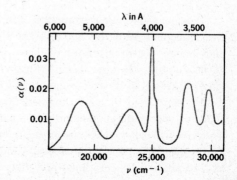

FIG. 11-20 The absorption spectrum due to the ion $[Mn(H_2O)_6]^{++}$. [*From C. K. Jorgensen, Acta. Chem. Scand., 8: 1502 (1954).*]

which predicts a group of three absorptions around 25,000 cm^{-1} and another group of three around 30,000 cm^{-1}, gives the best correlation between the energy-level diagram and the observed spectrum.

The above examples illustrate the chief goals and results of the discussion of this section. The positions of the principal d-electron absorption bands are understood, and the parameter Δ, measuring the magnitude of the interaction between the ligands and a metal ion, can be evaluated. Other spectra of other octahedral ions can also be understood, and the value of Δ determined, from comparisons of the observed spectra with the energy-level diagram. In a similar way one can construct energy-level diagrams for octahedral complexes of ions with different numbers of d electrons and can understand the principal features of the spectra of these ions. Furthermore, other geometries, i.e., square planar, tetrahedral, and so forth, can be studied, energy-level diagrams for these geometries can be constructed, and the spectra of ions with these geometries can also be treated. It should, however, be mentioned again that a more complete and detailed study must take into account the orbitals of the ligands as well as those of the metal ion. Then one constructs suitable orbitals from these two types of localized orbitals. This ligand field approach will not, however, be dealt with here.

Again it should be pointed out that other electronic transitions, leading to charge-transfer bands, occur with coordination compounds. Although these bands are generally very intense, they usually occur farther out in the ultraviolet region than do the d-d bands treated here. They do not, it might be added, contribute to the characteristic colors often observed with transition metal complexes.

EMISSION AND DECAY PROCESSES

Various types of electronic transitions that lead to the absorption of electromagnetic radiation and raise the absorbing molecule or ion to some high-energy electronic state have been dealt with in the preceding parts of the chapter. Now we will investigate the ways in which a molecule, or ion, can get rid of its excess energy and return to the ground state after it has been raised to such a high-energy electronic state. Two general types of energy-dissipation processes can be recognized. In one type, which we will call *nonradiative processes*, energy is transferred to molecules that collide with the excited molecule and carry away some of this energy as translational, or rotational and vibrational, energy. No emission of radiation is observed in such processes. The second type of dissipation processes, on the other hand, involves an emission of radiant energy. Such radiation can be detected and analyzed, and as we will see, such analysis leads to the further classifications of *fluorescent emission* and *phosphorescent emission.*

11-7. Nonradiative Processes

As was discussed in Sec. 10-1 and illustrated in Fig. 10-2, the transition associated with an electronic absorption band produces a higher energy electron configuration and often leaves the molecule in one of the higher vibrational states of the new electronic state. For molecules in solution it appears that the molecular collisions are very effective in removing, probably by one vibrational level step at a time, the excess vibrational energy. This energy goes into the thermal, and perhaps vibrational, motion of the molecules of the solvent and is not detected as emitted radiation. It appears, from ultrasonic dispersion measurements and theoretical calculations, that a typical time required for the dissipation of excess vibrational energy by such a process is of the order of 10^{-10} sec. When this is compared with a typical vibrational period of 10^{-13} sec, it is seen that many vibrations, say a thousand, do occur while the excess vibrational energy is being lost.

Since the principal mechanism for the vibrational deactivation of a molecule involves molecular collisions, it can be expected that restricting or eliminating such collisions will slow down the process. A procedure that has been often used, for reasons which will be made clear in the remainder of the chapter, to effect a slowing down of this process consists of dissolving the material under study in a solvent which, when cooled, sets to a rigid glass. One solvent often used is boric acid; another is a mixture of ether, isopentane, and ethanol, referred to as EPA.

The simple diagram of Fig. 10-1 showing the potential curve of the ground electronic configuration and that of a single excited state configuration is not typical of the situation that exists for polyatomic molecules and is inadequate for a complete discussion of radiationless energy dissipation. A number of different electronic configurations must be expected to have energies that lead to potential-energy curves in the region covered by this diagram. In this regard Fig. 10-20 is more typical. Furthermore, the potential energy for a given electronic state will be a function of all the internal coordinates of the molecule, and for polyatomic molecules the potential energy would have to be represented by a surface in this many-dimensional space. The net effect of these two features is that potential-energy curves or, more properly, surfaces of different electronic states will cross one another, and a representative arrangement of potential curves is that shown in Fig. 11-21.

The occurrence of a crossing, or nearby, potential surface with that initially reached by the absorption process leads to a second type of radiationless process. This type can, moreover, lead to the return of the excited molecule to its ground state. When two potential surfaces or, to simplify the discussion, two potential curves cross as in Fig. 11-21, it is possible for the molecule, originally in the excited electronic configuration corresponding to the curve labeled S, to change over into the configuration corresponding to the curve labeled S'. The crossing of the potential curves facilitates this process, known as *internal conversion*,

FIG. 11-21 Energy dissipation by vibrational deactivation and internal conversion. (The dashed curve suggests the course of these nonradiative processes.)

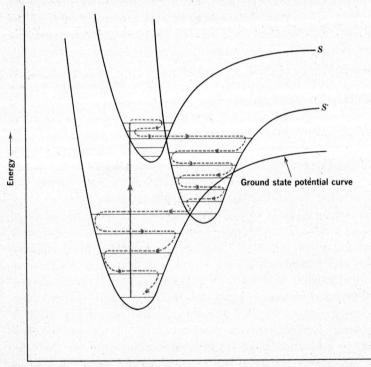

because at the crossover point the potential energies of the two electronic states are equal and the vibrational kinetic energy of the molecule in either state would be zero.

For polyatomic molecules, potential curves often exist with suitable relative positions so that combinations of vibrational deactivations and internal conversions can return the molecule to its ground state before any emission process has had a chance to occur. Other molecules, however, either do not have such crossing potential curves or have electronic states in which the molecule becomes trapped. In such cases emission does occur, and we will now investigate how this happens.

11-8. Fluorescence

If the efficiency of internal conversion processes that return the molecule to its ground state is not too great, various emission processes can occur. The simplest mechanism that is consistent with some of the observed emission is illustrated in Fig. 11-22. The observation that the emission band generally appears at longer wavelengths, i.e., lower energy, than the absorption band suggests that vibrational deactivation within the potential curve of the upper electronic state is essentially

FIG. 11-22   Fluorescent emission from the same electronic state as initially reached by the excitation process.

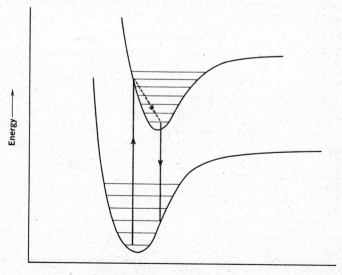

Energy ⟶

Representative internal coordinate ⟶

complete before much emission occurs and, therefore, that the emission transition of Fig. 11-22, rather than the exact reverse of the absorption transition, is to be drawn. Absorption and emission bands which illustrate this behavior are shown in Fig. 11-23.

Since most fairly intense absorption bands that are observed occur from the ground state to an excited state with the same multiplicity as the ground state, the emission process of Fig. 11-22 is a transition with no multiplicity change. It is now becoming customary, although other conventions are used, to use the term *fluorescence* for emission transitions that occur between states of the same multiplicity. This definition includes, therefore, emissions from states reached from the initial excited state by internal conversion as long as the second state has the same multiplicity, usually a singlet state, as the ground state. We will now see that fluorescent transitions, as defined above, can and generally do occur within about 10^{-4} sec after excitation. (Transitions connecting states of different multiplicities, usually triplet to singlet transitions, will be defined as phosphorescence and, in contrast to fluorescence, often continue for periods up to seconds after the absorption process is ended.)

FIG. 11-23 The absorption and fluorescent emission spectrum of anthracene dissolved in dionane showing the occurrence of the emission band at longer wavelengths, as suggested by the transition arrows of Fig. 11-22. [*From G. Kortum and B. Finckh, Z. physik Chem. B52, 263 (1942).*]

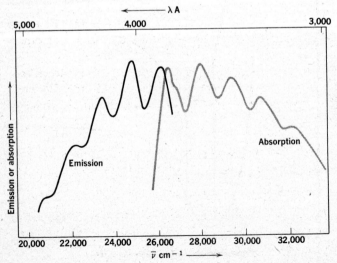

Let us now consider the rate, or probability, for an emission process of the type illustrated in Fig. 11-22. The experimental results that one might try to understand would consist of measurements of the change of intensity of the emitted radiation with time after the radiation beam causing the excitation to the higher-energy electronic state had been turned off. Information is needed, therefore, about the process of spontaneous emission. A brief derivation will show that a coefficient for spontaneous emission can be deduced and that it is related to the coefficient of induced emission, or absorption, derived in Chap. 4. We will then be in a position to use the measurable absorption coefficient to deduce the behavior of the spontaneous-emission process.

Let us consider molecules with a ground electronic state designated as g and a higher electronic state designated as h. Consider the sample containing these molecules to be in a black-body cavity in which the radiation density $\rho(\nu)$ is related to the frequency and the temperature by Planck's radiation law

$$\rho(\nu) = \frac{8\pi h \nu^3}{c^3} \frac{1}{e^{h\nu/kT} - 1} \tag{11}$$

At equilibrium the ratio of the number of molecules N_h in the higher-energy state to the number N_g in the ground state will be given by Boltzmann's distribution as

$$\frac{N_h}{N_g} = e^{-h\nu_{gh}/kT} \tag{12}$$

where $h\nu_{gh}$ is the energy difference, per molecule, between the two states. Now we must investigate the mechanism by which this equilibrium is established and maintained.

Molecules can be excited from state g to state h by transitions induced by the radiation in the cavity. Recalling the Einstein coefficient of induced absorption $B_{g \to h}$, introduced in Eq. (35) of Chap. 4, one writes

$$\text{Rate of } g \to h \text{ transitions} = N_g B_{g \to h} \rho(\nu_{gh}) \tag{13}$$

Transitions downward can occur by either induced emission or spontaneous emission. One can write the net rate of these processes as

$$\text{Rate of } h \to g \text{ transitions} = N_h[B_{h \to g}\rho(\nu_{gh}) + A_{h \to g}] \tag{14}$$

where $A_{h \to g}$ is Einstein's coefficient of spontaneous emission. The nature of $A_{h \to g}$ will be determined by relations established here. (We know, however, from the discussion of Chap. 4 that $B_{g \to h} = B_{h \to g}$.)

At equilibrium the two opposing rates must be equal, and one can obtain from the above rates the relation

$$\frac{N_h}{N_g} = \frac{B_{g \to h}\rho(\nu_{gh})}{B_{h \to g}\rho(\nu_{gh}) + A_{h \to g}} \tag{15}$$

Now one can replace N_h/N_g by the Boltzmann expression for this quantity, and one can also replace $\rho(\nu_{hg})$ by the black-body expression of Eq. (11). Rearrangement of the resulting equation gives, with

$$B_{g \to h} = B_{h \to g}$$

the desired relation

$$\begin{aligned} A_{h \to g} &= \frac{8\pi h(\nu_{gh})^3}{c^3} B_{g \to h} \\ &= 8\pi h(\bar{\nu}_{gh})^3 B_{g \to h} \end{aligned} \tag{16}$$

We can further relate $B_{g \to h}$ to the observed integrated intensity of the absorption band, $\int \alpha(\bar{\nu})\, d\bar{\nu}$, by Eqs. (36) and (46) in Chap. 4. Thus

$$\begin{aligned} A_{h \to g} &= \frac{64\pi^4 (\bar{\nu}_{gh})^3 |\mu_{gh}|^2}{3h} \\ &= \frac{8\pi (1,000) c (\bar{\nu}_{gh})^2}{N} \int \alpha(\bar{\nu})\, d\bar{\nu} \end{aligned} \tag{17}$$

With this result, the value of $A_{h \to g}$ can be calculated from the observed integrated intensity of the corresponding absorption band.

The lifetime of an excited state that spontaneously emits after the exciting radiation is turned off can be calculated as a half-life, i.e., the time it takes for the number of molecules in the excited state to decrease to half its value. One can write the rate equation

$$\frac{dN_h}{dt} = -(A_{h \to g})N_h$$

or $$\tag{18}$$

$$d \ln N_h = -(A_{h \to g})\, dt$$

Integration over the time interval $t = 0$ to $t = t_{\frac{1}{2}}$ in which N_h goes from N_h to $\frac{1}{2}N_h$ gives

$$\ln \frac{\frac{1}{2}N_h}{N_h} = (A_{h \to g}) t_{\frac{1}{2}}$$

or $$\tag{19}$$

$$t_{\frac{1}{2}} = \frac{\ln 2}{A_{h \to g}}$$

Finally, substitution of the expression for $A_{h \to g}$ obtained in Eq. (17) gives

$$t_{\frac{1}{2}} = \frac{N \ln 2}{8 \pi c (1,000)(\bar{\nu}_{gh})^2 \int \alpha(\bar{\nu}) \, d\bar{\nu}}$$
$$= \frac{0.55 \times 10^9}{(\bar{\nu}_{gh})^2 \int \alpha(\bar{\nu}) \, d\bar{\nu}} \tag{20}$$

Alternatively one can relate the half-life to the oscillator strength f of the transition discussed in Sec. 4-9. If one inserts the relation of Eq. (78) of Chap. 4, one has

$$t_{\frac{1}{2}} = \frac{2.4}{(\bar{\nu}_{gh})^2 f} \tag{21}$$

A typical strong absorption band due to an allowed electronic transition has $\int \alpha(\bar{\nu}) \, d\bar{\nu} = 10^9$ and a band maximum at, perhaps, 3,000 A, or 30,000 cm^{-1}. The emission from the excited state reached by this absorption should, according to the above analysis, have a half-life, due to the emission process, of

$$t_{\frac{1}{2}} = \frac{0.55 \times 10^9}{9 \times 10^8 (10^9)} = 0.6 \times 10^{-9} \text{ sec} \tag{22}$$

Such lifetimes are comparable with, or shorter than, typical non-radiative processes involving internal conversion treated in the previous section. It is clear, therefore, that any decrease in the efficiency of collisional deactivation, as by freezing in a glass or cooling to liquid nitrogen temperature, will allow the fluorescent emission to occur to a significant extent.

Many absorption bands are less intense, i.e., occur with a smaller integrated absorption coefficient, than that cited for typical completely allowed transitions. Emissions corresponding to these bands occur, in view of Eq. (20), with a correspondingly longer half-life. One finds in practice that fluorescent emission can be prolonged to half-lives of as much as 10^{-4} sec in cases where the value of $A_{h \to g}$ is small enough and nonradiative processes are relatively ineffective.

11-9. Phosphorescence

Phosphorescent emission is here defined as resulting from transitions that connect electronic states of different multiplicities, i.e., states with different net electron spin angular momenta. It is now recognized, primarily as a result of the early work of G. N. Lewis, that the most important phosphorescent bands of organic compounds arise from transitions between a triplet excited state and a singlet ground state.

The potential-energy diagram that represents a situation that can lead to phosphorescence is shown in Fig. 11-24. Absorption of radiation from the ground singlet to an excited singlet can occur to an appreciable extent; i.e., the transition can be allowed. Collisional deactivation can then drop the energy past the point where the potential curve of the singlet state crosses that of the triplet state. Although internal conversion between states of different multiplicities is apparently not easy, this process can occur and can lead to triplet-state molecules if the collisional deactivation does not carry the molecule too quickly past the potential crossing point. Once a triplet electronic state is formed, further vibrational energy will be lost and the molecules will occupy the low-lying vibration levels of the triplet electronic state.

Emission from this triplet state to the ground state will constitute phosphorescence. Since such transitions will be forbidden by the prohibition against spin changes, the spontaneous-emission process will

FIG. 11-24   Arrangement of potential-energy curves of singlet S and triplet T states that can lead to phosphorescence.

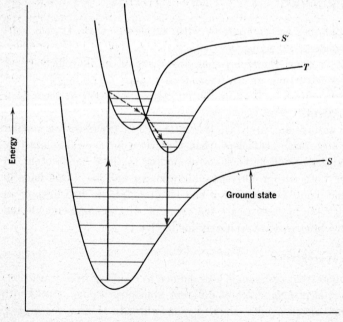

Energy ⟶

S'

T

S

Ground state

Representative coordinate ⟶

occur with low probability, i.e., $A_{h \to g}$ will be very small, and the phosphorescent emission will continue over relatively long periods of time. Half-lives for phosphorescence of the order of seconds, or longer, are not uncommon. (One should recognize that the relation between the $B_{g \to h}$ and $A_{h \to g}$ coefficients and the relation between $A_{h \to g}$ and $t_{\frac{1}{2}}$ require a roundabout mechanism, such as that of Fig. 11-22, in order to populate a long-lived excited state.)

The process of internal conversion between a singlet and a triplet state is sufficiently difficult, even if the potential curves cross, that phosphorescence is seldom observed in liquids at ordinary temperatures. Again the process of forming a glass with the material as a solute and cooling the system to liquid nitrogen temperatures is often resorted to. With this procedure many organic compounds undergo appreciable excited singlet to triplet internal conversions, generally referred to as intersystem crossing, and are observed to emit radiation as phosphorescence.

It should be mentioned that the lifetimes of excited states is a subject of great importance in photochemical studies. The occurrence of a long-lived high-energy species, such as the triplet states that lead to phosphorescence, often provides the means whereby photochemical reactions can occur. In this way the study of electronic spectra, and particularly fluorescence and phosphorescence, and photochemistry are intimately related.

INDEX